Attachment, Relationships and Food

Using attachment theory as a lens for understanding the role of food in our everyday lives, this book explores relationships with other people, with ourselves and between client and therapist, through our connection with food.

The aim of this book is twofold: to examine the nature of attachment through narratives of feeding, and to enrich psychotherapy practice by encouraging exploration of clients' food-related memories and associations. Bringing together contributions from an experienced group of psychotherapists, the chapters examine how our connections with food shape our patterns of attachment and defence, how this influences appetite, self-feeding (or self-starving) and how we may then feed others. They consider a spectrum from a "secure attachment" to food through to avoidant, preoccupied and disorganised, including discussion of eating disorders.

Enriched throughout with diverse clinical case studies, this edited collection illuminates how relationships to food can be a rich source of insight and understanding for psychotherapists, psychoanalysts and other counselling therapists working today.

Linda Cundy is an attachment-based psychoanalytic psychotherapist, supervisor, independent trainer and author. She is the Attachment Theory Consultant to the Bowlby Centre in London.

Attachment, Relationships and Food

From Cradle to Kitchen

Edited by Linda Cundy

 Routledge
Taylor & Francis Group

LONDON AND NEW YORK

First published 2022
by Routledge
2 Park Square, Milton Park, Abingdon, Oxon OX14 4RN

and by Routledge
605 Third Avenue, New York, NY 10158

Routledge is an imprint of the Taylor & Francis Group, an informa business

© 2022 selection and editorial matter, Linda Cundy; individual chapters, the contributors

British Library Cataloguing-in-Publication Data
A catalogue record for this book is available from the British Library

Library of Congress Cataloging-in-Publication Data
Names: Cundy, Linda, editor.
Title: Attachment, relationships and food: from cradle to kitchen / edited by Linda Cundy.
Description: Milton Park, Abingdon, Oxon; New York, NY: Routledge, 2022. | Includes bibliographical references and index.
Identifiers: LCCN 2021008968 (print) | LCCN 2021008969 (ebook) | ISBN 9780367561314 (hardback) | ISBN 9780367561307 (paperback) | ISBN 9781003096559 (ebook)
Subjects: LCSH: Eating disorders—Treatment. | Food—Psychological aspects. | Attachment disorder—Case studies—Treatment.
Classification: LCC RC552.E18 A88 2022 (print) | LCC RC552. E18 (ebook) | DDC 616.85/26—dc23
LC record available at https://lccn.loc.gov/2021008968
LC ebook record available at https://lccn.loc.gov/2021008969

ISBN: 978-0-367-56131-4 (hbk)
ISBN: 978-0-367-56130-7 (pbk)
ISBN: 978-1-003-09655-9 (ebk)

Typeset in Times New Roman
by Apex CoVantage, LLC

To the memory of Christian, who kept me nourished with love, companionship, support, laughter and great food for many decades.

And to all absent friends – loved ones who are no longer with us but who are associated for me and my fellow authors with the intimacy of sharing food; feeding and being fed. Their company is greatly missed.

Contents

Acknowledgements

So many people have contributed to the preparation of this book, from the initial concept through to its final stages. Chance conversations and deep discussions have provided rich food for thought; friends and colleagues have shared my enthusiasm for the project, helping to keep it on track during challenging times. I extend my appreciation to everyone who has played a part, including Dina Chioni, Su Fox, Rabbi Herschel Gluck, Dini Grussgott, Charanjot Kaur and Deep Kaur from the Guru Maneyo Granth Gurdwara in Slough, Will McFadden from Furloughed Foodies and Yusuf at Migrateful. Also, many thanks to Tamar Posner, Nina Roberts, Julia Segal, Shabibi Shah, Janet Smith, Christine Tseng, Judy V (you know who you are) and Dvina Vydelingam. Thanks, too, to Kate White, Ulla Gustafsson and Sharon Beavan for holding us in mind and bringing relevant attachment research to our attention. Maggie Turp's ongoing support and wisdom have been invaluable to me throughout the whole process of writing and editing, and conversations with Annie Power have kept me grounded.

I am deeply grateful to Brett Kahr for his encouragement with this book and for contributing the Foreword, a delectable entrée to whet the reader's appetite for what follows; and also to Jeremy Holmes and Julia Buckroyd for their enthusiastic endorsements.

My gratitude also goes to each of the authors who put so much time, thought and passion into their chapters, who worked with me collaboratively and with generosity of spirit to pull everything together into a satisfying whole, while bringing their own distinctive 'signature flavour' to the table. It has been a privilege and a delight to work with each of them.

Finally, my thanks to the editorial team at Routledge for making this book possible.

About the editor and contributors

Linda Cundy (editor) is a UKCP-registered attachment-based psychoanalytic psychotherapist and supervisor in private practice and an independent trainer, consultant and writer. She has taught on psychotherapy courses for almost thirty years, including a long association with the Wimbledon Guild, where she developed and led a post-graduate diploma in attachment-based therapy. A number of her articles have been published in professional journals, and she has written/edited three books to date, *Love in the Age of the Internet: Attachment in the Digital Era*; *Anxiously Attached: Understanding and Working with Preoccupied Attachment*; and *Attachment and the Defence Against Intimacy: Understanding and Working with Avoidant Attachment, Self-Hatred and Shame*. Linda has worked in the areas of adult mental health and bereavement and has been appointed Attachment Theory Consultant to the Bowlby Centre.

Penny Forster is a senior psychotherapist specialising in the treatment of eating disorders. Initially trained in group therapy and integrative psychotherapy, she went on to train more extensively in attachment-based psychodynamic therapy, completing a post-graduate diploma in attachment-based psychotherapy. She was an independent psychotherapist with the Eating Disorder Unit at the Priory Hospital Roehampton for many years, seeing individual patients and running groups as part of their extensive therapy programme, and currently works with colleagues as a partner in the Chelsea and Harley Street Eating Disorder Service, seeing patients individually and running a weekly support group for those who are approaching recovery.

Julie Friend is a chartered counselling psychologist working in private practice in central London. She began her career as a secondary school teacher of modern foreign languages, soon finding that she was more interested in understanding the "imperfect" pasts of her pupils than she was in their grammatical understanding of the French past perfect. She subsequently trained in counselling psychology at the University of Roehampton. However, her interest in attachment theory led her to continue her training with a postgraduate diploma in attachment-based therapy, and this informs not only her psychotherapy practice but also colours her worldview. In terms of her personal relationship to food, she is of the mindset that, however challenging things may seem, there are always at least three things to look forward to in her day: breakfast, lunch and dinner.

Graeme Galton is an attachment-based psychoanalytic psychotherapist and member of the Bowlby Centre, where he is a training supervisor and teaches on the clinical training programme. In addition to his private practice, he worked for sixteen years in the National Health Service as a psychotherapist and clinical supervisor, and is a Consultant Psychotherapist at the Clinic for Dissociative Studies, a small specialist outpatient mental health service for people suffering from severe trauma and dissociation. He is a member of the European Association for Psychotherapy and holder of the European Certificate of Psychotherapy, the European-wide standard for psychotherapy training. Graeme edited the book *Touch Papers: Dialogues on Touch in the Psychoanalytic Space* (Karnac, 2006) and co-edited *Forensic Aspects of Dissociative Identity Disorder* (Karnac, 2008).

Charlotte Hastings is a psychodynamic counsellor who also draws on her training in systemic family therapy and attachment theory to inform her work. She studied anthropology at university, and her previous career in education led to her appointment as head of drama in a special needs school. Partly informed by a 1970s childhood split between her grandmother's home-cooking and her working mother's boil-in-the-bag dinners, she developed what she calls Kitchen Therapy, integrating talk therapy with cooking in sessions, designed to enhance personal and social well-being for individuals, families and groups. She has contributed articles on Kitchen Therapy to professional journals, blogs and the media, and her Kitchen Sessions podcasts feature interviews with people from many backgrounds about the place of food in their lives.

Professor Brett Kahr has worked in the mental health profession for over forty years. He is Senior Fellow at the Tavistock Institute of Medical Psychology in London and also Visiting Professor of Psychoanalysis and Mental Health in the Regent's School of Psychotherapy and Psychology at Regent's University London. A Consultant Psychotherapist at The Balint Consultancy and a Consultant in Psychology to the Bowlby Centre, Kahr is also a trustee of the Freud Museum London, of Freud Museum Publications and of the United Kingdom Council for Psychotherapy. Moreover, he serves as chair of the Scholars Committee of the British Psychoanalytic Council. Kahr is the author or editor of fifteen books and series editor for more than seventy further titles. His most recent books include *How to Flourish as a Psychotherapist*; *Bombs in the Consulting Room: Surviving Psychological Shrapnel*; *Celebrity Mad: Why Otherwise Intelligent People Worship Fame*; and *Dangerous Lunatics: Trauma, Criminality, and Forensic Psychotherapy*. A long-standing educator and broadcaster, he has, over the decades, delivered more than 3,000 public talks on psychotherapy and has delivered over 1,000 broadcasts on psychological topics on radio and television, having formerly worked as Resident Psychotherapist at the BBC.

Andrea Oskis is a Senior Lecturer in psychology at Middlesex University, London. Her teaching and research expertise extend across a range of areas, including developmental, clinical, biological and health psychology, and she has published academic papers on many of these subjects. She specialises in interview assessments of attachment style, parenting and early experiences of care and abuse. Her research is conducted as part of the Centre for Abuse and Trauma Studies (CATS), which is based at Middlesex University. Andrea is also a UKCP-registered attachment-based psychoanalytic psychotherapist in private practice in North London. Contributing to this book combines two of her great interests, as she also trained as a chef at Leith's School of Food and Wine.

Sarah Pennock trained to be a therapist after a twenty-year career in live television. Following her initial specialist training in addiction psychology, she worked in residential addiction treatment centres, outpatient programmes and addiction support agencies. Later, on completing a postgraduate diploma in attachment-based therapy, she moved into private practice in Marylebone, London. She also facilitates workshops on attachment for the general public and for businesses and provides training seminars on attachment and addiction.

Jenny Riddell is a psychoanalytic psychotherapist working with individuals and couples in private practice. A registered member of the Bowlby Centre and BSCPC (British Society of Couple Psychotherapists and Counsellors), her specialist interests are in how a couple grieves, infertility, affairs, and working with couples in later life. She has authored and co-authored several chapters on the subject of couples and couple therapy. Jenny also supervises, trains and is academic supervisor on a variety of psychotherapy trainings. She is a member of the British Psychoanalytic Council, BAPPS (the British Association for Psychoanalytic and Psychodynamic Supervision) and COSRT (the College of Sexual and Relationship Therapists), as well as the UKCP and BACP.

Foreword

My dinner with John Bowlby: food for thought versus food for the soul

Professor Brett Kahr

Many decades ago, as a young schoolboy, I spent an afternoon at a friend's house, studying some thick textbooks very obsessionally in preparation for what seemed to be an important examination. As early evening approached, my friend's mother invited me to stay for supper, and I cheerfully accepted this kind invitation. Keen to be a good hostess, the mother asked, "So, Brett, what sort of food would you like? I could prepare some chicken or maybe some steak?" Before I had a moment to answer, my school friend's father, seated nearby, interrupted and shouted jokingly at his wife, "Don't be ridiculous, the boys are hard at work prepping for their exams. They don't want to be interrupted with *food*. They are much more interested in *food for thought!*"

As an aspiring scholar, I found the father's comment rather lofty and, also, somewhat inspiring. Surely, anyone can enjoy ordinary food – whether carrots or potatoes or pasta or fish – but only a very diligent and dedicated student can fully appreciate the benefits of food for thought.

I must confess that, as the years unfolded, I spent a very great deal of time indulging in food for the mind rather than in the more edible variety.

In 1983, as a young psychologist with a keen passion for psychoanalysis, I organised a series of lectures at my university, an institution which, at that time, paid little attention to the work of Sigmund Freud and his followers. Eager to meet as many of the key figures in the psychoanalytical community as possible, I wrote to all of my heroes and invited them to speak, including one of my very favourite researchers, the luminous Dr John Bowlby, who would subsequently become immortalised as the veritable father of attachment theory and attachment-based psychotherapy.

To my surprise and delight, Dr Bowlby graciously accepted my offer. As a budding psychoanalytical historian, I knew that I wished to spend as much time with Bowlby as possible, and so I boldly enquired whether he might be willing to arrive in Oxford a few hours *before* the lecture so that I could interview him about his career over a cup of tea and, also, whether he might remain in town *after* the lecture so that I could treat him to a fancy supper. Bowlby, then well into his seventies, could readily have refused the invitation to both tea and dinner and could simply have restricted his visit to the delivery of his public talk before returning to his home in London. But, to my astonishment, he accepted all of my suggestions; and, on 20 February 1984, I enjoyed the deep privilege of spending both the afternoon and the evening with this remarkably generous and brilliant man.

At 3.00 p.m. on the day in question, I met John Bowlby in the entrance of Corpus Christi College in the heart of Oxford; and as he walked through the small sixteenth-century doorway, I gawped with amazement as I caught my very first glimpse of this tall and distinguished looking man. Timidly, I introduced myself and then escorted him to a quiet, pleasant café on Broad Street, not far from the college. As Bowlby and I munched on our croissants and sipped our Earl Grey, he regaled me with no end of reminiscences about some of the leading lights within the British Psycho-Analytical Society who had trained him or who had worked alongside him, such as Dr Ernest Jones, Dr Karin Stephen (the sister-in-law of Virginia Woolf) and, in particular, Mrs Melanie Klein – the iconic pioneer of child psychoanalysis who had supervised his early clinical work.

As we drank our tea and consumed our snacks, Bowlby became increasingly relaxed and infinitely generous with his gossipy and, often, shocking revelations. Sensing my great interest in British psychoanalysis of the 1930s, Bowlby continued to offer a whole range of compelling anecdotes; and at one point, this very traditionally masculine septuagenarian even began to mimic his former supervisor, Mrs Klein, by imitating her high-pitched and somewhat grandiose voice. I could not quite believe that this rather austere and "old school" gentleman, educated at boarding school and at the University of Cambridge, could become so relaxed that he would dare to make himself vulnerable in this way and provide me with an almost pantomime-like imitation of his one-time great teacher. Needless to say, I enjoyed John Bowlby's performance as Melanie Klein with great gusto.

After an extremely pleasant tea, in which Bowlby revealed much about his early years of training and about his intellectual development, he and I then strolled to the offices of the Department of Experimental Psychology, located on South Parks Road, just in time for his 5.00 p.m. lecture. Bowlby had originally intended to speak on the subject of "Psycho-Analysis as a Natural Science" – the title advertised on the flyers – but only moments before the talk commenced, he explained that, since our initial correspondence, he had changed his mind about the topic of his presentation, and he then handed me a piece of paper with a new title, scribbled in his distinctive handwriting, and explained that he would now prefer to lecture on the revised subject of "Defensive Processes in the Light of Attachment Theory." In retrospect, I appreciate that this talk, delivered in 1984, may well hold distinction as one of the very first Bowlby lectures with the word "Attachment" in the title. At that time, virtually no one in the field of psychology spoke about attachment at all. Bowlby really led the way in this regard.

I then introduced this iconic psychoanalytical superstar to a packed audience of approximately one hundred guests (including the distinguished psychiatrist and psychotherapist Dr Anthony Storr), and I welcomed Bowlby warmly to Oxford. Needless to say, John Bowlby presented a magnificent talk, articulated with tremendous confidence and wisdom, and the audience and I certainly enjoyed his remarks unreservedly. After he finished speaking, I thanked Dr Bowlby for his contribution to our series of lectures and then led a round of appreciative – indeed enthusiastic – applause.

Subsequently, after Dr Bowlby's memorable presentation, I transported our distinguished guest speaker to a very elegant nearby restaurant, accompanied by two female psychology trainees, each of whom would come to enjoy a distinguished career in the field of clinical psychology in years hence. Over supper, Bowlby became increasingly relaxed. Although he behaved in a completely appropriate and gentlemanly manner, I suspect that he very much enjoyed flirting innocently with these intelligent young women. And, over a delicious supper, Bowlby regaled us all with a detailed preview of his book-in-progress, namely, a psychoanalytical study of the life of the great evolutionary theorist Charles Darwin. Bowlby explained that Darwin suffered from deep depression and also from a range of debilitating psychosomatic symptoms, emphasising that, although other experts regarded this illness as an expression of a medical disease, he had recently accumulated sufficient evidence to demonstrate that Darwin's physical pains and his profound sadness could actually be traced more convincingly to early loss and bereavement. My female psychology colleagues and I sat utterly entranced as we enjoyed the privilege of this snapshot of what ultimately became Bowlby's final major publication, his now classic book, *Charles Darwin: A Biography*, released in 1990, the very year of his death at the age of 83.

I have shared these memories of my first encounter with John Bowlby for several reasons. First of all, I suspect that anyone who has purchased a book entitled *Attachment, Relationships and Food: From Cradle to Kitchen*, inspired by the blue-sky work of Bowlby, might well be eager to devour any and all reminiscences about this inspirational leader in the field of mental health. Second of all, I wish to propose that food played an extremely important role during my initial encounter with Dr Bowlby.

Although I have often "dined out" on my stories of tea and supper with the father of attachment theory, I have always talked about his physical appearance, his kindness, his anecdotes, his gossip, his wisdom and even his flirtatiousness with my young female contemporaries. I must confess that I had never before considered the impact of having first conversed with Bowlby over tea and supper, and certainly, I may well have underestimated that our Oxford meals might have contributed hugely to our increasing conversational comfort with one another. In retrospect, I secretly suspect that food and drink actually provided us with a setting in which we could relax and begin to embark upon a series of rich dialogues. It may well be the case that Bowlby could have reminisced equally skilfully without a cup of tea or a glass of wine in his hand; but I believe that the atmosphere of a plentiful table may well have facilitated his growing ease of comfort and communication. Moreover, Bowlby might well have appreciated the fact that *I* paid the bill, both at the teashop and, subsequently, at the restaurant, and thus looked after him, in spite of my very young age at that time.

He and I never mentioned food as we spoke about Melanie Klein and Charles Darwin and related subjects, but our actual meals may well have helped to promote something of a pleasant attachment; and over the next six years, I had the privilege of corresponding with Bowlby, of visiting with him and of interviewing him, and, in later years, of socialising with his lovely wife, Ursula Bowlby, and their very pleasant children. I feel honoured to have enjoyed such a wonderful experience with one of the world's greatest minds, and I feel particularly happy that a crispy croissant and a juicy steak might well have fostered this amazing opportunity.

I regret that Linda Cundy, the progenitor and editor of *Attachment, Relationships and Food: From Cradle to Kitchen*, did not have the opportunity to meet John Bowlby in person. I strongly suspect that, had she done so, she would have made a very favourable impact indeed, and Dr Bowlby would have become entranced by this beautifully prepared and highly original collection of essays, which, in my estimation, constitutes a very important contribution to the study of attachment psychology.

With great creativity, Cundy has assembled a wide-ranging group of experienced psychologists, psychotherapists and counsellors who, collectively, have addressed the impact of food on intimate relationships in a very engaging manner. Each chapter has impressed me not only as rather wise but also as unusually well written.

In the pages that follow, readers will be treated to a feast of clinical observations and theoretical insights about the role of food in the development of the secure attachment relationship, examining how edible meals not only promote intimacy and safety but also how food enhances these vital foundations of human functioning. Although the mental health literature contains no shortage of material on the psychopathological side of food and drink (i.e., the devastating consequences of anorexia nervosa, bulimia and obesity, as well as alcoholism and substance misuse), the work of Cundy and her colleagues truly underscores the ways in which the physically and emotionally nourishing meal can provide the very bedrock of creativity and sturdiness of character.

I shall not attempt to offer summaries of these delicious chapters. Happily, the authors have provided us with easily digestible treats, so I know that readers will be warmly nourished. But I shall report that, as I studied this typescript, I found myself thinking about so many of my own patients – not only those with eating disorders *per se* but, especially, those *without* such struggles. While immersing myself in this text, I became increasingly aware of the ways in which healthy parenting and, in particular, the healthy provision of food really does contribute to mental health, perhaps even more so than we may well have recognised.

In her own engaging chapter on "The Last Supper: Attachment, Loss . . . and Food," Linda Cundy has concluded, "We love people through food; through feeding others, delighting in being fed by them, and by sharing food." This succinct encapsulation provides us with a veritable leaping-off point to from which to explore this universal topic – one which remains relatively marginalised in discussions, even by those devoted to Bowlby's notions of attachment security. Fortunately, Cundy and her colleagues have composed a magnificent platform which might well prompt us all to embark upon even more interesting psychological conversations in years to come.

With great admiration, I strongly recommend this lovingly prepared book. It has provided me not only with rewarding food for thought but also with food for the soul.

Preface

Linda Cundy

Attachment theory is an evolutionary model concerned with our innate human instincts. Man's history with food – indeed, prehistory – defines us as a species. There is reason to believe that our distant ancestors' brains grew larger and more complex once a shellfish diet was discovered (Broadhurst et al., 2007; McKie, 2002) – the omega fatty acids found in high density in fish may well have fed our distinctive cortex – and our use of fire marked us out as unique. While Koshima monkeys season their sweet potatoes with seawater, they eat them raw; cooking is only known among our human line. We are the only species to farm our raw ingredients, and this shift away from a hunter–gatherer way of life to a settled agricultural one enabled the development of rich cultural diversity, trading and civilisations.

Bowlby's theory, influenced by both Darwin and Freud, addresses the macro and the micro, the species and the personal. Alongside an evolutionary perspective, at the heart of his work is his concern with the individual in his or her historical, political, cultural and unique relational context. Each of these domains influences what and how we eat. In fact, Bowlby's understanding of what it is to be human rests on the issue of feeding. As Oskis reminds us in Chapter 3, he rejected the prevalent concept of "cupboard love," viewing the infant as fundamentally attachment-seeking rather than driven by the pleasure principle (1958).

René Spitz's classic "Hospitalism" study (1945) supports this. Spitz observed and compared two groups of disadvantaged children; infants in a residential nursery attached to a women's prison where their mothers were serving sentences and a group in a "foundling home." This latter group showed shocking developmental delays and failures (including failure to crawl, walk, speak or feed themselves), severe disturbance and astonishingly high mortality rates, despite good levels of hygiene and nourishment. In "both institutions adequate food is excellently prepared and varied according to the needs of the individual child at each age." (p. 61). However, during a measles outbreak, 23 out of the 88 "foundlings" under the age of 2½ died. So what was responsible for this level of suffering? Spitz concluded that, as with the more recent case of Romanian orphans, deprivation of human contact and stimulation was the pathogenic factor, and the "presence of the mothers [in the penitentiary nursery] could compensate even for numerous other shortcomings" (Ibid., p. 55). Dramatic *relational* starvation, it seems, compromises the infant's immune system (National Scientific Council on the Developing Child). Spitz filmed the children he observed, and some of this disturbing footage can be viewed online (Emotional Deprivation in Infancy: Study by René A. Spitz, 1952).

Though relationship with a caregiver is essential not only for survival but also well-being, food still matters. "What we eat enters our bodies and becomes part of us in an intimate way. Food forms and reveals us" (Basil, 2019, p. 3). Where there is food, there is attachment of some kind. From difficulties breastfeeding to the timing of weaning; from food phobias and fads as expressions of anxiety to food used to reward, seduce, silence, distract or attack; from dieting and dating to dinner table conversations and plate-throwing rows; from turning vegan to the special diets of sickness; from snacking alone in front of a screen to traditions of hospitality, feasting or fasting, experiences of attachment, separation and loss are played out in kitchens and dining rooms the world over. Food and relationships are inseparable.

It is not the grand architecture and extravagant artefacts but the evidence of ordinary everyday practices that give the deepest insight into a civilisation. Equally, it is in the details of our domestic lives, so mundane as to be easily overlooked, that we see most clearly our cultures, our values, our unconscious motivations, our relationships with other people and with ourselves; in short, who we are. Narratives about cultural heritage, intergenerational influences, identifications, bonding and conflict all have a valid place in the consulting room, and our relationships with food offer access to all of this. In her object relations theory, Melanie Klein proposed that for the infant, ingesting milk and the bodily processes involved in expelling waste products provide the model for the psychological processes of introjection and projection (Klein, 1952). As clinicians, I'm sure we are all familiar with the countertransference experiences of feeling devoured by a client or vomited over as unprocessed psychic material is discharged with energetic force in the session. Cooking metaphors spice up a therapy session, or more concretely, clients may bring breakfast or gifts of food into the consulting room with them. Not only storytelling but also preparing meals and sharing them are therapeutic activities in themselves, helping to bring together couples, groups and communities where fractures exist.

In this book we look at relationships with other people, with oneself – and with one's therapist – through our connection with food. We examine how early relating shapes patterns of attachment and defences and, in turn, how these may influence appetite, self-feeding (or self-starving) and how we then feed others. As psychotherapists, we rarely explore a client's attitude to food unless it is seen as problematic, and this overlooks the rich and sometimes spicy diet of stories that can be told that define each person as an individual in his or her own unique relational ecosystem. The focus here is not specifically on eating disorders, though these worrying manifestations of disturbed attachment are addressed (Penny Forster, Chapter 5). Instead we assume a spectrum from a "secure attachment" to food through to avoidant, preoccupied and disorganised.

Each author is a psychotherapist whose work with individuals, couples, groups or communities is informed by attachment theory. Some also have previous training or parallel careers involving cooking (cookery teacher, chef), or are highly specialist in the field of eating disorders. Others are just interested in food! Material will be drawn from research findings, interviews, the consulting room and lived experience to bring attachment theory to life. This book is a mezze; each chapter has its own flavour, seasoned and spiced according to the interests of the person who prepared it, including literature, anthropology, nutrition and psychophysiology. What they have in common is the same foundational "stock" – attachment.

While these chapters were being written, the world experienced a global crisis unprecedented in recent times: the Covid-19 pandemic. At times of threat to life, we instinctively reach out to connect with our nearest and dearest in any way possible and want to protect them. Inevitably, during the time of lockdown when social distancing, self-isolating or shielding became necessary, our relationships with food were also impacted dramatically. Food insecurity was evoked in generations of people who had never known true hunger, leading initially to panic buying. The shock of empty supermarket shelves and rationing of some food staples was a jolt to those of us in the developed world. For a time in my part of London, eggs became as scarce as precious stones. People stockpiled tinned foods they would never ordinarily eat. We had to change how we cooked, no longer planning a meal and casually popping out for ingredients; it was a matter of "what do we have and what can we do with it?" People whose incomes were hit hard changed food shopping habits, and brand loyalty was put aside in favour of economy. Food poverty became a political hot potato as many parents whose employment was threatened worried about how to feed their children. In the United Kingdom an unlikely hero appeared; young footballer Marcus Rashford, who himself had grown up in poverty, took on the British government to champion the cause of the food poor. Food banks – how dreadful that these are needed in twenty-first century Western democracies – were initially forgotten by people who made a habit of donating a box of cereal, tin of sardines, or pack of pasta with the weekly shop. We were in the grip of primitive anxiety. Generosity of spirit toward others, it seems, was only possible when there was plenty to go around; in survival mode we prioritised feeding ourselves and our own families. Meanwhile, in other parts of the world, the poorest feared that they and their children would succumb to starvation before the Coronavirus got them.

But during the lockdown, experienced by more than half of the world's population, people also began to connect through food in new ways; they shared recipes for meals cooked with those few basic ingredients that were still available and gave cookery lessons online to others who had never needed to make a meal but were now holed up alone. We live-streamed from our kitchens and sat down to eat with family and friends via Skype. We were reminded that we can bake our own bread rather than rely on shop-bought (the disappearance of yeast from supermarket shelves attested to this), and growing our own vegetables in gardens and on balconies helped many connect with the natural world, introducing their children to the delights of nurturing and valuing the ingredients on their plates.

We needed to be imaginative with cooking. A friend was shielding her partner throughout lockdown. After three months of isolation they began to feel stifled by a kind of claustrophobia, longing for a change of scenery. Her creative response was to turn to a favourite cookbook, *Dishoom* (Thakrar, 2019). Each day she not only prepared a new dish from it but evoked the accompanying environment: one day it was akuri and masala beans in a simple Irani café, the next found her drinking cocktails and dining at the lavish Bombay Taj Mahal Hotel, then lunch of aloo sabzi served by 90-year-old Mr Kohinoor. She wrote about these "adventures" in her Coronavirus Chronicles blog, illustrated with photographs of the dishes she had made, to entertain her friends.

There is a question used in the Adult Attachment Interview (AAI, George et al., 1984) to help identify the interviewee's pattern of attachment: "What did you do as a child when you were ill or frightened?" Typically, children turn to one of their parents to be cared for, but as adults, we look also to our health care systems. In the United Kingdom, our National Health Service is the ultimate symbolic attachment figure, there to protect us, make us well, save lives. Frontline medical workers are greatly valued, and during lockdown the public wholeheartedly supported the decision by supermarkets to give them priority food shopping. The same public spiritedness was shown the world over. And quickly, grassroots community kitchens sprung up, initiated and staffed by volunteers who prepared and delivered meals to neighbours in need.

We are a social species, after all.

References

Basil, P. (2019). *Be My Guest: Reflections on Food, Community and the Meaning of Generosity*. Edinburgh: Canongate.

Bowlby, J. (1958). The nature of the child's tie to his mother. *International Journal of Psycho-Analysis, 39*(5), 350–373.

Broadhurst, C.L., Cunnane, S.C., & Crawford, M.A. (2007). *Rift Valley Lake Fish and Shellfish Provided Brain Specific Nutrition for Early Homo*. Published online by Cambridge University Press. https://doi.org/10.1079/BJN19980004.

Emotional Deprivation in Infancy: Study by René A. Spitz, 1952. www.youtube.com/watch?v=VvdOe10vrs4.

George, C., Kaplan, N., & Main, M. (1984/1996). *Adult Attachment Interview* [Unpublished]. Berkeley: University of California.

Klein, M. (1952). Some theoretical conclusions regarding the emotional life of the infant. In M. Klein (Ed.), (1988) *Envy and Gratitude, and Other Works 1946–1963* (pp. 61–93). London: Virago.

McKie, R. (2002). It's a shore thing: Diet of fish made man brainy. *The Guardian*. www.theguardian.com/uk/2002/may/26/medicalscience.research. Accessed on 27 September 2019.

National Scientific Council on the Developing Child. (2012). *The Science of Neglect: The Persistent Absence of Responsive Care Disrupts the Developing Brain*. Working Paper 12, Harvard University. https://developingchild.harvard.edu/wp-content/uploads/2012/05/The-Science-of-Neglect-The-Persistent-Absence-of-Responsive-Care-Disrupts-the-Developing-Brain.pdf.

Spitz, R. (1945). Hospitalism: An inquiry into the genesis of psychiatric conditions in early childhood. *Psychoanalytic Study of the Child, 1*, 53–74.

Thakrar, S. (2019). *Dishoom: From Bombay with Love*. London: Bloomsbury.

Chapter 1

The last supper

Attachment, loss . . . and food

Linda Cundy

> The main facts in human life are five: birth, food, sleep, love and death.
>
> (Forster, 2005, p. 57)

To this, Bowlby would have added separation. The big themes of attachment theory are the nature and purpose of the attachment bond and the impact of separation from and loss of our attachment figures. Throughout life we make important relationships, face temporary and permanent losses, and hopefully recover from these. But what of food?

Attachment and separation

The last supper

I met Leanne when I worked for Hackney Bereavement Service. In her late twenties, she was struggling to cope following the death of her father a few months earlier. She described herself as a "daddy's girl" and was clearly a bright young woman, but depression masked any spark of curiosity, creativity or motivation. An only child, she was the first in her extended family to pursue further education, but at the time she took up her place at a university several hundred miles from home, her mother had breast cancer and died shortly after. Leanne returned, ostensibly to care for her father. But the reality was rather different.

Leanne told me that she had always been timid and dependent. She applied for a university place to make her parents proud but experienced the separation as unbearable, cutting her off not only from the family home but also the working-class community she grew up in. She lacked the internal resources to adapt to this new world, and she was worried and distressed about her mother's illness. Her parents had kept the true extent of the disease hidden from their highly-strung daughter, but parental secrecy created further anxiety in the child – anxiety, separation and then loss. So her return home was rather to be *cared for* by her father. Perhaps this also fulfilled a need in him, to continue nursing and supporting a vulnerable loved one, a way of coping with his own grief at losing his life partner.

It seems he was by nature more a nurturing maternal figure than a father, and an important manifestation of his love was his cooking. So while Leanne found work with the local council, father Eddie ran the home, shopped and prepared her evening meals.

When Eddie was himself diagnosed with an advanced cancer, he faced his illness courageously troubled only by the knowledge that his daughter would soon be left alone. He tried teaching her to prepare basic dinners, but Leanne would have none of it – she would not countenance the need to cook for herself. So in order to continue caring for her from beyond the grave, Eddie filled the freezer with her favourite homemade meals.

Leanne was devastated when her father died. Her doctor signed her off work with depression and she became reclusive. When just one of her father's home-cooked dinners remained to be defrosted she finally asked for help.

We humans are a profoundly social species, and our young are utterly dependent on their parents for survival. Babies come into the world ready equipped with behaviours designed to elicit care, and the caregiver's most fundamental function is to keep the infant alive. Feeding is a critical component of this (how many times have I heard, from people severely neglected or abused as children, "at least there was food on the table"?). But in time, the child must develop skills to go out into the world, keep himself safe, find his own food and eventually to feed others. It is part of the attachment figure's role to pass on the skills to fend for and feed oneself.

One approach to understanding Leanne's difficulties is to reflect on the family's three-person dynamics. Did "daddy's girl" Leanne long to shut out her mother, to have her nurturing father to herself? May she have felt excluded from the parental couple's relationship, especially during the months of her mother's illness and treatment when Eddie was so involved in supporting his wife? Was Eddie's subsequent death felt to be a punishment for her Oedipal triumph? So many questions. And, when viewed from an attachment perspective, further questions arise concerning the family narrative.

Leanne's is a moving tale of a father's love and care – the parental urge to keep his child alive and nourished. But perhaps the Tupperware containers filled with his beef stews and fish pies were also manifestation of an enmeshed family dynamic? The attachment-seeking and caregiving functions of their relationship worked well, but the encouragement to explore the world, develop expertise and grow into a secure *autonomous* adult was missing. (I am aware of a certain bias here, the assumption that separation and independence are normal, healthy, inevitable. I accept that human development allows for wide variation, but I view the *capacity* for autonomy to be culturally appropriate in the Western world.)

I did not learn the family history, the ingredients that spiced life with anxiety and seemed to tinge the outside world with danger, making all food other than father's unpalatable for Leanne. Perhaps there was a clue in the age of her parents (both had been in their forties when their daughter was born), the absence of siblings, some reason why her arrival in the world, or her survival, was especially precious and precarious. Possibly Eddie's attachment history could have helped us understand his need to protect and feed his daughter long beyond usual dependency. Or, as her mother's cancer was diagnosed when Leanne was a teenager, perhaps a developmental opportunity was missed; adolescents typically experiment with separation and individuation, loosen bonds with family and begin to invest in new relationships. Teenage protest and rebellion, against a mother whose breast was cancerous, would likely have been curtailed. And now, twice-bereaved, Leanne lacked skills or resources to sustain herself.

The imperative for Eddie to continue caring for – and feeding – his daughter even beyond death was far from unique. In past years archaeologists have unearthed mysterious objects dating from the Bronze and Iron Ages in numerous sites in Europe. These ceramic containers have spouts, and recent finds in Germany contain traces of animal milk (Dunne et al., 2019). It appears that these were feeding bottles for small children – evidence of weaning practice some three thousand years ago. What is notable is that these were grave goods, buried alongside young bodies. It seems the parental urge to nourish their young continued beyond the child's death. Part nourishment, part transitional object, these feeders indicate a belief in an afterlife, with the bond between parent and offspring continuing despite separation by death.

In this chapter, I explore the close connection between feeding and attachment and the impact of separation and bereavement on appetite, eating habits and the sense of self. Eating together is central to parent–child relationships, is part of couple bonding and of family life. So when an attachment figure dies, our relationship to the world – including what and how we feed ourselves – is shaken up. People enjoy talking about food, and I have listened to and interviewed, many people – family, friends, clients, even strangers on trains – about their own experiences. Some of their stories provide vignettes.

In general, I will refer to the infant or child as "he," and the mother (the person who provides "mothering," whether birth mother or not, and regardless of gender) as "she."

Early feeding

From the start of life, feeding is a relational activity. Whether breast or bottle, feeding time provides an opportunity for intimate connection. Skin-to-skin contact stimulates oxytocin, the bonding hormone, in both partners. Through touch, gaze, facial expression and vocalisation, the nursing dyad come into synchrony; they find each other.

One vital task of early caregiving is regulating not only the infant's hunger but also his affect states. How the baby is held and fed depends on the caregiver's capacity for sensitive attunement, and that, in turn, is related to her own attachment history, as well as current support and stresses (Sette et al., 2015). A mother's capacity to be fully present and enjoy the infant, or her unease with intimacy and baby's dependency needs, her own barely contained anxiety, or her struggle to be reliable and attuned, have origins in her own past and often her own infancy. The pattern of attachment that develops between baby and a parent – secure, avoidant, ambivalent or disorganised – is shaped long before conception (Benoit & Parker, 1994; Fonagy, 1991; Steele et al., 2016); *mother's* early relationships thus contribute to the infant's sense of self and self-worth, how he comes to perceive his place in the world. The intergenerational relationship is ingested with each feed and forms the basis of the baby's developing personality.

Mother may have the capacity to meet the baby's needs for nutrition and attunement more or less on demand at first (Winnicott's "good enough mother," 1971), putting time aside for a relaxed, unhurried meal. The baby experiences his bodily needs and emotional hunger for connection as important. Or this family may opt for the structured approach to feeding advocated by Frederic Truby King, whose childcare methods were particularly influential following the Second World War, or, more recently, by Gina Ford. Here, the infant is trained from the start to fit into a routine, allowing mother to attend to other commitments and to her own needs. The little one discovers the place he can occupy in the life of this family – and the mind of this parent. He adapts, learning to contain his own anxiety and, perhaps, make do with less intimate contact. His awareness of his hunger for food and for attention and how he later feeds himself develop within this particular relational ecosystem: his appetites perhaps feel shameful.

A chronically anxious mother conveys her agitation through how she holds and nourishes her baby. If her anxieties concern his survival, she may become intrusive and potentially misattuned in her management of feeds; she is likely to resort to controlling behaviours in her attempts to feed her child, and conflict may develop between them (Messina et al., 2000). Her cortisol is taken in with the milk, and his digestive system is often troubled. Feeding becomes stressful for him, torn between the pain and fear of hunger and a tense encounter with his stressed mother, and his own base levels of stress hormones are likely to be set high.

Here is an extract from a letter written in 1850 by Jenny Marx, wife of Karl: at that time the family was in London, almost destitute, after being effectively banished from France, Germany, Belgium, Switzerland etc.

> Let me describe for you, as it really was, just one day in our lives and you will realise that few refugees are likely to have gone through a similar experience. Since wet-nurses here are exorbitantly expensive, I was determined to feed my child myself, however frightful the pain in my breast and my back. But the poor little angel absorbed with my milk so many anxieties and unspoken sorrows that he was always ailing and in severe pain by day and by night.
>
> (in Wheen, 2000, p. 158)

The baby being nursed, little Henry, did not survive.

Alternatively, a depressed parent may provide functional feeding, but without the pleasurable relational connection that babies so crave and need to thrive. Food is then equated not with love, pleasure, safety and comfort but with fuel.

Of course, mother's state of mind is also affected by other factors, including her support system, the influence of her partner (if she has one), other demands on her energies, her own health, recent or past trauma, or loss. It is possible that the pregnancy and birth give rise to fantasies about this particular baby that influence how mother relates to him, as explored by Piontelli in her observational study, *From Fetus to Child* (1992). Even when she has created secure attachment with a previous child or children, if this pregnancy has been an ordeal for her or has become associated with tragedy or pain, it is possible that her reserves are over-stretched. It is then difficult to distinguish between the newborn who has ordinary needs from one who is "insatiable" and has "been trouble from the start." She may resent paying him attention, and that influences the feeding contact.

A baby who cannot or will not breast feed, due to birth defects, colic or other difficulties, is often experienced as rejecting. Mothers who are unable to breast feed commonly feel inadequate, and their shame may take the form of withdrawing from intimacy or perhaps overcompensating with the bottle.

If a woman has been victim to attack, persecution or sexual assault, we can imagine that pregnancy and early motherhood may feel traumatic – how she might confuse the piercing, persistent cries of a hungry infant with the taunts or jeers of an abuser, or the little one's vulnerability with her own at the time of assault. Mothers with a history of unresolved trauma manifest their own disturbance in how they attend to their babies' needs, including their hunger, often leading to infants' failure to thrive (Ward et al., 2000). Research using the "still face" procedure with mothers diagnosed with borderline personality disorder – or complex post-traumatic stress disorder, as Herman (1992) renamed it – and their 8-week-old infants found these mothers to be more intrusive and insensitive to their baby's cues than the control group (Crandell et al., 2003). Fraiberg and her colleagues, assigned to support young mothers with a background of trauma and abuse where the baby was at risk of harm, found that these women, when in self-absorbed states of mind, did not hear their infants' cries of hunger or distress. (Fraiberg et al., 1975) Parents with a traumatic past struggle to manage their own fear, hopelessness and rage and may dissociate when agitated. They have few internal resources to help them care for a dependent infant and, under the strain of sleepless nights and frequent demands, may not only fail to provide reliable, safe, enjoyable feeding experiences for the little one; rage, terrifying shouting and physical attack may be triggered by a hungry baby's desperate communications. A chilling description of such a scenario is outlined by Daniel A. Hughes (2018).

I worked with Samira at a mental health centre in the 1980s. She had recently been discharged from psychiatric hospital, where she had been sectioned following a psychotic episode. Samira showed signs of true hysteria, or conversion disorder – psychological distress converted into mysterious bodily symptoms. In particular she suffered from partial paralysis not caused by neurological damage. She also had an eating disorder, surviving on a restrictive diet of sweets and cigarettes.

Samira had been subjected to physical and sexual abuse by her father, but she understood her difficulties to originate from the start of life and her mother's "poisonous milk." Two siblings had died in infancy before she was conceived and Samira believed that her mother harboured murderous wishes toward all her babies (Kahr's "infanticidal attachment," 2007). She explained that she alone had survived the infanticidal attacks on her insides by rejecting her mother's breast milk and becoming phobic of food.

In my attempt to make sense of this story it occurred to me that Samira's mother may also have suffered abuse and violence within the home. Separated from her own family back in Egypt, she may have been vulnerable and stressed, and the cortisol in her milk may well have unsettled her small infant's stomach. Her unresolved grief for those children who had indeed died in infancy would also have taken its toll, infecting the early feeding of her baby. Later, when she failed to protect her daughter from the beatings and incestuous abuse, Samira's resolved was fortified; she both protected herself and punished her mother by continuing to refuse her food, equating self-denial with survival (the "no entry defence": Williams, 1997).

Weaning: the first experience of loss

For most of us, weaning is the first experience of loss, marking the end of a precious physical intimacy. How this potentially painful experience is managed, and the timing, is again influenced by many factors including cultural practices. Mary Ainsworth had worked at the Tavistock Clinic with James and Joyce Robertson on their observational research into young children separated temporarily from their families. Then in 1954, she moved to Uganda, hoping to further study the impact of separation on attachment behaviours and defences; she had heard that it was local tradition to send children away to stay with extended family at the time of weaning to help them "forget the breast." What a rich source of data that would have provided – except that it was no longer practiced by the time Ainsworth arrived (Bretherton, 2003)!

Weaning opens the way to new experiences, with new tastes, textures and aromas to explore and, if handled sensitively and timed in accordance with the individual child's capacities, the gains outweigh the losses. However, when scheduled to suit the adult's needs there can be difficulties. Parents who prefer their children to develop quickly and make few demands may impose early weaning, while a mother who craves intimacy and fusion might delay, perhaps continuing to breast feed for longer than the child requires. This keeps the father (the one doing the fathering) excluded and keeps the child infantilised, trapped in an enmeshed relationship. Pincus and Dare (1978) acknowledge that breastfeeding excludes the father, whose envy for the suckling infant may be aroused alongside his erotic feelings associated with breasts being roused. So alongside practical considerations, personal needs and the infant's readiness, a further factor in moving on from breastfeeding and in weaning may concern the relationship between the parental couple.

Sitting and eating together as a family or group and learning culturally appropriate table manners prepare us for making our own way in the world (Visser, 2017). Anthropologist Jared Diamond (2006) points out that, unlike all our ape relatives, human toddlers continue to depend on their caregivers for food long beyond weaning, and this lengthy period of dependency allows for our induction into the family's culture; specific cuisine, rituals at table, portion size, who cooks and who is served, the order in which food is served or taken, who is entitled to the "best" foods, notions of hospitality and so on. Age, gender, class and religion are often factors. Where meals are taken (on the floor by the cooking fire, in the men's longhouse, at the kitchen or dining table, or in front of the television) and what they are called (tea, dinner, supper) become part of one's identity.

A friend recently described his family's routine of "tea" when his father came home from work at around 6 o'clock each evening. His mother cooked and the family sat together eating in silence, focused on emptying their plates. This was always followed by "pudding," usually supermarket-bought with Bird's custard or tinned fruit with ice cream. In his early twenties he had a girlfriend from a more middle-class background and was invited to join her family for "dinner," the evening meal served at around 7:30. This family drank wine with their meal and ate "dessert," and discussed current affairs during their leisurely repast. He felt acutely embarrassed, exposed and ashamed of his origins. He commented that he is now middle class himself and brought his own children up to converse at the dinner table – and electronic devices are banished at mealtimes.

Separation

Separation is not always developmentally driven, nor the choice of the child. Bowlby observed the detrimental impact on children of long separation from their families, recognising this as the hidden root of much disturbance. (Attachment theory was later concerned with what is missing from insecure relationships rather than literal "maternal deprivation.")

In the Robertsons' studies of children temporarily separated from their parents, they noted a pattern of reactions that mirrors those typical of mourning in adults (Robertson & Robertson, 1989). After a period of protest comes searching and pining, followed by a descent into depression. If the separation continues longer, the child appears to recover and adapt to his situation, although with new defences that play out when parents return. They filmed 17-month-old John when he was sent to a residential nursery for nine days while his mother gave birth to her second child. He appeared to be securely attached to her and was initially open and trusting with nursery staff. His father visited on a number of occasions, but as the days passed John fell into a depressive state. Initially he ate well, fed by nursery nurses, but mealtimes became fraught and even his father could not help him. John was clearly hungry and wanted to eat but simply couldn't swallow. We must assume that, in his mind, his mother had gone and would never return, and grief prevented him from taking in his food. (According to notes accompanying the Robertsons' films, "for several weeks after returning home John showed extreme upset, often refusing his mother's comfort and the food she offered." (1969))

Pining and depression are often accompanied by appetite loss or, like John, an inability to swallow anything down. This supports Bowlby's hypothesis that attachment is the most fundamental instinct, taking priority over the need for nourishment (Bowlby, 1969). However, later in life, depressive moods may lead us to use food for comfort, a substitute for the now missing relationship – or as an attack on the self. This can be viewed as a protest to the absent Other, communicating that he or she is needed to protect the binge-eater from harm. (I address this later in a vignette about Seema.)

Generally, children feel safest when their caregivers are nearby, even if the attachment is not secure. One woman I worked with was a tragic exception. Her mother was chaotic, a heroin addict who brought frightening people back to their flat. As a small child, Amy was often shut in the kitchen while mum went out in search of a fix. Sometimes she was gone for hours, seemingly forgetting her daughter. And there was never food in the kitchen so Amy resorted to searching the bin for anything still edible. Eventually she was removed from home and taken to a foster placement. Amy remembered walking up the garden path in the company of a social worker she had never met before. Rather than feeling scared, she was calm. The smell of sausages, mashed potatoes and gravy wafted on the air as they waited for the door to open and that aroma was all she was aware of. This story is also familiar to me from my brief spell as a residential social worker in an adolescent unit, where young people from chaotic homes would arrive hungry as well as in urgent need of containment, structure and stability.

"How does one perform reverse alchemy, going from a normal newborn with almost unlimited potential to a diseased, depressed adult? How does one turn gold into lead?" (Felitti, 2002, p. 45). Working in an obesity programme in the 1980s, Vincent Felitti found a powerful connection between morbid obesity in adult life and multiple adverse experiences in childhood. His original study, for the Kaiser Permanente health care provider in the United States, addressed one of the most widespread health conditions with huge cost implications, and from this original work the entire ACEs (Adverse Childhood Experiences studies) project has gone on to discover links between early deprivation, loss and trauma with many other physical, mental health and social problems including addictions, heart disease, cancers and diabetes.

Amy, in her short life, had already experienced numerous forms of trauma, abuse and neglect. It is a credit to her that she created structure and purpose in her adult life and the ability to contain herself and her appetites. Rather than binge on high-sugar, high-fat foods, she took care of her body and appearance (although she couldn't cope with intimate relationships). Perhaps her self-respect owed much to the reliable attachment she developed with her foster mother, the one who introduced her to sausages and mash.

Individuation

Food fads or phobias are common in childhood. In rejecting the foods eaten by everyone else the child is asserting his individuality, attempting to persuade his family to accommodate or adapt to his preferences. This marks a further phase of separation and individuation but can create conflict with his parents, or between them if one parent takes a hard line and perceives the other to be indulgent. Winnicott lists: "some of the reasons why a mother hates her baby, even a boy: ... He is suspicious, refuses her good food, and makes her doubt herself, but eats well with his aunt" (1992, p. 201).

Separation and individuation are revisited during adolescence, and the young person often marks himself out as "other" from his parents' generation by what he eats. He may again reject his parents' "good food," decide on a vegetarian or vegan lifestyle, or follow particular diets. These choices may reflect a growing awareness of social and political issues – or of social pressures. What and how a young person feeds himself (or denies himself) is a great indicator of the relationship he has formed with himself – secure, dismissing, preoccupied or unresolved.

Fonagy and Moran (1990) researched a group of insulin-dependent children and adolescents who were disorganised in managing their medication, leading to frequent dysregulating hypo- or hyperglycaemic episodes – a form of self-harm. They discovered that, more than dietary advice or behavioural therapy, psychoanalytic psychotherapy had a beneficial impact on how these young people managed their diet and insulin injections. It was not a lack of information but a resistance to self-care that was at issue, reflecting underlying insecurities.

During the physical and emotional upheavals of puberty, our bodies may feel alien to us, and we can become hyper-aware of the gaze of others. Concerns with body size, weight and newly developed feminine or masculine physical features can be difficult to manage. Peer pressure and, nowadays, social media further undermine the adolescent's self-perception. Having a body that is the "wrong shape" is equated to being unlovable, unlikely to find a partner or possibly even a peer group. Acne is also a curse for many (Penny Forster addresses this is in her chapter on eating disorders). Whether restricting calories, bulking up muscle with protein powders or cutting out fatty foods to clear the skin, diet and dieting seem to offer a way to feel better about oneself and be more attractive to others. When taken to extremes, these preoccupations can evolve into disorders, but as an expression of genuine self-care they mark a renegotiating of the teenager's relationship with the family in preparation for moving out into the world and making a new kind of attachment.

Food and couples

Food is an integral aspect of courtship. In the early stages, cafés and restaurants provide an ideal relaxed and safe environment for conversation without commitment. Later, a romantic or exotic dinner date conveys the message that the partner being treated is special. The Valentine's Day box of chocolates is almost obligatory, with the choice of confectionary communicating layers of meaning; the financial position of the purchaser, his or her "good taste," how well the gift-giver understands the tastes of the receiver, how much he or she is prepared to spend or how much thought is given to the gift. And "if the way to a man's heart is through his stomach," then food has a starring role in seduction.

Can you remember the first time you dined out with someone you were "see-ing"? Where did you eat? Who suggested the venue? What did your partner order? Who paid? Did you notice your date's social behaviour and table manners? How he or she behaved toward the waiter (if there was one)? Eating together is an opportunity to check out compatibility of values, aspirations, social background, financial status, generosity, empathy and tact.

What was the first meal you cooked for your partner? And that your partner made for you? What could be more intimate or erotic than preparing a meal for a romantic partner that he or she bites into, tastes, savours and swallows? The ingredients and nutrients taken inside and digested literally become part of the Other. More domestic qualities are on display when someone cooks for their date, perhaps trying to impress with culinary skills by preparing a romantic candlelit dinner for two. Or instead of cooking, maybe it's sharing a takeaway with a bunch of friends and watching a movie together. Food is a third element in couple rela-tionships. Eating together, we learn a great deal about one another's lives and histories, tastes, preferences and aversions. We may also discover new ingredients and recipes, flavours and textures. We are gauging whether or not we can adapt to each other, implicitly and explicitly negotiating our different needs. What may have to be sacrificed in order to make necessary compromises? One partner is wheat intolerant, the other is not. One loves hot spicy food, the other prefers light fresh flavours. Can such differences be accommodated? One is vegan, the other a committed carnivore. Are important values challenged? Is it worth it?

Being introduced to your partner's family often involves eating together too. In most cultures it is considered good manners to take a gift of food when visiting; a box of chocolates and bottle of wine, or fresh dates, or home-grown lychees. On these occasions, the family is also making judgments. An Orthodox Jewish woman told me about her experience of an arranged introduction to a suitable young man. After a couple of meetings together he was invited to join her large family for a Friday evening Shabbat meal. His manners were impeccable, but he was reserved and only spoke when spoken to. She felt he would not be a strong enough personality to fit in with her lively, if rather querulous, clan competing for food and attention.

Over the years as a couple, food habits and traditions develop. New memories associated with sharing meals are created; favourite restaurants, holiday treats, dishes made to feed a fever or to celebrate achievements and milestones. Food and feeding can bind couples together. However, Richard Wrangham, who proposed that the manipulation of fire for cooking made us human, theorises eloquently about the origins of pair bonding in our species. He suggests that while both part-ners derived benefits from cooking food in terms of security, status and nutrition, the division of labour has been iniquitous for women:

> The idea that cooking led to our pair-bonds suggests a worldwide irony. Cooking brought huge nutritional benefits. But for women, the adoption of cooking has also led to a major increase in their vulnerability to male

authority. . . . Cooking created and perpetuated a novel system of male cultural superiority. It is not a pretty picture.

(Wrangham, 2010, p. 177)

Food and power are bedfellows, and sometimes women, wanting their share of power, use their role as feeders to get it. As Priya Basil wryly noted:

Mumji spent the first half of her married life cooking to impress Papaji and the second half cooking to oppress him. She seemed to believe that by deciding what went on his plate she could rule all his appetites.

(Basil, 2019, pp. 87–88)

The family eats

According to the saying, "a family that eats together, stays together." If only it were so easy! But family life involves power struggles, rivalries, alliances, insecurities, negotiations, adaptation. Coming together and separating. New arrivals to accommodate, losses to grieve. Each family flourishes or survives (or self-destructs) in a particular social, historical, cultural and economic environment. Day-to-day life can be challenging at the best of times, but everybody needs to eat.

Let me ask you some

- What was the place of food in your family of origin? Who shopped, cooked, cleaned up? Who made the decisions about what went on your plate? And the size of portions?
- How did your family cope with different food preferences, dietary needs, appetite or eating habits?
- What foods were associated with special occasions?
- Are there favourite recipes handed down from previous generations?
- What memories, good and bad, are associated with food for you?

Stories we tell about food give a rich insight into our relational world and family dynamics, the flavour of our personal ecosystem.

The shadow of the Second World War hung over my own early life and the food on the table. While my mother showed her love by dishing up home-baked cakes and trifles concocted with ingredients not available during the rationing years when she was a young woman, my father's prisoner of war experiences left him with a damaged digestive system. He was dangerously intolerant to spices, so "exotic" foods were avoided in favour of bland but hearty fare. This gave me something to rebel against in my adolescence!

In his early teens, chef Nigel Slater returned from his home economics lessons each Wednesday proudly carrying cakes and other dishes for his father's approval. But his stepmother was insecure and decided that would be her day in the kitchen, preparing three-course dinners and baking dazzling cakes of her own to tempt her man. The young Nigel's offerings were put in the fridge until stale.

Valentine Warner writes:

> I can vouch that none of my joy in eating could be ascribed to my grand-mother, except perhaps my joy at being clever with leftovers. . . . Her devout [Christian Scientist] faith meant that food to her was primarily sustenance and little more. She regarded our approach to eating as overindulgent and frivolous, endeavouring to improve us fractionally by insisting upon saying grace when she came to stay.
>
> (2019, p. 46)

But Priya Basil's Sikh grandmother had been a wonderful cook who practiced "exaggerated hospitality," always overfeeding family and guests. "She [wielded] ingredients like weapons" and would not share her recipes. Wanting to be the only one who could create these special dishes, she took her culinary secrets to the grave.

Loss and bereavement

Illness and anticipated loss

The evolutionary urge to keep our loved ones alive is not confined to parent–child relationships; adult attachments evoke similar anxieties when there is risk of sepa-ration or loss – the attachment system kicks in, and we usually resort to our default patterns of attachment seeking and defences against abandonment.

Mario and Gary had been together for eight years. They met soon after Mario moved to London from Rome and moved in together quickly. Gary was older by ten years, and he provided Mario with a comfortable home and security in this new city. Mario was accepted into his large, warm family and friendship circle. All went well except that Gary sometimes drank heavily and then Mario felt aban-doned and angry.

One evening, Mario was preparing dinner when Gary's secretary called to say he had been taken ill and was being rushed to hospital – he had had a stroke. Mario was frantic. For a few hours it was unclear whether his partner would pull through and, if he did, what damage had been done. Thankfully, Gary returned home and the recovery went well, but Mario was now anxious, hypervigilant – and controlling. He tried to prevent Gary smoking and drinking and imposed a dietary regime intended to help him lose weight. Arguments began when evidence was discovered of Gary eating fast food while Mario was at work. He insisted that his partner install a phone app to track his whereabouts, and he searched Gary's pockets for receipts from food outlets. Not surprisingly, Gary resented this level of intrusion. He protested by provoking, drinking more heavily and consuming more junk food. He understood that he was putting his life at risk, but now felt trapped in a suffocating relationship.

Mario's original preoccupied anxieties had to some extent had been contained by his relationship with a reliable partner and his supportive extended family but were triggered again by the threat of loss. Gary was generally secure but experienced his partner's neediness and controlling tendencies as suffocating. While his withdrawal suggested an avoidant defence, the risk-taking with food and alcohol had features of attacks on the self, more associated with unresolved trauma. And, indeed, he had experienced his recent stroke as traumatic. Each partner needed sensitive support from the other, and they sought couples' therapy to help them.

I spoke to Jan, who told me that she had always cooked for her husband, Adam. He had a "tough persona," and this was the only way he would let her care for him. As he became more ill, he lost his appetite and she felt rejected, helpless and impotent. She felt shut out as his cancer progressed, and she couldn't help him fight the illness that eventually took him from her.

The foods we eat express who we are; our social, cultural and family context, our values and self-perception, as well as connecting us powerfully to memories (remember Proust and his madeleine). I have a friend who now lives in a care home. She accepted this as a necessity and resigned herself to the loss of her previous life. Her only complaint concerns the meals. These are cooked daily in-house with fresh ingredients, and there are always several options available. However, my friend's distress is focused on what she eats, and her appetite has diminished. Never a cook herself, her husband had prepared wonderful, nutritious dishes for her throughout their lives together, and they enjoyed dining out in good restaurants together. After he died, she lived on ready meals heated in the microwave. The freshly made lunches at her care home would seem an improvement on this state of affairs. However, I believe her complaints contain and express her grief at losing her husband, then her home, the life she made for herself and – perhaps even more disturbing for this bright woman – her sense of self, as dementia robs her of her words and so much more. Her grieving has been replaced by grievance.

Matthew had been retired for several years and took on house-husband role while wife Judy continued to work full time. When he was diagnosed with a terminal illness, family routines needed to change, domestic roles reversed. Matthew was prescribed a high fat diet to slow the weight loss caused by his illness, and Judy struggled to care for him and continue to work as best she could. She dealt with the impending death of her husband by filling every moment with activity, trying to stay on top of all demands, leaving no space to confront her feelings. In her journal she wrote:

> *small spaces of time get eaten into, completely devoured by the need to shop, clean, cook, pick up prescriptions or just sit with Matt. He has to eat so much more that it entails more trips to the supermarket that need to fit into an already busy schedule. We run out of blue-top milk, eggs, ice cream, crumpets, bread, cheese . . . every day or two. I will start organising online shopping to get the basics delivered, but first I must find time to make space to store these extra groceries. Time – I just don't have enough. And I do wonder*

if his consultants' insistence on this high fat diet is in some way to hasten his end – a quick heart attack rather than a long, slow and painful decline.

There is the sense here of a manic defence, rather like the stage of bargaining that Kübler-Ross (1969) identified in those confronting death. "If I wear myself out looking after him and still manage all my other commitments, maybe I can earn more time and he will live longer, or won't be taken from me."

In Greek mythology, Zeus gave his daughter Persephone to Hades as his wife (in one version of the myth she is abducted.) She was taken to the Underworld, where her distraught mother Demeter travelled to bargain for her return. A compromise was reached, and Persephone was permitted to return for part of each year. Her annual arrival marked the start of spring and she stayed until harvest time. When she was summoned back by Hades, winter fell. Thus, the goddess of the Underworld became associated with grain and the earthly cycle of crops. This compromise spared Demeter the agony of permanent loss.

After Matthew died, Judy told me she had thoughts of bargaining for his return. She would have been happy to have him back for just a month or two each year, maybe even less. Jan said the same about Adam.

Bereavement

The initial reaction to bereavement is often bodily, a feeling that our insides have liquefied, turned to churning acid that cramps the stomach. We may feel cold and empty and crave calories, or unable to swallow anything down. But as days and weeks pass, the bereaved must confront the new reality and gradually adapt themselves to a changed world.

In many cultures, news of a death galvanises support from extended families, neighbours and communities. A Turkish friend worked into the night in her kitchen preparing meals for her recently widowed sister-in-law. In Bahrain, as in other Muslim countries, funerals happen within 24 hours of a death and are followed by a period of mourning. During this time, the eldest son provides food for the family, allowing them to focus on prayer and mourning. Likewise, in Jewish tradition the bereaved family sit shiva for seven days and they are forbidden to prepare food, so the community ensures they are well nourished. Shiva baskets, condolence gifts of fruit, pastries and snacks are also given. In many cultures a funeral is followed by a wake, where the family share food and drink with mourners who gather to celebrate the deceased person's life and "give him a good send-off." And in Taiwan, families of the deceased refrain from eating meat for either forty-nine or one hundred days to show respect to the dead and facilitate the bereaved person's journey to heaven. However, bereavement in Taiwan is a time of isolation; the grieving family are not visited by the community but rather are shunned and have to fend for themselves. The funeral meal is shared only with the closest relatives due to superstition about death and a fear of ghosts.

Pining and searching

Nigel Slater's mother died when he was 9. His father was unaccustomed to expressing love through words or physical contact but found a way to convey that he held his son in mind: marshmallows. The young Nigel had described them in a school essay as: "the nearest food to a kiss. Soft, sweet, tender, pink" (Slater, 2013, p. 102) And so:

> Each night for the next two years [after Mum died] I found two, sometimes three fluffy, sugary marshmallows on my bedside table. It was the good night kiss I missed more than anything, more than her hugs, her cuddles, her whispered "Night-night, sleep tight."
>
> (Ibid.)

But Slater senior was too inhibited to provide the longed-for goodnight kiss; marshmallows had to substitute.

Flavours and aromas evoke memories, associations. It is natural that we turn to such reminders in the hope of reconnecting with lost loved ones. Katya moved to the United Kingdom twelve years ago and married a British man. They have young children, and she works as a carer. She had a difficult relationship with her father and rarely visited her family since leaving Poland. But after her maternal grandmother died a few months back, she began craving the foods she ate as a child, the spicy sausages, dumplings and cabbage rolls her grandma used to make. Her British family dislike these unfamiliar dishes, and Katya has little time to cook separately for herself but has started to shop at Polish delicatessens for ingredients that remind her of her cultural identity and early life with her beloved babcia.

Journalist Matt McAllester "lost" his mother twice. The warm, affectionate relationship they shared when he was young was destroyed by her encroaching depression and alcoholism. And later, when she died, he was taken aback by the urgency of his need to reconnect with her:

> I wanted to put back together what had long ago been broken. . . . I wanted back the woman I had known for the first ten years of my life, the woman who placed heavenly, delicious food at the centre of our family and of my relationship with her. . . . I couldn't call her up and ask for cooking advice any more, but perhaps I didn't need to; her [recipe] books could teach me everything she had known.
>
> (McAllester, 2011, pp. 48–49)

Early in my career, working at a mental health day centre, I was tasked with running a cookery group with clients. I met each week with a handful of them who lacked kitchen skills to discuss what they wanted to make, then compiled a shopping list with them and taught basic food preparation. One group member was Joe, a very vulnerable man who had learning difficulties (that may have been psychogenic) as well as profound depression. He had been resident in the local psychiatric hospital for many years until "care in the community" closed it down and he was moved to a shared home. I don't recall the dish Joe wanted to cook, but it was something he remembered from his distant past, and as we chopped the onions and boiled potatoes together he started to talk – a rare occurrence – quite eloquently about his mum and his childhood. He became distressed because she had died and his siblings felt he was too volatile to attend her funeral. He didn't know where she was buried or, if she had been cremated, what had happened to her ashes. Joe talked more about himself during that time in the kitchen than ever before, and I learned things about his life that he had not shared with anyone previously.

Depressive withdrawal

Judy kept a journal to help her cope with her bereavement. Here is an extract:

> *3 months since Matt died. Ollie is out this evening with friends – I'm glad he's feeling up to it. He may stay over at Daniel's, but if he does come home it will be late. It is my first long evening alone. I've been decorating the spare room but when the light got too poor I went to the supermarket. I want to cook spaghetti with cherry tomatoes and asparagus, as Matt used to make it. Perhaps it will help me feel his presence still here in the house. It's a meal we used to have every week when Ollie was out or away – he doesn't like any of the vegetables so I haven't eaten it for a while. I will need to use the whole pack of asparagus as I won't find another use for it. And can I be bothered to use garlic? Probably not. The spaghetti in the cupboard is a pack I bought with the expectation of cooking it for Matt – for the last few months he wasn't able to cook for us anymore. And I've just been reduced to tears by a pack of cheese.*

Despite the hope of feeling close to her dead husband, Judy's withdrawal from the world and depressive mood are beginning to be evident. At times, bereaved individuals feel vulnerable and exposed without the presence of a protective Other somewhere nearby. The environment becomes a place of potential danger. Perhaps some atavistic, ancestral memory is stirred when eating alone, at risk of ambush or attack from predators (Wrangham, 2010).

At other times a grieving person may feel invisible, as if he or she is becoming a ghost. In our nuclear family-based society, some who have lost a partner are confronted with eating alone. One elderly widower, whose wife of nearly fifty years had died, commented that food tastes different without company; there is no pleasure in it, or sense of occasion. A woman noticed that she no longer eats dinner at the table but perches on the edge of her sofa, often while watching television or even working on her laptop. She wonders if she will eat at restaurants again – something she and her partner enjoyed – now she is on her own and their children have moved away. "I don't mind having a coffee and a snack in a café during the day but I won't eat out alone in the evening – of course I won't."

Relationships entail each person adapting to the needs, wishes and personalities of the other. We are, to a considerable extent, the product of our relationships, so when we lose someone close, our sense of who we are comes into question. According to Bowlby, depressive mood following loss is part of dismantling one's sense of self (1980). The period of withdrawal from usual activity is a time of deconstructing and, eventually, reconfiguring who we feel ourselves to be. And what we enjoy eating, when we choose to have mealtimes, how we feed ourselves, is part of that painful process.

This, from an interview with Dvina, a relative of mine widowed two years previously:

> *David loved food, he LOVED food! But he only ever wanted to eat curries, three meals a day. He would get up early every day to steam the rice for breakfast, even when we were both working. . . . But while he was receiving chemo they always had to be freshly cooked, not reheated. When he became really ill, I just couldn't manage to cook three fresh meals a day, so his sister came over from Mauritius and took over the kitchen while I cared for David. What he didn't eat went in the fridge and at the end of the day, when Mary and I were both exhausted, we would have his leftovers. And now, all I eat is toast and my grandson's leftovers. I have no appetite for cooking. My grandson has lost his taste for Mauritian food too.*

Prior to David's death, this couple had been the hub of social life for extended family and friends; their parties and Sunday lunches were legendary. I never left their home without a container or two of Dvina's wonderful curries and David's amazing fresh lemon and garlic pickle. Now, widowed, Dvina's past identity seems redundant to her and her relational world has shrunk. She is greatly loved, and I very much hope she will find a new way to live, comforted by David's continuing presence in her internal world.

Readjusting

Food waste! A woman who had lost her teenage son talked about how hard she found it to cook the correct amount of food. For months, both she and her husband continued to prepare an extra portion. Quantities in recipes all seemed inaccurate, and they felt guilty about the amount of food that went to the compost heap or recycling.

A man who had been the carer for his elderly mother until her death bemoaned that sliced bread came in such large loaves that it frequently turned mouldy before he could finish it. (It was news to him that he could freeze half the loaf for later use.) And a younger man whose girlfriend died redirected the rage of grief at the food industry. He felt discriminated against as a single person with the additional cost of buying ingredients in smaller packages and taunted by the "buy one, get one half-price" offers.

Gemma's friend recently asked about her "signature recipe." *I don't have one, though there are ingredients I put in lots of dishes. But I've just realised that many of them are quite new, things I didn't use when Dev was alive like onion seeds, paprika and fresh thyme. But I especially love cumin. Dev's skin smelled like cumin, warm and spicy, and I don't ever want to forget that.*

Bereavement changes us physiologically. Our bodies, cut off from the sustaining body of our loved one, become alien to us. Appetite, taste, weight, body shape, digestive functions – all are subject to alteration. While some comfort-eat, others lose all interest in food. Or perhaps, sooner or later, we embrace the opportunity to introduce new ingredients into our diet and enjoy, no longer compromising over what we eat. Of course, there may be guilt attached to redefining ourselves in this way, as if it is a betrayal of the dead to change one's eating habits. Perhaps those who are avoidant in their attachment style move on more quickly to abandon previous habits and traditions, including those regarding food, while preoccupied individuals cling to the past and struggle to make choices for themselves.

Relocating the lost object

> There is a time in life when you expect the world to be always full of new things. And then comes a day when you realise that is not how it will be at all. You see that life will become a thing made of holes. Absences. Losses. Things that were there are no longer. And you realise, too, that you have to grow around and between the gaps.
>
> (Macdonald, 2014, p. 71)

Macdonald's words exquisitely describe the transformation in one's sense of self that bereavement necessitates. For Bowlby, mourning is a natural process that ultimately enables adjustment to the new reality. When a loved one is no longer seated at the breakfast table with us in the morning or preparing dinner with us in the kitchen, they come to occupy a different space in our internal world of memories. This process takes time, often meets with resistance, and is the fundamental task of mourning. (Bowlby, 1980)

If we are what we eat, to paraphrase Brillat-Savarin ("Tell me what you eat, and I shall tell you what you are" 1971), when our diet changes, so do we. Taking refuge in fast food and biscuits, the extra kilos may feel like protective arms around us, keeping us hidden and safe in a newly unsafe, unfamiliar reality. Or ditching the fry-up and taking up carrot juice for breakfast reshapes the body, requiring a new wardrobe and raising questions about who we are now and how we present ourselves – in Victorian mourning black crepe, or eye-catching colours and figure-hugging outfits? And a healthy eating regime could be a step towards searching for a new partner.

I spoke with Stella a year or so after her partner died. She told me:

> Nick and I were together for twenty-six years, since we met at uni. We had a great life together, and three kids. We ate out a lot and loved big family lunches at the weekend – he was a real foodie. It's not surprising that I put

on quite a few kilos. Now, without intending it, I'm back to the weight I was when we met. I guess I just don't get pleasure from eating in the same way. I miss him like hell, and I'd rather have him back, but I'm happier with my body and feel healthier than for years.

Carlos is alone since his wife of fourteen years died. Now, two years after losing her, he is trying to move on with his life. He has tried Internet dating and taken one or two dates out to restaurants, but not to those that he and Maria loved, and he hasn't yet prepared a meal for them. He always enjoys cooking, taking every opportunity to invite family and friends over for dinner, and hopes that one day he will meet someone he'd like to introduce to everyone and impress with his culinary skills – but not just yet.

At special celebrations and important events, it is traditional to think of those loved ones who are no longer with us, to include them in our ongoing lives. We raise a glass to "absent friends and family" at weddings, christenings, Christmases and so on. In many cultures, offerings of food are made to the ancestors at special occasions (for instance, Día de los Muertos – the Mexican Day of the Dead). Though no longer present, the deceased can become an internal resource if we can manage to "grow around and between the gaps" left when a loved one dies. Bowlby (1980) described this process as the gradual relocation of the lost object.

In a few cultures, the deceased are literally taken into the self as an internal resource. In the practice of endo-cannibalism, "failure to eat a dead parent might mean poor health, or barrenness, or weak children, since the life essence has not been properly 'topped up'" (Visser, 2017, p. 12). Thankfully most of us manage to introject our "good attachment objects" without resorting to eating them.

Seema's wife, Jill, died suddenly from an undiagnosed heart condition. In a state of shock and unresolved recent trauma, Seema resorted to binge-eating to manage the intensity of her grief. As the pounds piled on she became isolated, ashamed to be seen in the social circle that had always been an important part of the couple's life together. Some months later she told me: "as I sat there today with the chocolates and biscuits in front of me I suddenly thought: *what* are *you doing?! No-one is going to step in now to stop you from going too far*. Jill had always kept me in check before, with food and with drink. She was always firm when she thought I'd had enough. Sometimes I resented her for it but really I was grateful." Jill was no longer present to protect her from losing control over her appetites, but her voice lived on in Seema's mind as she struggled through those difficult months alone. She was learning to contain herself, the legacy of having been loved, held and contained by her wife.

There were other occasions that Seema heard that restraining voice but chose to keep on eating, an active angry protest to Jill in the hope she would magically return to life to resume her protective role. But Seema knew it for what it was and could observe her own behaviour with amusement and self-compassion, knowing she could now take responsibility for her own choices.

For Matt MacAllester, preparing the Christmas meal was the culmination of his journey, through cooking, to mourn his mother.

> This was my chance to piece together the sort of big family meal and celebration my mother used to make the focal point of our year. It was just that, well, this was my meal, not hers. . . . I wanted her with me, yes, but I did not want her running the show.
>
> (2011, p. 208)

He wanted to prepare a celebratory feast for his wife, family and friends, and hoped his mother would have been proud of the culinary skills he had developed. But his attachment to the living was stronger than his need to keep her in the forefront of his mind; having reconnected with the exciting, fun-loving, passionate mother he had lost long ago, she had become a new, inspiring internal object, and he could build from that.

Su's siblings have migrated to different continents, but every year, on the anniversary of their father's death, they all prepare a curry to remember him – he had grown up in India. And Judy and her son Ollie have started a tradition marking the anniversary of Matthew dying by eating New York cheesecake, "partly to remember all the cheesecake Matt ate to keep up his calories – and partly because it's a tough day and we just deserve cake!"

Ben was in his early twenties when his father, Mark, died. Mark had been a carpenter and as a youngster Ben sometimes accompanied him as he worked, helping to carry tools and assemble flat-pack furniture. But Ben went to university and had a desk job rather than following in his dad's footsteps. A year or so after Mark died, things started to break or go wrong in the family home. The fridge gave up the ghost and needed replacing. Ben needed to dismantle the surrounding cupboards to remove it, using his father's screwdrivers and working out how Mark had constructed them. A couple of weeks after the new fridge freezer was installed, Ben told his sister; "Dad visited me in a dream last night. He said: 'that dairy drawer in the new fridge is an inefficient use of space. You should go back to keeping the cheese in a Tupperware box.' And he was right!"

Conclusion

We love people through food; through feeding others, delighting in being fed by them, and by sharing food. How we go about it is influenced by cultural, religious and historical factors. We accommodate each other's dietary needs and preferences as best we can. We make choices about what we eat based on identifications, aspirations, values and necessities. But our patterns of attachment, formed in the early years with our parents and within our families are also added to the mix. And when we lose a loved one, our appetite for both food and life are impacted.

I end with questions: what is your idea of the perfect meal? Why? Who would you share it with? And what might this say about your own relational history, and relationship with yourself?

Many thanks to all the individuals who have shared their stories with me and permitted me to share them with you. Clinical material has been disguised to protect client confidentiality.

References

Basil, P. (2019). *Be My Guest: Reflections on Food, Community and the Meaning of Generosity*. Edinburgh: Canongate.

Benoit, D., & Parker, K.C.H. (1994). Stability and transmission of attachment across three generations. *Journal of Child Development, 65*(5), 1444–1456.

Bowlby, J. (1969). *Attachment and Loss. Volume 1. Attachment*. London: Hogarth.

Bowlby, J. (1980). *Attachment and Loss. Volume 3. Loss: Sadness and Depression*. London: Hogarth.

Bretherton, I. (2003). Mary Ainsworth: Insightful observer and courageous theoretician. In G.A. Kimble & M. Wertheimer (Eds.), *Portraits of Pioneers in Psychology* (Vol. 5). Hillsdale, NJ: Erlbaum.

Brillat-Savarin, J. A. (1971). *The Physiology of Taste: Or Meditations on Transcendental Gastronomy*, translated by Fisher, M. F. K. New York, NY: Alfred A. Knopf.

Crandell, L.E., Patrick, M.P.H., & Hobson, R.P. (2003). "Still-face" interactions between mothers with borderline personality disorder and their 2-month-old infants. *British Journal of Psychiatry, 183*, 239–247.

Diamond, J. (2006). *The Third Chimpanzee: The Evolution and Future of the Human Animal*. New York: Harper Perennial.

Dunne, J., Rebay-Salisbury, K., Salisbury, R.B., Frisch, A., Walton-Doyle, C., & Evershed, R.P. (2019). Milk of ruminants in ceramic baby bottles from prehistoric child graves. *Nature, 574*, 246–248. https://doi.org/10.1038/s41586-019-1572-x.

Felitti, V.J. (2002). The relation between adverse childhood experiences and adult health: Turning gold into lead. *Permanente Journal, 6*(1), 44–47.

Fonagy, P., & Moran, G.S. (1990). Severe developmental psychopathology and brittle diabetes: The motivation for self-injurious behaviour. *Bulletin of the Anna Freud Centre, 13*(4), 231–248.

Fonagy, P., Steele, H., & Steele, M. (1991). Maternal representations of attachment during pregnancy predict the organisation of infant-mother attachment at one year of age. *Child Development, 62*, 891–905.

Forster, E.M. (2005). *Aspects of the Novel*. London: Penguin.

Fraiberg, S., Adelson, E., & Shapiro, V. (1975). Ghosts in the nursery: A psychoanalytic approach to the problems of impaired infant-mother relationships. In J. Raphael-Leff (Ed.), (2003) *Parent-Infant Psychodynamics: Wild Things, Mirrors and Ghosts*. London: Whurr.

Guide to the James and Joyce Robertson Film Series, Young Children in Brief Separation. (1969). London: Robertson Centre.

Herman, J.L. (1992). *Trauma and Recovery: From Domestic Abuse to Political Terror*. London: Pandora.

Hughes, D.A. (2018). *Building the Bonds of Attachment: Awakening Love in Deeply Traumatized Children* (3rd ed.). Lanham, MD: Rowman & Littlefield.

Kahr, B. (2007). The infanticidal attachment. *Attachment: New Directions in Psychotherapy and Relational Psychoanalysis, 1*, 117–132.

Kübler-Ross, E. (1969). *On Death and Dying: What the Dying Have to Teach Doctors, Nurses, Clergy and Their Own Families*. New York: Scribner.

Macdonald, H. (2014). *H Is for Hawk*. London: Jonathan Cape.

McAllester, M. (2011). *Bittersweet: Lessons from My Mother's Kitchen*. London: Bloomsbury.

Messina, S., Reisz, S., Hazen, N., & Jacobvitz, D. (2000). Not just about food: Attachments representations and maternal feeding practices in infancy. *Attachment and Human Development, 22*(5), 504–533.

Pincus, L., & Dare, C. (1978). *Secrets in the Family*. London: Faber and Faber.

Piontelli, A. (1992). *From Fetus to Child: An Observational and Psychoanalytic Study*. London: Routledge.

Robertson, J., & Robertson, J. (1989). *Separation and the Very Young*. London: Free Association.

Sette, G., Coppola, G., & Rosalinda, C. (2015). The transmission of attachment across generations: The state of art and new theoretical perspectives. *Scandinavian Journal of Psychology, 56*(3).

Slater, N. (2013). *Toast: The Story of a Boy's Hunger*. London: Fourth Estate.

Steele, H., Perez, A., Segal, F., & Steele, M. (2016). Maternal Adult Attachment Interview (AAI) collected during pregnancy predicts reflective functioning in AAIs from their first-born children 17 years later. *International Journal of Developmental Science, 10*(3–4), 113–120.

Visser, M. (2017). *The Rituals of Dinner: The Origins, Evolution, Eccentricities and Meaning of Table Manners*. London: Penguin.

Ward, M.J., Lee, S.S., & Lipper, E.G. (2000). Failure-to-thrive is associated with disorganized infant-mother attachment and unresolved maternal attachment. *Infant Mental Health Journal, 21*(6), 428–442.

Warner, V. (2019). *The Consolation of Food*. London: Pavilion.

Wheen, F. (2000). *Karl Marx*. London: Fourth Estate.

Williams, G. (1997). *Internal Landscapes and Foreign Bodies: Eating Disorders and Other Pathologies*. London: Karnac.

Winnicott, D.W. (1947). Hate in the countertransference. In (1992) *Through Paediatrics to Psychoanalysis* (pp. 194–203). London: Karnac.

Winnicott, D.W. (1971). *Playing and Reality*. London: Tavistock.

Wrangham, R. (2010). *Catching Fire: How Cooking Made Us Human*. London: Profile.

Chapter 2

"He's got a good appetite"

How do men experience attachment and food?

Graeme Galton

[F]ood is the most basic medium of communication from the first day of our lives. . . . The process of feeding sets up a whole tableau of feelings that affect not just our relationship with food, but our experience of closeness and intimacy.

(Orbach, 1993, p. 33)

Che tu abbia tanti figli maschi da nutrire.

(May you have sons to feed) Italian saying

Introduction

The literature on dysfunctional attitudes to food and eating increasingly recognises that men are affected by this issue too (Schoen, 2015). However, there has so far been little consideration of the role of the family in the formation of this specific aspect of maleness, particularly the undoubted links between food, feeding, attachment and being a little boy. How do boys and men experience attachment and food? How do they absorb and express their attachment pattern of behaviour through their relationship with food and eating? Preparing this chapter has given me a welcome opportunity to consider the influence of social mores, culture and family dynamics concerning gender while reflecting on how my male clients have talked about food and what this has revealed about their relational world, their attitude to their body and their place in the family.

Gender, culture, attachment and food

Analysing data from the United States and Canada, Baker and Milligan (2011) note evidence of baby boys being introduced to solid food earlier than baby girls. What might explain this? The authors conclude that, although males and females are equally likely to be breastfed, this continues for about a week less for boys than girls and solid food is introduced between one and two weeks earlier. Is there a feeling in parents that these boys need something more substantial than breastmilk at an earlier age than girls? Perhaps there is an unconscious bias in mothers and other caregivers that baby boys are not getting enough, that they need plenty of food to build them up and reinforce their masculine strength. Does this imply that in Western culture today there is a corresponding notion that eating plenty of food will make baby girls fat and diminish their femininity? Feminist theorists have long been concerned with the complexity of the mother–daughter relationship in patriarchal society. According to Orbach, "most women live with feelings of self-disgust and dislike" (1993, p. 59) in relation to their own bodies and appetites, and this is inevitably transmitted from mothers to their daughters. Findings by Johnson and Birch (1994) suggest that mothers more often restrict the food intake of preschool girls than that of boys. Thus, girls are socialised early on to eat less, to have fewer needs, to take up less space than their male counterparts.

But what about mothers and sons? If boys are "Other" and men are privileged in society, what is the nature of the mother-son relationship? How is this expressed through the way boys are fed? In an oft-quoted piece of research, Brunet and Lézine (1966) found a different pattern of behaviour among Italian mothers; while female babies were fed for an average time of twenty-five minutes, the mothers fed their boys for an average of forty-five minutes. The authors suggest that through this early inequality, daughters learn to accommodate the needs of others, whereas sons take in a different message with the milk; they may recognise and express their instinctual needs and expect these will be responded to.

Also from the original research comes data regarding breastfeeding (99 percent of boys breastfed compared to 66 percent of girls). While these statistics in some ways reinforce the idea that boys are "fed up" to develop their strength and to "have good appetites," it seems that these mothers, unlike their North American counterparts, weaned their daughters earlier than their sons. Perhaps their mothers' own needs – for continuing this most intimate of relationships with their boys – was part of the equation?

It may be argued that attitudes and lifestyles have changed in the fifty years or so between these two pieces of research, but anecdotal evidence supports the continuing preference for little boys and the existence of a different kind of bond between mothers and their sons in Italy, and no doubt other countries too, with a strong preference for chubby-cheeked little boys – "cicciotti." In her study of twins in Italy, Piontelli observed the greater maternal draw toward one rather the other: "In opposite-sex pairs choice was frequently and quite blatantly dictated by gender. Mothers adored their little boy" (Piontelli, 2002, p. 65).

So cultural attitudes to gender play a part in the way babies are nourished, preparing each infant for life within his or her community. The individual's relationship to food is thus framed by perceptions of masculinity and femininity.

> If the parents' expectations of their children are determined to such a degree by the child's sex, they will inevitably react accordingly from the very first moment they hold the child in their arms. This simple fact ensures that children of different sexes have completely different experiences of life.
>
> (Belotti, 1976, p. 31)

Including how they are fed.

Research into patterns of attachment highlight cultural aspects too, with a higher prevalence of avoidant/dismissing attachment found in Northern Europe and North America as opposed to Southern European and Latin cultures, where there is a greater prevalence of the ambivalent/preoccupied pattern. While the former is characterised by an emphasis on self-sufficiency (and is therefore more common where individualism is the norm), preoccupied attachment promotes dependency on others, with separation being discouraged (where extended family structures predominate). Orbach draws our attention to corresponding cultural attitudes to food, for instance describing English disdain and "the tension between those who perceive food as an aesthetic statement and those who continue to hold a fairly utilitarian attitude towards it," contrasting this with "other Western countries [where there is] a genuine love of food, and the hospitality it represents" (Orbach, 1993, pp. 32–33). If we transcribe this into the language of attachment, she suggests that the stereotypical British attitude to food is rather more dismissing, restricting, self-denying or purely functional, while the food-loving countries tend to be more communally minded, emotionally engaged, but potentially more preoccupied and enmeshed.

While attachment research does not generally find differences in patterns of attachment based on gender, there are inevitably not only cultural biases but also familial and individual expectations, preferences, pressures and fantasies invested in boys and girls. In some situations, sons are raised to separate early, breaking the close bond with mother to go out into the world in search of success, while in others, preferential treatment around food, with all that may imply, seems to keep boys tethered to mothers in enmeshed relationships. Women, particularly disenfranchised ones, may look to their sons to provide status for the family, perhaps also wishing to live vicariously through the boys' experiences and achievements. Early feeding may suggest something of the family expectations, aiming to give sons strength and stamina to study, work hard, get on in the world.

> An Indian mother . . . preconsciously experiences her newborn infant, especially a son, as the means by which her "motherly" identity is crystallized, her role and status in family and society established. She tends to perceive a son as a kind of saviour and to nurture him with gratitude and even reverence as well as with affection and care. For a range of reasons, the balance of nurturing may be so affected that the mother unconsciously demands that the child serve as an object of her own unfulfilled desires and wishes, however antithetical they may be to his own.
>
> (Kakar, 2002, pp. 28–29)

Her special nurturing, that may include feeding her son the "best" food and larger portions than allotted to his sisters, may come with a high price tag. Such boys may be both indulged and coerced.

Something similar is described by Belotti from an observation of a 13-month-old Mark with his (Italian) mother. Mark eats and sleeps well, though he is not yet walking. He is generally a contented infant who enjoys interacting with people. However, he is picked on by other children. His mother

> uses every possible method to get him to walk, play, and above all defend himself when attacked by other children. She complains that he does not react against the attacks of his companions. "What kind of boy are you?" she often says and then she draws him passionately to her breast saying "You're mummy's little man."
>
> (Belotti, 1976, p. 53)

This mixed message, "grow up quickly to be a strong, *masculine* man – but still depend on me, love me more than anyone, and never leave me" is a challenge for these boys and men to negotiate.

In some traditions, it is the duty of sons, especially the eldest, to care for elderly parents and, if necessary, provide for the family, while daughters are married out to become part of a different family; other cultures keep their daughters close with the expectation that they will help with younger siblings and take on the care of the older generation. Sons carry the family name but do not have the same familial responsibilities as their sisters. This is likely to have repercussions not only on how and what children are fed but also on kitchen duties.

Regarding gender, there is an interesting recent development in Japan. Historically, Japanese society has encouraged women to be slim and delicate while, according to Castro-Vásquez, men's bodies were more or less ignored. There is now a growing concern about obesity, with both men and women presenting as overweight or obese in a culture where this is perceived as having a "disreputable body." Shame is a powerful sanction in Japan. What is curious is that while one in five women aged between 40 and 74 currently have high metabolic syndrome ("visceral fat syndrome" or *metabo*) or are considered at risk of developing it, that figure is one in every two men in the same age range. While a sedentary lifestyle and adoption of a Western fast food diet are blamed, the reason for this gender discrepancy is not so clear. Anecdotally, one possibility is the higher level of alcohol consumption among men. However, when "metabo" men come into contact with the health care system, the professionals enlist the assistance of their wives: "A firmly dedicated wife was key to complying with guidance" (Castro-Vázquez, 2018).

Some of these overweight men reject the "obese" label; they

> contended that regardless of being corpulent, they were healthy and thus slimming down was unneeded. They uphold a form of embodiment underpinned by the "emotionalization of the fat body" to suggest that their embodied experiences were not appalling but appealing and a symbol of wellbeing in a country where sizeism, anorexia and bulimia remain endemic.
>
> (Ibid.)

Meanwhile, another phenomenon is developing, to some extent fuelled by fashion. Just as Western women's bodies were once shaped by the fashion industry, so in Japan it is young men who are now the focus. But there are other reasons why they choose to become "herbivorous boys" (*sōshokukei danshi*). One factor is a conscious rejection of the stereotype of the suit-wearing, office-working Japanese man who is a slave to his employer. Generally, *danshi* are perceived as "weak and feminized" due to their preference for aesthetics and the beautification of the male body. They are seen as "incomplete men" (Ibid.). But tellingly, these herbivorous boys "live with their parents, enjoy homemaking, and do not smoke, drink, or maintain the slovenly rooms associated with bachelors, they exhibit little interest in sex, romance, or corporate advancement" (Bardsley, 2011, p. 133).

Research has not helped us understand these men's early attachment histories, but their current ones are relevant; while "*metabo*" depend on their wives for dietary care, "herbivorous boys" show little interest in adult romantic relationships and are unwilling to separate from their parents. Either these young men prepare their own meals in the parental home or their families of origin must accommodate their preference for a vegan diet.

Fathers and sons

What of boys' relationships with fathers? Again, the Italian twin study found that soon after the babies were born, "fathers of dizygotic twins were more openly biased towards one child. Again, gender made choice especially easy in the case of opposite-sex twins. Fathers, like the mothers, usually doted on their boys but also chose on the basis of apparent constitution" (Piontelli, 2002, p. 68), perhaps, Piontelli wonders, anticipating a future of "sharing manly interests, teaching them a sport and indulging in man's talk" (Ibid.) – so a father's wish to have a child who is like himself, to confirm his own identity, to continue the family name and values. But this may lead to an overidentification by the adult, with his son perceived as an extension of himself and as a vessel to project his own needs and feelings into. If the little boy's "constitution" is very different, making this paternal fantasy unlikely, the son may be rejected, a disappointment in the eyes of his father. There may even be a question about the true paternity of this child that can create friction within the family. Just as mothers are more likely to project self-dislike onto their daughters, the same can be true of fathers with their same-sex children. In any culture where his partner has worked to make herself and the son into an indivisible couple, it would not be surprising for a father to feel excluded, envious and resentful and perhaps become more hostile to and critical of the "rivalrous" boy, with a wish to push him out of the home quickly. Sons may identify with their fathers, idealise them as role models with qualities to aspire to, fear and despise them, or determine to grow into a "different kind of man." Some boys are fatherless.

We may hope and believe that gender-based stereotypes are a rarity now in the twenty-first century. Even if that is the case, most of you who are reading this chapter and most of our clients were born into a world where expression of gender identity was shaped from the start by these values. How we were all fed played a part.

In the therapy room

As Orbach reminds us, "food is the most basic medium of communication" (1993, p. 33). Relationship and eating are closely associated, and the place of food in the lives and stories of men conveys their unique experiences of attachment. Using examples drawn from clinical practice and public life, this chapter explores possible links between early attachment experiences for boys and the meaning of food and eating that they take into adulthood. In approaching the writing of this chapter, I have used the binary concept of sexual difference rather than the more complex and nuanced distinctions of gender identity, although these would also have been relevant to this inquiry. I have chosen not to increase the complexity by considering gender identity (Schoen, 2015). With apologies, I have made a simplistic distinction between male and female that does not consider other categories of gender identity, such as transgender, gender neutral, non-binary, agender, pangender, genderqueer, two-spirit and third gender.

Preoccupied caregiving using food

Michel was in his sixties when he began therapy. He had come to me somewhat reluctantly, saying that his adult daughters and his wife had told him he needed therapy to deal with his headaches and irritability. It soon became clear that Michel was chronically anxious, although he was quite unaware of this. His headaches and irritability were the most obvious expressions of this anxiety, which he tried to manage by keeping himself busy all the time. He was always working on a project, always planning for the future, particularly financial planning to keep the family safe against imagined catastrophe. Michel was a retired engineer but was now busier than ever with numerous business-related activities and commitments. He never looked back, never spoke about the past, never reminisced about his earlier life; he was always looking forward. He was not an obvious candidate for attachment-based therapy.

One focus of his manic activity was preparing and serving food for his family. Whenever his daughters and their families were staying with him, Michel would spend all morning sitting at the kitchen table preparing an elaborate lunch. By mid-morning, he would also have begun preparations for the evening meal. If any of the family were going out for an extended time, he ensured they were well-stocked with food. All this he did happily and efficiently and without fuss, but it was relentless and left him exhausted.

As we explored this pattern of behaviour and tried to understand its origin and meaning, it emerged that Michel's mother had done the same when he was a child. Her first question after breakfast was to ask what he wanted for lunch. She had lived through near starvation during the Nazi occupation of her country during the Second World War, and one way that she expressed her love for her son had been to keep him well fed so he would never go hungry as she had done. Although money was tight, she served elaborate meals made from the best quality ingredients she could afford. He was an only child and she called him her "prince"; with all the royal feasts she served him, it was surprising that Michel had not become overweight. She had a preoccupied attachment pattern of behaviour, characterised by a high level of emotional expressiveness and an encouragement of dependency, and this constant feeding had been her way of showing love for her son. Michel had inherited his mother's preoccupied attachment pattern and expressed it in the same way; preparing lavish meals was a way of showing his love for his family and friends. It also provided a somewhat manic outlet for his need to be busy and his need to be planning for the future against vaguely imagined hard times. Although very loving, his anxious mother had not been best placed to help Michel regulate his own agitation. Keeping herself busy with food preparation and fussing over him pushed away her anxious feelings, and he now replicated this pattern of behaviour to manage his own affect. Michel's father was seldom mentioned in the therapy, remaining a somewhat vague figure in the story, and it was not clear how much Michel had experienced him as a paternal role model. Certainly, Michel appeared to be identified with his mother, and it was her attachment and care-giving style that he adopted with his own family. With his father being such an insubstantial presence in the childhood home, it is not surprising that a strong mutual identification would develop between mother and her only child, her "prince."

As the therapy progressed, Michel could never quite understand my interest in his childhood experiences, and he could not see how they were relevant to his life now. However, he continued to come to the sessions, and he tolerated my wish to understand his past and my tendency to make links with the present. It seemed to me that, because Michel was always more comfortable when he was the one feeding others, he found it difficult to take in the therapeutic feeding that I was offering to him. Nonetheless, when the therapy ended after about six months, Michel's anxiety had begun to diminish. Although he still had a preoccupied attachment pattern and was still a "feeder," he was generally happier and less irritable with those around him.

The needs of the son or the father?

While feminist writers addressing the subject of eating disorders in women are concerned with the mother–daughter relationship, men's struggles with food and the role of the father are often overlooked. But men's issues with identity and "masculinity" that can contribute to serious problems with eating (anorexia, bulimia, over-eating leading to obesity) may have origins in problematic attachment between boys and their fathers.

The British actor Christopher Eccleston, writing in his autobiography, describes himself as a lifelong anorexic and dysmorphic (Eccleston, 2019). For many years this was a "guilty secret" because it was shameful for a working-class male from the north of England to have an eating disorder. His body dysmorphia was present, he believes, from when he was a young child; by the time he left home he had been suffering with it for many years. He would look at himself in the mirror, aged 6 or 7, and be critical of his physical appearance, thinking that he had a pot belly and knobbly knees. He describes himself as "a lifelong body-hater" (Ibid., p. 99). At the same time, food was particularly important in the home as he grew up and was a deeply emotional matter. His mother was an especially good cook whose day was planned around mealtimes. However, the dinner table became a battleground with his father, who insisted young Christopher finish what was on his plate. In the face of this emphasis on food and eating, he felt oppressed. Food became associated with family control and pressure. "Mealtimes became all-consuming for me in a very negative way" (p. 96).

Without a secure base at home, when Christopher left to study drama in London he had a crisis of identity, a feeling that he did not belong in his own skin. He felt out of place and intimidated by the other students, experiencing his world as hostile. But the one part of his life he could now control was food. By not eating, he put a boundary between himself and the outside world, using anorexia as "the rigid 'no' that keeps food, people and needs at bay, away from the reality of life" (Dana, 1987, p. 59). He was trying to manage his sense of being the wrong person in the wrong place, to avoid the shame he felt because of his northern working-class origins. His body became his preoccupation and his project. He writes; "When I looked at myself in the mirror, I was constantly seeing fat. Actually, I was skeletal" (Eccleston, 2019, p. 102). He could now avoid associations with the hated mealtimes of his childhood by barely eating but, whatever he did, he still *felt* fat and ugly. He worked hard to give others the impression that he was a tough male in keeping with cultural expectations of the era, but he felt quite different from this inside. He writes; "I felt emasculated to be suffering what I felt at the time to be a female condition" (Ibid. p. 104). This added to his burden of shame.

It is ironic that, in trying to hide aspects of themselves they deem shameful, anorexics make themselves more visible. However, in the 1980s it was unlikely that a man's thinness would be recognised as evidence of anorexia, as this was generally perceived as a uniquely "female problem." Also, Christopher's skeletal looks worked well for his career, giving him a distinctively striking appearance. He likens acting to the modelling industry; to achieve the image that was in vogue, high cheek bones and a cadaverous look, he needed to starve himself. Believing he lacked any ability as an actor, he did everything he could to at least make himself look the part.

There was an intersection between the demands of his career, as he saw them, and his distorted and controlling relationship with his body and food intake that can be directly traced back to his childhood home and insecure attachment to his father. Christopher's father was very thin, and he used to tell the family that as a child in the 1930s he had been hungry much of the time. These anguished memories of hunger made eating a deeply emotional issue in the Eccleston household. His father's own basic survival needs for food were barely met, and it was intolerable for him to see his child leave meals unfinished. In a reversal of roles, the son was forced to eat to meet the father's unconscious hunger, but the domineering insistence on finishing what was on the plate also expressed the father's urge to care for his son, to ensure his survival. This was incompatible with the son's need to be a separate person, in charge of his own body. Christopher both identified with his father and rejected him. He rejected him by engaging in the dinner table battles about eating, but he also modelled himself on his father, both in body shape and in feeling hungry most of the time.

The urge to disentangle himself from his father and to be acknowledged as a person in his own right had begun with conflict at the dinner table. Later, when he moved away from his father, the need to separate from him psychologically continued, with the battle morphing into a refusal to feed himself. Alongside this difficult relational dynamic, cultural notions of masculinity also played a role in the genesis of his eating disorder. The north of England was traditionally a centre of industry, and most boys would eventually be employed in manufacturing, dock work or other physical labour. So the feeding up of sons prepared them for strenuous, "manly" work, and often the role of father was to toughen up their sons in readiness. There was also high unemployment and poverty when Christopher was a child, so his father's anxiety to build up his son's strength had an extra urgency about it.

Historically, male roles in society and within the family and prescribed notions of "masculinity" have changed, but they add a potent if often unspoken ingredient in a boy's upbringing. Implicit and explicit messages are absorbed in interactions with other people. In many countries now there are wider possibilities for men than previously, and fathers may play a very different part in the lives of their children than their own fathers did. Paternity rights are often enshrined in law, varying in generosity from country to country. Male role models are unlike those in our parents' early lives (and possibly our own). One obvious example is the division of labour in the home; certainly, until the 1960s or even later, while men went out to work to support the family, women stayed home to look after children and provide food for everyone. The kitchen was her domain. This is still the case in some cultures. For many men of those generations, there was no expectation to cook the dinner, and boys were rarely taught how to prepare their own meals; they were dependent on women to feed them. If his wife became ill or died, or they divorced, a man would struggle to cook and care for himself or his children and may then need to rely on family members to help out.

Regarding notions of masculinity, in current society there is a greater emphasis now on body image driven by social media and consumerism. In the name of self-care and good health, gym membership, exercise regimes, diets and protein powders are marketed vociferously at young men. While there is a positive aspect to this development, an awareness of the importance of exercise and nutrition for individuals whose work life is increasingly sedentary, it is a matter of degree whether this amounts to enjoyment of the body and self-care or calculated consumer society pressure that promotes similar discontent, body shaming and disease with the body for men as women have long experienced. Boys' and men's bodies are increasingly under scrutiny, objectified – and often found wanting. Where there is also a history of insecure attachment, there is a greater risk of shame, self-hatred and the development of eating disorders.

Overeating to feed an attachment need

When Daniel arrived at my consulting room for our first meeting, he was a big presence. He came through the door breathless and flushed after climbing one flight of stairs to my office. He shook my hand enthusiastically and lowered himself onto the sofa. Daniel was in his fifties, well-spoken, well-dressed, full of exuberance and the owner of a successful business consultancy employing around one hundred people. He was also overweight and clearly unfit. As he told me about himself, he explained how depressed and hopeless he was feeling despite his apparent ebullience. His relationship with his wife was not good, and he was frequently arguing with his son, who was away at university. His doctor had instructed him to lose weight or his health would be at serious risk.

Daniel's parents had been quite poor when he was growing up. They ran a café in a rundown neighbourhood, and the family lived in a small flat above the premises. He remembered various frightening and embarrassing events in his childhood, including visits from debt collectors, mice infestations and not having enough money to buy his school uniform. His parents had struggled to make a success of the business, and this took most of their time and energy, so there was little of either left for Daniel and his brothers. His parents were not actively unkind to Daniel, but there had been a degree of benign neglect. However, they owned a café, so the children never went hungry. Indeed, there was plenty of stodgy and comforting food, and his parents made sure that both he and his brother had as much to eat as they wanted. His mother used to talk about the need for him to build up his strength, and he was encouraged to indulge his desire for food.

At school, Daniel felt his shame and embarrassment were palpable. Neglect and poverty led him to feel anxious and insecure and, above all, inferior. Nonetheless, he was a good scholar and gradually found escape in his ability to do well in exams. He was eventually offered a place at a prestigious university to read mathematics and became the first person in his family to have a university education.

At university, Daniel reinvented himself. He told no one about his background, where he had grown up or his parents' jobs, and he worked hard to acquire an accent like those around him. After graduating he set up a company with a friend. Over the years the business thrived; he bought his partner's share of the business and was now the sole owner. However, when he came to see me, Daniel was having something of a midlife crisis. He was acutely aware of the things he had not done in life, seeing failure and inadequacy in all his decisions and relationships. He also had some business worries and was feeling depressed and hopeless. His career involved a lot of business lunches, and these were often lavish meals at expensive restaurants. As his mood had declined, his eating and drinking had increased, and by the time I met him, he was very overweight. He explained to me how difficult it was to manage his weight as the professional demands of entertaining clients at good restaurants were intrinsic to his business. His wife was worried about his health and his doctor was telling him to change his lifestyle, but Daniel felt that nothing could be done and seemed to be accepting of the consequences.

He already recognised that the years of lavish lunches at nice restaurants were partly a reaction to the poverty and neglect of his childhood; he was literally filling himself up with extravagance and excess to show that he was successful and affluent. Rather than running a local café, as his parents had done, he was dining in high-class restaurants. What we eventually understood was that, at the same time, he was still full of self-loathing, still carried the shame of poverty, even though he was now far from poor. His internal picture of himself as not good enough, not interesting enough, not important enough to hold his parents' attention persisted. He was literally making himself into a big presence so that he was unmissable. At the same time, he hated his body and was attacking it by stretching it out of shape. He also had a strong sense of his own ageing and mortality and it now seemed as if he was doing so much damage to his body that he was killing himself with rich food and expensive wine. He told me that he could not imagine himself living more than a few years longer and did not expect to reach his sixtieth birthday. He had an exercise treadmill at home, and he used this intermittently under the encouragement of his wife, but his weight stubbornly refused to shift.

We did not actually spend much of the psychotherapy specifically talking about food or eating, nor did we try to change his behaviour around his eating or his weight. I understood Daniel's problems as primarily relational. A lot of the therapeutic work focused on his childhood and on his relationships, both in the past and in the present, and in particularly on his current problematic relationship with his son. I was able to help him make better guesses about what his son was thinking and feeling. He had been seeing his son as a projection of himself, wanting him to achieve even more financial and social success than he himself had done, to take even greater strides away from his own impoverished childhood on his behalf. This ambition had become the battleground with his son. In one session, I said to him, "With all your ambitions for your son, it sounds as if you are trying to fatten him up, rather than helping him to feel OK about himself."

In childhood, Daniel's parents had sought to compensate for their unavailability by providing an abundance of calorific food, and this became equated with attachment, providing a false security. Having to work long hours, their time was scarce, but their food was plentiful, and Daniel had felt the comfort of filling his stomach rather than the comfort of their presence and attention. This pattern became internalised, and when his attachment needs for safety and support were activated, he turned again to eating. His unmet longing for love and proximity appeared to be satisfied by his encounters with food rather than through meaningful, intimate relationships with people. Also, just as his parents had been unable to see Daniel's needs as separate from their own, he struggled to view his own son as a person in his own right. One of the things we did in therapy was to help Daniel recognise and manage his preoccupied attachment pattern with his son, for example, by helping him find ways to offer supportive guidance without being overly controlling, and to see his own son's needs as separate from his own. Daniel worked hard on himself and his relationships in the therapy. Gradually, his relationship with his son improved, as did his mood; he became less depressed and less anxious. Unsurprisingly, as his relationships improved, he began eating less and lost some weight. By the time he left therapy, after about a year, he was noticeably less overweight, less flushed and less breathless and was starting to feel better about himself.

Cooking as a link with a secure base from childhood

Some men do not talk much in therapy about food and eating but do talk about cooking; I have had more men than women describe to me their use of cooking for affect regulation, particularly as a calming activity. David, a man in his thirties who worked as a project manager, told me that he would come home at the end of a stressful day, his head full of work-related thoughts, and look forward to being "at work" in the kitchen within a minute or two of walking through the door. He would put on music and quickly become absorbed in the activity of cooking. These were not elaborate dinner party set-piece menus he was preparing but everyday meals for himself and his wife. He said he could lose himself in cooking more than in any other activity. His pleasure was more in the process of cooking itself and how it made him feel rather than the dishes he produced, or the meaning of providing the meal for his wife, or the sharing of the meal with her. Affect regulation was his immediate motivation for cooking rather than attachment need.

We explored where his love of cooking might have originated. His mother had been a good cook, but he did not get involved in the food preparation with her when he was growing up, and his father had not cooked at all at that time; he worked away for long periods, leaving David at home with his mother and younger brother. He missed his father greatly during these absences and describes himself as being quite clingy to his mother when his father was away. We came to understand that he might have been anxious at these times that his mother would leave too. During these periods when his father was absent, the kitchen had been the focus of family life, and David would spend his time after school in that cosy environment, doing his homework while his mother prepared the evening meal. The kitchen became his secure base to return to.

When David was 11, his father was transferred abroad to work for several years and David's mother and brother moved with him. However, instead of joining them, he was sent to an English boarding school. He felt abandoned by his parents and was desperately unhappy for the first year or two. Eventually, he adapted to the new environment, found his place amongst the other boys and grew to like it well enough. However, at boarding school, as well as having no access to his parents, the kitchen was out of bounds. Meals emerged from the school kitchens and were served to the boys in the dining hall. Food during these years was stripped of its relational ingredient.

Leaving school for university, David rediscovered the environment of the kitchen as a secure base that helped him regulate his feelings. He began to cook for himself for the first time, and gradually it became an important part of his routine and a significant way to manage stress, especially around essays and exams. Later, when he started working, the kitchen remained his favourite room in the house, and he continued to use cookery as a way of unwinding after a long day at work. The kitchen represented a link with childhood security, just as being kept out of the kitchen had represented separation, loss and alienation at boarding school. He used the homely activity of cooking to connect with the comfort and safety experienced in the kitchen of his childhood.

Although David spoke in sessions about cooking, he never mentioned food or eating. As well as the security of the kitchen, cooking was for David a creative process without pressure or obligation. His job involved dealing with people and carried a lot of responsibility. In contrast, when he was working in his kitchen he was quite often alone, and he felt no responsibility or pressure. This freedom was crucial to his pleasure. Perhaps he was able to relax so much when he was cooking in part because he did not *have* to do it. His wife was not particularly interested in cooking and appreciated him taking on the role of providing meals but did not expect it of him. He had the luxury of feeling no expectations from others, no pressure on him. There was no obligation to cook; no one was expecting to be fed by him every evening. He could unwind in his own domain for a time, creating a transitional space between his work and home lives in which to sink into reverie and "play." In the Winnicottian sense, he could enjoy the experience of being self-absorbed on his own in his kitchen because of his childhood experience of being alone in the presence of his mother as she prepared their meals.

> Gradually, the ego-supportive environment is introjected and built into the individual's personality, so there comes about a capacity to actually be alone. Even so, theoretically, there is always someone present, someone who is equated ultimately and unconsciously with the mother, the person who, in the early days and weeks, was temporarily identified with her infant, and for the time being was interested in nothing else but the care of her own infant.
>
> (Winnicott, 1958, p. 36)

He had internalised his mother and was now connecting with her as he prepared ingredients to cook. In terms of his attachment style, David seemed to have a broadly secure attachment to his wife, as well as to his now ageing parents. I wonder if those cosy evenings of his childhood, spent in the kitchen with his mother, were an important developmental ingredient in his capacity now to have secure attachments as an adult.

Food has no taste without the company of others

In contrast to David and Michel, Stephen did not like cooking, had never liked cooking, and felt he was a poor cook. Neither did he enjoy food nor being in the kitchen; he fed himself simply to keep himself alive. The only time that Stephen gained any pleasure from meals was when he ate with other people. He told me that he had no interest in eating by himself; it was if food had no taste without the company of others.

Stephen was 71 years old and had been in therapy with me for several years, primarily battling his tendency towards depression. When he began therapy, he could barely get out of bed in the morning and occasionally missed his sessions with me for this reason. Gradually, his depressive state and his general functioning had improved, but he remained susceptible to low mood. His parents had likewise found it difficult to get much joy from life, including a failure to find pleasure from food and cooking. His childhood memories of his mother in the kitchen were a joyless experience. He never felt the slightest wish to help with food preparation and his parents did not involve him. Neither of them were good cooks, and mealtimes were regarded as necessary but sombre affairs.

Stephen was divorced and lived on his own; his children were now grown up with families of their own. Despite his parents' emotional struggles, Stephen had always found pleasure in being with other people and had a wide circle of friends who were important to him and with whom he kept in regular contact. His emotional and physical health were relatively good when the Coronavirus health crisis first struck in 2020 and there were several months of lockdown in the United Kingdom. People were restricted to their homes; non-essential shops, offices and factories were closed, and workers who could work remotely from home were instructed to do so. Overnight, for most people, contact with others was dramatically reduced. People over 70 were regarded as particularly vulnerable and were told to shield from infection by isolating themselves in their homes. Stephen was in this vulnerable group, so from one day to the next, all his contact with others had to move online, using remote video calls and telephone. His therapy with me was fortnightly at this point, and suddenly sessions had to move online.

At the beginning of the confinement, Stephen managed quite well with the restrictions and the isolation. However, after a few weeks he came to his online session in a state of distress, telling me that the previous fortnight had been dreadful. He outlined a string of disasters and disappointments. One particular meal had turned out badly and the food had been awful; he had felt like a failure; he had become lonely and stopped eating; he had lost weight; he had become depressed and had stopped replying to emails; he had miscalculated his food order from the supermarket and had accidentally run low on food. In the space of two weeks he had moved from being high functioning to barely functioning at all. Fortunately, a friend had become concerned when she did not get a reply to her message and had alerted his sons, who had responded quickly and helpfully. However, Stephen had scared himself with how quickly he had gone into decline. In the therapy, we were able to understand that, for him, eating was a *relational* activity that lost its meaning when done alone. The forced isolation had led to him unintentionally starve himself.

We immediately increased the frequency of the sessions (for extra therapeutic "feeding"), and his children kept a much closer eye on him. I think the additional caregiving he then received from those around him activated a self-caregiving part of himself, and he was quite quickly able to look after himself well enough once more. With the support of his family and friends, Stephen regained some confidence with food and cooked a couple of modest meals that he felt were a success so that he could feel he was a good enough cook. He was also able to set up some online classes and activities to help him feel more connected with others. For his birthday, he had an online party, with his friends toasting him from their homes. Sharing a meal with the people close to him was the thing he had missed most during the lockdown so, as soon the restrictions were eased slightly, he organised a picnic in the park with his son and his family and felt reconnected with them again.

The attachment needs of the parent projected as the needs of the child

Separation and reunion are themes that run through all these men's encounters with food. Christopher's anorexia was an internalised battle to separate from his father; for Daniel, food had been a substitute for parents who were absent or distracted; Michel's preoccupied feeding brought the family together at the dinner table; Stephen lost all interest in eating when he could not share the meal with others; and David tried to be cooking in the kitchen within a few minutes of arriving home from work, after being separated all day from his secure base (and, perhaps, to neutralise the anxiety he had felt when sent away from his family to boarding school).

In some of these cases, the attachment needs of the parents had been expressed through their attitude to food, to mealtimes and to the child's eating. This was certainly the case in Christopher's family, when his father insisted that he eat everything on his plate; it was also true for Daniel's parents, who gave him plentiful food to compensate for their scarce attention while they struggled to earn an adequate living, and for Michel's mother when she began preparing the next meal as soon as the last was finished. These well-meaning parents were unconsciously projecting their own attachment-related anxiety into the child through how they were fed. In the cases of Daniel and Michel, this was internalised and carried into adulthood, replicated in their own parenting. For both, separating the parent's needs from the child's was an important task of the therapy, understanding where the anxiety originated and making sense of it.

Were the parental attachment interactions that shaped these men's relationships with food influenced by them being male? Undoubtedly, yes. For Daniel and Christopher, parental approval had been conditional on them eating heartily as befitted the expectation of boys. Traditionally, boys are served larger portions than girls and often with the "best" ingredients, whether the most nutritious or the most extravagant. This was in keeping with prevalent ideas about masculinity, both within the family and the wider culture. Daniel had been told specifically that he needed to build up his strength; as long as he had a "healthy appetite" his parents could be assured that they were doing a good job of raising him. Would these individuals have been overfed in this way if they had been girls? Michel's mother called him her "prince," and she went to a lot of trouble to serve him meals to match this idealised view of him. As noted earlier, mothers are more likely to exalt their sons than their daughters. Stephen felt deeply incompetent at feeding himself and feeding others, despite valuing meals as relational experiences. Would he have felt more agency around food and feeding if he had been encouraged to cook as he grew up and had been expected to share in the cooking for his family? David was able to use cooking for affect regulation perhaps partly because, as a man, no one had expected him to take responsibility for preparing meals, leaving him free of pressure to enjoy his kitchen, recreating his secure base and connecting with the mother and childhood home he had internalised. For each of these men, the way attachment needs are expressed through food and feeding was influenced by the specific place of the little boy in his family of origin, but also by the complex identifications that existed between boys with their mothers or their fathers.

Conclusion

The social constructs of femininity and masculinity, of what it means to be a girl and what it means to be a boy, can only be understood within the specific cultural context of the individual and her or his family. For all of us, just like the clinical examples in this chapter, attitudes to food and eating are passed down within families from one generation to the next, like recipes. This is linked with and parallel to attachment patterns of behaviour, which also tend to be consistent through the generations. Hopefully, existing research into the intergenerational transmission of attachment patterns can be expanded to increase our understanding of the ways that attitudes to food and feeding form part of this transmission process. For example, there is emerging evidence that a caregiver's attachment pattern of behaviour is likely to influence their feeding practices with their child (Messina et al., 2020).

We need to recognise that these attitudes are not the same for men and women, and we need to better understand how these differences express themselves. This will help psychotherapists such as myself be more attuned in the therapeutic feeding of our clients.

References

Baker, M., & Milligan, K. (2011). *Sex Differences in the Care of Young Children in Canada and the U.S.* www.semanticscholar.org. Accessed on 12 July 2020.

Bardsley, J. (2011). The Oyaji gets a makeover: Guides for Japanese salaryman in the new millennium. In J. Bardsley, & L. Miller (Eds.), *Manners and Mischief: Gender, Power, and Etiquette in Japan* (pp. 114–135). Berkeley, CA: University of California Press.

Belotti, E.G. (1976). *What Are Little Girls Made Of? The Roots of Feminine Stereotypes.* New York: Schocken.

Brunet, O., & Lézine, I. (1966). *I Primi Anni del Bambino.* Rome: Armando.

Castro-Vázquez, G. (2018). A healthy, chubby Japanese man (*genki na debu chan*). *American Journal of Men's Health*, *12*(4), 1138–1150. Accessed on 18 August 2020.

Dana, M. (1987). Boundaries: One-way mirror to the self. In M. Lawrence (Ed.), *Fed Up and Hungry: Women, Oppression and Food* (pp. 46–60). London: The Women's Press.

Eccleston, C. (2019). *I Love the Bones of You: My Father and the Making of Me.* London: Simon & Shuster.

Early food and feelings

> The early simple path between eating and feeling happy.
>
> (Gopnik, 2011, p. 6)

Food and feelings become mixed and mingled from early doors – via cupboard doors more precisely, according to early theories of relationships which were based on food and feeding. Cupboard love theories were either behaviourist (with one of the most well-known theorists being Pavlov, known for his classical conditioning of dogs) or psychoanalytic, pioneered by Freud. The common feature in cupboard love is that an infant attaches to his or her caregivers because they provide food. Thus, a relationship with the caregiver is a by-product of "the early simple path between eating and feeling happy" (Gopnik, 2011, p. 6).

Food was central to the development of attachment theory; Bowlby disputed cupboard love and instead trod the path first laid by Darwin, proposing that attachment is a biological instinct genetically "wired" into us because of our evolutionary history and is present at birth. Our attachment behavioural system is therefore designed to ensure our survival and, for children, to limit long-term separations from a primary caregiver (Sbarra & Borelli, 2019). Around the same time, over in Wisconsin, Harlow (1958) was testing this very idea in rhesus monkeys and found that monkeys separated from their birth mothers chose something comfortable to cling to, only moving to an inanimate food source when driven by hunger, and that this clinging was a uniquely attachment behaviour. For Bowlby, who insisted that his theory be supported by research, this provided strong evidence that the nature of love in the earliest relationship between mother and baby could not be boiled down to food alone.

In his own work, Bowlby observed that across all human cultures young, vulnerable infants display specific emotional and behavioural reactions following separation from their stronger, older, wiser caregivers, including protest, despair and – eventually – detachment. He suggested that the set-goal of the attachment behavioural system was proximity to an emotionally available and responsive caregiver, especially during an experience that is either physically or psychologically dangerous or distressing, such as hunger. By obtaining proximity to the attachment figure, the infant not only gets fed but receives soothing and social interaction – in other words a relationship – as part of this. Freud considered this secondary to the "satisfied need for nourishment" (Freud, 1940, p. 188), whereas for Bowlby "the young child's hunger for his mother's love and presence is as great as his hunger for food" (Bowlby, 1982, p. 28). So cupboard love theories are not entirely wrong; associations between food and relationships are important, as we shall see later. We might just need to look beyond the cupboard for the primary significance, which is not food and eating but attachment to that person who opens the cupboard.

What feelings are we feeding?

Right from the start food becomes a way to feed our feelings, and throughout life feelings influence when, what and how much we eat. One of the most reliable, everyday examples is that many of us tend to be bad-tempered or irritable as a result of hunger – a feeling that has come to be known as "hangry" (MacCormack & Lindquist, 2019). But sometimes the greatest insights into feelings occur when we eat but are not even hungry. Sometimes the food itself allows us to work backwards to find the feelings and the context; opening a bottle of champagne tends to signal the celebration of success, whereas Nigella Lawson suggests her chocolate fudge cake is "the sort of cake you'd want to eat the whole of when you'd been chucked" (Lawson, 2011, p. 47). The power of sugar to soothe appears to be present from the very beginning, with effects demonstrated in those as young as one day old (Blass & Smith, 1992).

Nigella's philosophy takes us to an area of food literature and research that still has many unresolved questions: emotional or comfort eating; the kind of eating where the body is in no real need of calories and feelings take over. Since feelings are often seen as "fuzzy" (Lowry et al., 2009), it may be useful to have a scientific definition of comfort eating, but immediately we face a problem: "comfort eating," "emotional eating" and even "stress eating" all make appearances in the literature. All terms refer to altered eating behaviour, yet researchers differ in how they conceptualise the triggering context, with comfort eating and emotional eating referring to eating in response a broader range of negative feelings, including stress, sadness, anger and boredom (Tomiyama et al., 2015).

Sadness would likely be one of the feelings that motivates baking and eating Nigella's chocolate cake in its entirety, and research supports the comforting effects of chocolate to some degree. Eating milk chocolate after watching a sad film scene improved negative mood in a group of participants to a greater extent than consuming dark chocolate with 70–99 percent cocoa or no food at all, but effects were short-term, only lasting for three minutes (Macht & Mueller, 2007). Other work, however, found that chocolate did not have a special comforting effect in improving anger, sadness and anxiety after watching "feel-bad" film clips; in fact, "comfort food" had the same effect on emotions as "non" comfort foods or even no food at all (Wagner et al., 2014). The inconsistent findings likely reflect that responses to ruptured relationships, whether temporary or more long-term, as in the case of divorce or death, are inconsistent in and of themselves; separations can elicit a range of responses in the individual, including despair, anger and a lack of self-compassion (attacks on the self).

Does this mean that one might not have to eat a whole chocolate cake, or indeed any cake, after being "chucked"? The findings mentioned are just some of the conflicting results from the research on comfort eating and emotional eating. The issue seems to be that despite having a similar research interest, people follow different "recipes" and use very different methodologies for studies, which for some has led to the conclusion that "comfort food is a myth" (Wagner et al., 2014). The process of defining variables into measurable factors is fundamental to research methodology, and for comfort food this is challenging. For example, chicken soup is often a front runner for comfort food, coming in first place first for nearly half of the participants in one study (Wood & Vogen, 1998). One study, however, found that chicken soup was comforting only for those who considered chicken soup to be a comfort food (Troisi & Gabriel, 2011). This makes sense – the choice of comfort food depends on unique memories and remembrance and reward association with both good and bad times; what's comforting to me might not be to you. The experiential aligns with the empirical, and comfort foods have been shown to vary by age, sex, culture, the type of food itself and the feeling that elicits comfort eating (see Spence, 2017 for a review) – it is a big melting pot.

Taken together, findings from the psychological research indicate that we might have to go beyond the cupboard, beyond food and beyond emotions to find some clearer evidence regarding food and feelings. Some suggest that the emotions themselves are not responsible for comforting eating but rather the strategies used to regulate those emotions; for instance, there is evidence that individuals who regularly use suppression, a maladaptive emotion regulation strategy, consume more calorie-rich snack foods when emotional (Evers, 2010). Here, calorie intake could be seen as a form of suppression – a way of forcing out the unwanted feelings by replacing them with food that *is* wanted.

There is even disagreement as to what "basic" emotions are. For example, some speak of anger, others of rage. One way of trying to solve this problem is to see if individual emotions are associated with different physiological responses. While emotions feel quite distinct, research has generally failed to link these distinct feelings with distinct physiological changes. For example, there is no definitive "shopping-list" or tick-box criteria for anger. (Ortony & Turner, 1990; Rimé et al., 1990). Indeed, many have argued that while the *components* which make up emotions (thoughts, behaviours, events in the body and the world) are in some sense "real," emotions are human inventions (Russell, 2008). There are undoubted links between emotions and eating, but on closer inspection these seem to be broader rather than specific. Curiously, different negative emotions do not appear to have differential effects on *why* we eat. Eating to feel better, to relax or for desire or enjoyment can all happen when we feel broadly negative, whether angry, fearful, tense or sad (Macht & Simons, 2000).

The emotions we give names to are just the momentary co-occurrence of a host of behavioural, perceptual and experiential responses (Ortony & Turner, 1990). The same might be said of food; a shepherd's pie is no more than a collection of ingredients that are responded to in a certain way at that time, in this case by cooking minced meat and topping with mashed potatoes. A shepherd's pie is a human invention, and so the name faces the same issue as research on emotion, that "pies are not simply called pies because they are called pies" (Clarkson, 2009). In fact, shepherd's pie is not considered a "real" pie because, in accordance with the first law of pies, "no pastry, no pie" (Clarkson, 2009, p. 2). Of course, this pie law is a personal creation, but it raises an important point: laws for "real" emotions do not exist. There may be a single constituent of a pie, but there is no single constituent of an emotion. For example, we cannot say "no feeling hot, no fear" because there is no such physiological signature for each emotion. Nor is there one signature dish for a specific group of ingredients. In a different situation where my friend does not like mince, I might respond by cutting the meat into chunks and slicing the potatoes instead, and the result would be a Lancashire hotpot. With emotions, we run into problems if we are label-led or, in the case of the analogy, dish-led. Similarly, with comfort food we need to better understand the specific ingredients, or responses, that underlie this dish of comfort.

From feelings to physiology

> Man should not try to avoid stress any more than he would shun food, love or exercise.
>
> (Selye, 1956, p. vii)

According to Selye, stress, like food, is one of the unavoidable ingredients in life. Considered the father of stress research, Selye's work took the pathway from physics to physiology to feelings. The term "stress" had only previously been used by physicists to refer to the interaction between a force and its opposing resistance. Selye applied this to his work in medicine, showing that a diverse range of "stressors" had similar physiological effects in patients, including effects on bodily systems involved in regulating metabolism, the immune system, and other essential functions, including food intake. Selye defined stress as the "*nonspecific response of the body to any demand*" (Selye, 1975, p. 37, emphasis added), that is, anything that disrupted the body's usual state. Bowlby shared Selye's view that stressors were environmental conditions that produced negative physiological states, but he was particularly interested in the personal experience of this, which he said is one of *distress* (Bowlby, 1982). Stress can lead to distress in a variety of ways, ranging from physiological (e.g., hunger for food) to psychologically or emotional (e.g., hunger for comfort). To our brain, these stressors are the same and our body will respond in the same way. An important part of Selye's work involved identifying specific hormones involved in the body's stress response. This specificity and quantification is the foundation of stress research today and enabled distinct measurement methods to be developed within the field, which makes stress research different to emotion research. This difference is not unlike the distinction between cooking and baking; cooking, much like emotion research, involves generalisation and substitution, whereas baking requires precision in all parts of its recipe application. Just like baking, stress research is all about specific ingredients and precise methods.

Our body has specific and dedicated stress response systems. Regardless of the type of stressor, if our brain perceives it to be threatening, the critical hub of the brain's stress response – the hypothalamus – will be activated. The hypothalamus is responsible for orchestrating the appropriate physical responses at the time, whether fight, flight or feed, because the hypothalamus is also responsible for hunger. We have two basic physiological response systems to stress: the sympathetic nervous system (SNS) and the hypothalamic-pituitary-adrenal (HPA) axis. These systems are interacting but distinct too. The SNS is associated with "fight-or-flight" responses, which come on rapidly and have classic visible signs, including sweaty hands, dilated pupils and increased breathing rate, and people will often describe having a "racing heart" or having "butterflies in their tummy." Collectively this is all part of the body getting ready to fight or flee. An important difference is that the SNS is not uniquely activated by threat – it can be activated by positive arousal, such as excitement, whereas activation of the HPA axis is fine-tuned to threat, making it a "cleaner" gauge of stress (Clow & Smyth, 2020).

The HPA cascade culminates in the release of the classic stress hormone cortisol. But cortisol also performs a wide range of "housekeeping" duties to protect the body's overall health and well-being, including important food-related drives, such as regulating the accumulation and storage of body fat and increasing appetite, food intake and body weight gain. Cortisol's role in food and feelings begins early, literally pre-food. Research suggests that the path may go from *mother's* stress, to food, to child's feelings, with elevated cortisol in mother's milk negatively influencing infant temperament (Grey et al., 2013). If a mother is stressed while pregnant, her child is substantially more likely to have emotional or cognitive problems, but interestingly, the quality of the child–parent bond can buffer some of these adverse effects, particularly regarding the child's later attachment behaviours (Bergman et al., 2010). For this reason, cortisol – and stress more generally – is the core of this chapter on food and feelings. Perhaps it is now time to shift our feeling-focus to stress.

Comfort eating or stress eating?

It makes no sense that we eat when we feel stressed. Stress promotes survival behaviours. Evolutionarily, feed, instead of fight or flight, is not a sensible strategy. The body's resources need to be prioritised to deal with the imminent stressor otherwise we risk danger from attack. (Death by chocolate could indeed be a reality if a predator crept up on us while we were tucking into our favourite confectionary.) Physiologically, our stress system works in line with this idea. Here, it is helpful that our systems for controlling stress and food share the same anatomy. When we are faced with acute stress, the hypothalamus will not only initiate the stress cascade of the HPA axis, but it will *inhibit* the systems normally responsible for stimulating feeding behaviour so that our appetite is supressed (Maniam & Morris, 2012). The end product of the stress cascade, however, cortisol, promotes food intake, particularly of certain kinds of foods. This is because it is sensible to eat *after* stress – the energy used to cope with the stressor needs to be replaced. If we are not required to fight the lion anymore, we can go back to eating that Lion bar. Indeed, those who are highly sensitive, as shown by their cortisol reactions, eat significantly more sweet food after stress (Epel et al., 2001).

At this point, however, the story is half-baked. Stress involves both physiology *and* feelings, and comfort and pleasure are powerful feelings that are linked to stress. Most individuals when stressed will *increase* their food intake and, crucially, the intake of foods just like Lion bars – foods that are calorie dense and high in fat and/or carbohydrates, especially sugar (Epel et al., 2004; Ip et al., 2019; Oliver & Wardle, 1999). These foods have stress-reducing effects that appear to be controlled by the amygdala – one of the brain's regions associated with emotion (Ulrich-Lai et al., 2015). All food, but especially these sorts of comfort foods, literally feed the feeling part of our brain, which is contained within the larger "reward system." Eating is therefore designed to feel good and be rewarding, but even more so when we feel stressed. Laboratory studies reveal that both acute physical and emotional distress increase comfort food intake in humans and animals even when they are not hungry and have no physiological need for calories (Dallman, 2010). This is because the body's stress system interacts with the reward system, hence the comforting feelings we get from eating those more palatable comfort foods (Adam & Epel, 2007). The feeling itself is a cocktail of increased comfort/pleasure/soothing *and* decreased stress. Sugar is particularly powerful; it not only inhibits stress-induced cortisol but at the same time it stimulates opioid release – one of the body's "feel good" chemicals (Tryon et al., 2015).

Another of the body's chemicals that comfort food increases is dopamine. It is interesting that such evidence has made its way into the culinary world – *The Dopamine Diet* is the name of a bestselling cookbook by Chef Tom Kerridge ("assured to make you happier in the process . . . it's a diet that will make you feel good!"). Dopamine appears to be involved in the motivational aspects of eating ("wanting"), whereas opioids more affect the hedonic experience of food ("liking") more (Berridge & Robinson, 1998). So, stress eating is indeed real, *but comfort eating is a key part of stress eating*, and this is known in the literature as reward-based stress eating (Adam & Epel, 2007).

Chronic stress, however, poses a potential recipe for disaster. No matter what, if our brain perceives threat and we are continuously "fire-fighting," then cortisol production is not switched off. And this is especially the case when it comes to attachment disturbances. Our attachments are one of the key resources we have for dealing with disruptions and demands in life. In my own clinical practice, I have found that attachment often has a seat at the table with chronic stress; attachments in and of themselves are "chronic," in the sense that they are built up from continuous interactions. If attachment experiences include unavailability, inconsistency and a lack of attunement, then this can be incredibly distressing. When stress reactions are persistent and sustained, the body will end up turning down its "stress-ometer," so to speak, to mitigate the damaging effects of cortisol (Fries et al., 2005). The brain and body's receptors for cortisol can get "burnt" over a prolonged period of hyperarousal, and as a result they will not work as well (McEwen, 2007). Chronic stress can therefore lead to *decreased* sensitivity to immediate stressors in the environment. (Tomiyama et al., 2011). And exactly this less sensitive, less reactive cortisol response to acute stress has been linked to greater stress eating in those with chronic stress (Tomiyama et al., 2011).

So, stress eating appears to have a specific signature, which is *high chronic* stress, but *low acute* stress reactivity. One study found that chronically stressed women showing low cortisol reactivity to an acute laboratory stress task consumed significantly more calories from chocolate cake in response (Tryon et al., 2013). Chronic stress also increases the salience of pleasurable activities, so comfort food will *feel* more comforting – sweet foods taste sweeter, and we want more of them (Dallman et al., 2003; Kuo et al., 2008). This may be what perpetuates the stress-eating cycle. Research has shown that stress-induced eating behaviours lead to a greater reduction in negative feelings in those with high chronic stress (Klatzkin, Baldassaro, et al., 2018). These are findings that we can take straight from the lab to the consulting room, and beyond. For those individuals for whom comfort eating becomes uncomfortable and a serious problem, an approach which goes further than the provision of dietary guidance and goals is necessary, particularly one that involves an exploration of adverse childhood experiences (see Williamson et al., 2002) and life events (see Bidgood & Buckroyd, 2005). So comfort food is most comforting to those who have experienced the most stress. But what *exactly* is the comfort that we are looking for?

Coming back to comfort – and to the cupboard

> If I'm being honest, for me all food is comfort food, but there are times when you need a bowlful of something hot or a slice of something sweet just to make you feel that the world is a safer place. We all get tired, stressed, sad or lonely, and this is the food that soothes.
>
> (Lawson, 2011, p. 31)

We have seen that when stress eating occurs, comfort and reward are part of this physiological recipe; they are powerful and prevailing feelings when it comes to food. Interestingly, the negative feelings we experience after a stressful event appear to link more to *wanting* to eat rather than *how much* one eats (Klatzkin et al., 2018). So what *do* we want when we "stress eat"? Nigella talks about feelings of safety and soothing – two concepts that attachment theory and research know very well. It is this sense of felt security – the experience of the world as a safe place in which to explore – that appears to regulate our attachment system (Sbarra & Borelli, 2019).

Attachment-related concepts are key ingredients that help make sense of the research on stress eating and its associations with cravings for comfort. Bowlby saw attachment behaviours as part of the infant's "capacity to cope with stress" (Bowlby, 1982, p. 344), the most stressful experience being separation from the caregiver. This original idea has been studied extensively, and we now know that stress is linked to a range of attachment experiences across the lifespan, from divorce to saying goodbye at the airport to just thinking about the death of a loved one (Simpson & Rholes, 2017). So might the stress underlying stress eating be related to attachment needs? If we look more closely at the research, this seems to be where the physiological research on stress eating and the psychological research on comfort eating meet in the middle.

For stress, the most consistent cortisol findings come from studies employing the gold standard of laboratory protocols – the Trier Social Stress Test (TSST; Kirschbaum et al., 1993; Oskis et al., 2019; Smyth et al., 2015). The task consists of public speaking and surprise mental arithmetic, all performed in front of a panel of experimenters in lab coats and recorded on camera. What makes this so stressful is that the experimenters are absolutely non-responsive; they do not smile or nod or encourage task performance in any way, and their only comments are rejecting ones. The task therefore involves negative evaluation and social rejection, likely evoking shame, which threaten our universal needs to attach and to belong. Research outside of the physiology laboratory has shown that comfort food produces its psychological effects via these very feelings. One study found that when participants consumed their comfort food of chicken noodle soup, they thought more about relationships (Troisi & Gabriel, 2011). Soup is an interesting choice. Some suggest that soup is the only truly ubiquitous and universal dish, and that every society since the very early times has had a liquid staple of some sort (Clarkson, 2010). But this does not mean that soup is universally comforting. In that particular study, soup only had comforting effects if it was personally considered to be a comfort food. This is important, given that some studies which have found no effect of comfort food have asked participants to choose their comfort foods from a list of twenty preselected food items (for example, Finch et al., 2019; Wagner et al., 2014).

In Troisi and Gabriel's (2011) second experiment, when participants' sense of belongingness was threatened, feelings of loneliness were attenuated when participants were instructed to write about an experience of eating a comfort food, but *only* for those who were securely attached. For participants with an insecure attachment style, writing about comfort food did not serve to buffer loneliness (Troisi & Gabriel, 2011). Following this, Troisi et al. (2015) found that securely attached participants actually enjoyed eating comfort food more compared to insecurely attached individuals when they experienced a threat to their sense of belonging. Findings also showed that real-life experiences of loneliness were associated with increased comfort food consumption, but again only for those secure in their attachment style, and this effect only held for comfort food and "not just any food they could get their hands on" (Troisi et al., 2015, p. 61). For those who are insecurely attached, it could be that food is just like people in life – uncomforting, because it never quite fulfils whatever need is at hand, and in true Goldilocks fashion, relationships feel like either too much (insecure avoidant) or too little (insecure anxious) – they are never just right. The conclusion from this research is that comfort food has "real significant, and consequential psychological roots"

(Troisi & Gabriel, 2011, p. 752) that are attachment-based. Comfort food *is* comforting, but only for those who know the comfort of relationships.

What is interesting is that studies not using an attachment-based stressor *do not* find the same picture emerging for comfort food. Wagner et al. (2014) found that comfort food, in this case chocolate, was no more effective in improving mood than eating other foods, or even no food at all. There is an important methodological difference, however; Wagner et al. (2014) chose to induce negative feelings in participants using 18 minutes of scenes from "feel-bad" movies compiled by the researchers. On the other hand, the belongingness threat of Troisi and Gabriel (2011) involved writing for six minutes about a fight with a close other – a stressor which activates the attachment system. Bowlby states:

> The goal of attachment behaviour is to maintain an affectional bond, any situation that seems to be endangering the bond elicits action designed to preserve it.
>
> (Bowlby, 1982, p. 42)

Troisi and Gabriel's (2011) findings suggest that comfort food fulfils a function of our attachment behavioural system – it maintains the affectional bond by reminding us of our close others. If attachment behaviour is "any behaviour that results in a person attaining or retaining proximity" to another individual (Bowlby, 1982, p. 39), then comfort food appears to achieve this set-goal for those who are securely attached – it brings that close relationship closer during an experience of stress. And so we find ourselves returning to cupboard love, as this most likely happens via a process of association, whereby a particular food comes to be associated with a "differentiated and preferred individual" (Bowlby, 1982, p. 39).

In those who are securely attached this process will also likely involve what Bowlby called the "internal working model" (Bowlby, 1982), also known as a "secure-base script" (Waters & Waters, 2006). This script is essentially a recipe for relationships, based on our early caregiving experiences, that we use over the lifespan. And just like a recipe, it includes "if-then" propositions that lead to the set-goal, such as "If I am stressed, I can approach my mother for help, she is usually available, sensitive and supportive. Then this closeness will comfort and soothe me and help me to deal with the stress." By relying on the secure-base script, secure individuals can stay relatively calm in times of stress. Therefore, just as a positive recipe can take the stress out of the kitchen, a positive secure-base script can take the stress out of the relational world. It may be that the "comfort food secure-base script" works in the same way to provide its buffering effects.

Comfort food or security food?

> This is the sort of cake you'd want to eat the whole of when you'd been chucked. But even the sight of it, proud and tall and thickly iced on its stand, comforts.
>
> (Lawson, 2011, p. 47)

Let us return to Nigella's chocolate fudge cake. Being "chucked" is the breaking of an affectional bond, which will therefore activate attachment behaviour. Whether a person eats the whole cake and if the cake provides comfort, however, depend on several factors, as we have seen so far. These include whether the separation becomes a chronic stressor and how reactive the person is to stress, which may lead to eating more of the cake and increase the desire for sugar- and fat-rich food. Perhaps most importantly, the person needs to identify chocolate fudge cake as a comfort food for it to trigger feelings of relational connection (preferably the cake will be associated with other close, supportive relationships, i.e., not the rejecting partner). The cake will more likely provide comfort and enjoyment if the individual is securely attached, and if feelings of isolation increase, the more inclined they will be to eat the whole of it. And if chocolate cake is a comfort food, just *writing* about the experience of eating it for those who are securely attached will help alleviate any feelings of loneliness "post-chucking." Nigella's claim that even the sight of the chocolate fudge cake is comforting also has research support; findings suggest that viewing images of high-fat, high-sugar "comfort foods," including cake, in the absence of intake can enhance positive feelings (Privitera et al., 2018).

The general consensus is that comfort food helps to restore our sense of felt security. This can also be seen in the list of qualities that the general public associates with comfort food, which include eliciting a sense of familiarity, being reserved for specific situations (such as when feeling sad or stressed) and being consumed when being alone (Locher et al., 2005). Here, it is hard not to be reminded of Bowlby's description of the attachment figure ("the face of the familiar caregiver," Bowlby, 1982, p. 281), and just as attachment behaviour is activated when a person experiences "separation or loss with various mixtures of protest, anger, anxiety or despair" (Bowlby, 1982, p. 375) and at times "should he find himself alone in a strange world" (Bowlby, 1973, p. 290), so comfort food is reserved for particular situations.

The first dish I cooked for myself in my own kitchen after leaving my family home was spaghetti bolognese, not because I had a craving for pasta (although now that I understand the link between carbohydrates and stress, perhaps that was somewhat in the mix at the time); I made that dish because I missed my mum. I was alone and I wanted to feel close to her. My mum's version of spaghetti bolognese has an evocative quality about it, but not one that takes me to the metropolitan city of Bologna or the Apennine mountains. Hers in no way resembles the original recipe for maccheroni alla bolognese that Pellegrino Artusi first published in 1891; she uses no sofrito, only a little chopped onion fried in olive oil (never butter), she uses minced pork instead of veal, tinned chopped tomatoes provide the liquid rather than wine or broth, and her featured herb, in line with our Greek Cypriot ethnicity, is dried mint, which gives the sauce a fresh, lively tang, rather than the deep, robust savouriness associated with the original recipe. Long spaghetti strands as opposed to squat macaroni are the pasta of choice. Finally, grated halloumi cheese is sprinkled on to the dish before serving, which unlike parmesan has a mellow rather than sharp saltiness. It's not an authentic dish; it's an attachment dish – my idea of *Noshtalgia*. It is fitting that this play on words involves the Greek words for pain and return/home. Food can be a powerfully comforting remedy to the pain of separation.

The attachment-related qualities of comfort food may shed light on some of the inconsistent research findings. One recent laboratory-based study found that eating "unhealthy" (i.e., processed foods high in sugar and/or fat) compared to "healthy" (fruits and vegetables) comfort food made no difference to participants' psychophysiological stress (Finch et al., 2019). But curiously, the authors recognise that participants would have perhaps felt more comfortable eating comfort food in the privacy of their own home and that the laboratory setting may have inhibited comforting effects, and this may be especially so for the eating of unhealthy foods, which could be linked fear of negative judgment from onlookers and consequently feelings of shame and being exposed. As we have seen, being alone is one of the qualities associated with the consumption of comfort food, and what Nigella calls "the smaller special project, the sort of indulgent eating that has something almost ceremonial about it when done alone" (Lawson, 2010, p. 7).

So perhaps the term *security* food is more fitting than comfort food. In writing this chapter I have come to think of food and feelings in line with the Circle of Security (Marvin et al., 2002), which symbolises a child's need to have a secure base from which to go out and explore the world and a safe haven to return to for physical and emotional nourishment. The idea is that parents need to be attuned to where their child is "on the circle"; in other words, does the child need to explore their environment, or do they need to return to familiarity for comfort? Similarly, in relation to food, we can think of where we are "on the plate." Comfort food is a familiar safe haven which restores our sense of felt security. Accordingly, Troisi and Gabriel (2011) found that securely attached participants experienced less loneliness after writing about their comfort food but not after writing about a new food. Food neophobia has been defined as reluctance to eat and/or avoidance of novel food and is considered to be protective in a potentially hostile food environment (Pliner & Hobden, 1992). Once again, this is programmed into the body's stress machinery; based on physiology alone, the authors of one study were able to estimate with 82 percent accuracy whether a single participant was preparing a dish with mealworms or with chicken (Brouwer et al., 2017). Curiosity didn't kill the chicken it seems – chicken is ordinary and familiar, whereas mealworms are extraordinary, hence cooking with these larvae correlated with bodily responses linked to curiosity, anxiety and even humour. So although we need novel foods for diversity in our diet, the unfamiliar can create anxiety. Rozin (1977) describes this relationship between new foods and anxiety as the "omnivore's paradox," which results from the dilemma of needing to both approach and avoid novel foods. This contradiction represents a "double bind between the familiar and the unknown, monotony and change, security and variety" (Rozin, 1987, p. 278). New foods can therefore never be comfort foods because they tend to evoke feelings of anxiety. But this does not make new food bad food. Once again, perhaps it is best to take advice from Nigella, where the best recipe for food and feelings comes from "mixing the comfort of the familiar with the exuberance of the new, and believing in balance" (Lawson, 2015).

From comfort food to comfort cooking

You have probably noticed that Nigella Lawson's words have been a regular feature in this chapter. If I were to use Bowlby's language, I would say she is my "cooking attachment figure," that is, my differentiated and preferred individual of the culinary world, whom I conceive as stronger and/or wiser when it comes to matters of the kitchen. One of my favourite books by Nigella is *How to be a Domestic Goddess*, subtitled *Baking and the Art of Comfort Cooking*. Can the act of cooking be comforting? Or might the feeling-theme of this chapter, stress, find its way into that too?

Where there is cooking of food, there is a cook. In the same way, Winnicott (1965) once said "there is no such thing as an infant," meaning that whenever there is an infant there is maternal care. The message is about looking beyond, whether it is the mother behind the baby, the caregiver who opens the cupboard, or the cook behind the meal. It has been suggested that "cooks have always been in the background – both ever present and unnoticed" (Symons, 2003, p. x). But the feelings that go with cooking are indeed noticeable; one need look no further than Tesco's food love stories advertisements which encourage you to "make the food you love for the people you love."

Some suggest that cooking for others feeds the process of empathy on the behalf of the provider, which in turn decreases stress for the recipient and empathic distress for the provider (Hamburg et al., 2014). This is reminiscent again of Winnicott, and in particular what he called the mirroring of the child in the mother's face. In the wider context, cooking in order to provide food is about the cook recognising the needs of the person who eats what has been provided (Alley, 2014). In this instance, cooking may be more linked to our other response to stress, known as "tend-and-befriend." Although "fight-or-flight" is our primary physiological reaction to stress and is crucial to understanding comfort eating, some have suggested that another striking aspect of the human stress response is the tendency to affiliate (Taylor, 2006). Comfort cooking may therefore involve empathy, social connection and tending-and-befriending.

Sometimes however, cooking is far from comfortable; it can be stressful enough to activate "fight-or-flight" responses. On MasterChef, tears, fearful wide eyes, sweaty brows and shaky hands carrying plates to the judges for reckoning are commonplace. Why and when did the kitchen become the jungle? When it comes to cooking for others, Nigella tells us that "the most important thing is to remind yourself that people are coming to have a good time, not to judge" (Lawson, 2017), and she draws our attention to a key issue when it comes to cooking: judgment. Fear of negative social appraisal has been associated with home-cooking in a range of ways, from using pre-prepared ingredients to feelings of obligation and duty about being a "good" parent or partner (Costa, 2013; Daniels et al., 2012). So if the context has the potential for judgment, then cooking can be stressful – our social self, as well as the food, is plated. It is exactly this uncontrollable threat of our social self being judged negatively that the Trier Social Stress Test uses to activate the HPA stress system. The signature stressful ingredient when we cook is the food potentially being judged by others; if the cooking itself is not judged, then our body's stress system is not triggered – there is no change in cortisol (Osdoba et al., 2015). Other research has shown that when we cook just for *ourselves* our body's other stress system, which is more associated with excitement and other forms of positive arousal, is turned on instead. One study demonstrated that when it is just us, our heart rate goes up during "crunch time" moments of a recipe, for example, adding the curry paste and taking a bite at the end – in other words, moments that are emotionally significant but not threatening. And it is not just our body that talks during these emotionally salient moments when we cook for ourselves – they *feel* more exciting and pleasant (Brouwer et al., 2019). Perhaps it does not always have to be the Trier Social *Chef* Test. And perhaps Nigella is right (again), after all.

Some takeaway points

When it comes to food and feelings, some things have (hopefully) now been straightened out. Food, in all manner of ways, occupies a considerable part of an average person's life (Köster, 2009). And crucially, food occupies a role in stress – a feeling that is essential to our life experience and for our survival. Research has shed much light on stress eating and "comfort food" because stress can be defined and objectively measured, in terms of how it affects the body and health. Cortisol provides a valuable insight into the links between mind and body and food; it is a window on comfort food in particular, where part of the comfort is, in fact, about feeling less stressed.

But any recipe involving a human being will always be complex, to say the least, and if we dig deeper we see that so much of what goes on between food and feelings is not really about the food. If comfort food has the power to comfort without even being eaten, then that says something significant. It is not about calories but nourishment of a different sort, provided by those we hold close – the person who opened the cupboard at the very beginning, or who cooks for us in the kitchen, or who sits with us at the table. MFK Fisher was correct when she identified that food is entwined with security. Both researchers and cooks appear to agree that comfort food serves to restore our sense of felt security and thus helps to regulate our attachment behavioural system. Bowlby said that "to suppose that nutrition is in some way of primary significance and that attachment is only secondary would be a mistake" (Bowlby, 1982, p. 249). It seems that Bowlby had much in common with MFK Fisher and Nigella Lawson.

To sum up, this chapter ends as it began with words of wisdom from MFK Fisher: "When I write of hunger, I am really writing about love and the hunger for it, and warmth and the love of it . . . and it is all one" (Fisher, 2017, p. 2).

References

Adam, T.C., & Epel, E.S. (2007). Stress, eating and the reward system. *Physiology & Behavior*, *91*(4), 449–458.

Alley, T.R. (2014). Food sharing and empathic emotion regulation: An evolutionary perspective. *Frontiers in Psychology*, *5*, 121.

Bergman, K., Sarkar, P., Glover, V., & O'Connor, T.G. (2010). Maternal prenatal cortisol and infant cognitive development: Moderation by infant–mother attachment. *Biological Psychiatry*, *67*(11), 1026–1032.

Berridge, K.C., & Robinson, T.E. (1998). What is the role of dopamine in reward: Hedonic impact, reward learning, or incentive salience? *Brain Research Reviews*, *28*(3), 309–369.

Bidgood, J., & Buckroyd, J. (2005). An exploration of obese adults' experience of attempting to lose weight and to maintain a reduced weight. *Counselling and Psychotherapy Research*, *5*(3), 221–229.

Blass, E.M., & Smith, B.A. (1992). Differential effects of sucrose, fructose, glucose, and lactose on crying in 1-to 3-day-old human infants: Qualitative and quantitative considerations. *Developmental Psychology*, *28*(5), 804.

Bowlby, J. (1973). *Attachment and Loss: Volume II: Separation, Anxiety and Anger*. London: The Hogarth Press and the Institute of Psycho-Analysis.

Bowlby, J. (1982). *Attachment and Loss. Volume I: Attachment* (2nd ed.). New York: Basic Books.

Brouwer, A.M., Hogervorst, M.A., Grootjen, M., Van Erp, J.B.F., & Zandstra, E.H. (2017). Neurophysiological responses during cooking food associated with different emotions. *Food Quality and Preference*, *62*, 307–316.

Brouwer, A.M., Hogervorst, M.A., van Erp, J.B., Grootjen, M., van Dam, E., & Zandstra, E.H. (2019). Measuring cooking experience implicitly and explicitly: Physiology, facial expression and subjective ratings. *Food Quality and Preference*, *78*, 103726.

Clarkson, J. (2009). *Pie: A Global History*. London: Reaktion Books.

Clarkson, J. (2010). *Soup: A Global History*. London: Reaktion Books.

Clow, A., & Smyth, N. (2020). Salivary cortisol as a non-invasive window on the brain. In *Stress and Brain Health: Across the Life Course*. London: Elsevier.

Costa, A.I.D.A. (2013). Conceptualization and measurement of personal norms regarding meal preparation. *International Journal of Consumer Studies*, *37*(6), 596–604.

Dallman, M.F. (2010). Stress-induced obesity and the emotional nervous system. *Trends in Endocrinology & Metabolism*, *21*(3), 159–165.

Dallman, M.F., Pecoraro, N., Akana, S.F., La Fleur, S.E., Gomez, F., Houshyar, H., Bell, M.E., Bhatnagar, S., Laugero, K.D., & Manalo, S. (2003). Chronic stress and obesity: A new view of "comfort food". *Proceedings of the National Academy of Sciences*, *100*(20), 11696–11701.

Daniels, S., Glorieux, I., Minnen, J., & van Tienoven, T.P. (2012). More than preparing a meal? Concerning the meanings of home cooking. *Appetite*, *58*(3), 1050–1056.

Epel, E., Jimenez, S., Brownell, K., Stroud, L., Stoney, C., & Niaura, R.A.Y. (2004). Are stress eaters at risk for the metabolic syndrome? *Annals of the New York Academy of Sciences*, *1032*(1), 208–210.

Epel, E., Lapidus, R., McEwen, B., & Brownell, K. (2001). Stress may add bite to appetite in women: A laboratory study of stress-induced cortisol and eating behavior. *Psychoneuroendocrinology*, *26*(1), 37–49.

Evers, C., Marijn Stok, F., & de Ridder, D.T. (2010). Feeding your feelings: Emotion regulation strategies and emotional eating. *Personality and Social Psychology Bulletin*, *36*(6), 792–804.

Finch, L.E., Cummings, J.R., & Tomiyama, A.J. (2019). Cookie or clementine? Psycho-physiological stress reactivity and recovery after eating healthy and unhealthy comfort foods. *Psychoneuroendocrinology*, *107*, 26–36.

Fisher, M.F.K. (2017). *The Gastronomical Me*. London: Daunt Books.

Freud, S. (1940). An outline of psycho-analysis. In J. Strachey, A. Freud, A. Strachey and A. Tyson (Eds.), *The Standard Edition of the Complete Psychological Works of Sigmund Freud* (Vol. 23, pp. 141–207). London: Hogarth Press.

Fries, E., Hesse, J., Hellhammer, J., & Hellhammer, D.H. (2005). A new view on hypocor-tisolism. *Psychoneuroendocrinology*, *30*(10), 1010–1016.

Gopnik, A. (2011). *The Table Comes First: Family, France and the Meaning of Food*. London: Quercus.

Grey, K.R., Davis, E.P., Sandman, C.A., & Glynn, L.M. (2013). Human milk cortisol is associated with infant temperament. *Psychoneuroendocrinology*, *38*(7), 1178–1185.

Hamburg, M.E., Finkenauer, C., & Schuengel, C. (2014). Food for love: The role of food offering in empathic emotion regulation. *Frontiers in Psychology*, *5*, 32.

Harlow, H.F. (1958). The nature of love. *American Psychologist*, *13*(12), 673.

Ip, C.K., Zhang, L., Farzi, A., Qi, Y., Clarke, I., Reed, F., Shi, Y.C., Enriquez, R., Dayas, C., Graham, B., & Begg, D. (2019). Amygdala NPY circuits promote the development of accelerated obesity under chronic stress conditions. *Cell Metabolism*, *30*(1), 111–128.

Kirschbaum, C., Pirke, K.M., & Hellhammer, D.H. (1993). The "Trier Social Stress Test": A tool for investigating psychobiological stress responses in a laboratory setting. *Neuro-psychobiology*, *28*(1–2), 76–81.

Klatzkin, R.R., Baldassaro, A., & Hayden, E. (2018). The impact of chronic stress on the predictors of acute stress-induced eating in women. *Appetite*, *123*, 343–351.

Klatzkin, R.R., Gaffney, S., Cyrus, K., Bigus, E., & Brownley, K.A. (2018). Stress-induced eating in women with binge-eating disorder and obesity. *Biological Psychology*, *131*, 96–106.

Köster, E.P. (2009). Diversity in the determinants of food choice: A psychological perspec-tive. *Food Quality and Preference*, *20*(2), 70–82.

Kuo, L.E., Czarnecka, M., Kitlinska, J.B., Tilan, J.U., Kvetňanský, R., & Zukowska, Z. (2008). Chronic stress, combined with a high-fat/high-sugar diet, shifts sympathetic sig-naling toward neuropeptide Y and leads to obesity and the metabolic syndrome. *Annals of the New York Academy of Sciences*, *1148*, 232.

Lawson, N. (2010). *How to Eat*. London: Hachette.

Lawson, N. (2011). *Nigella Bites*. London: Random House.

Lawson, N. (2015). My life in food. *The Guardian*, 3 October 2015.

Lawson, N. (2017). Nigella Lawson: "I have a deep need to feed people". *The Irish Times*, 30 September 2017.

Locher, J.L., Yoels, W.C., Maurer, D., & Van Ells, J. (2005). Comfort foods: An explor-atory journey into the social and emotional significance of food. *Food & Foodways*, *13*(4), 273–297.

Lowry, C., Lightman, S., & Nutt, D. (2009). That warm fuzzy feeling: Brain serotonergic neurons and the regulation of emotion. *Journal of Psychopharmacology*, *23*(4), 392–400.

MacCormack, J.K., & Lindquist, K.A. (2019). Feeling hangry? When hunger is conceptu-alized as emotion. *Emotion*, *19*(2), 301.

Macht, M., & Mueller, J. (2007). Immediate effects of chocolate on experimentally induced mood states. *Appetite, 49*(3), 667–674.

Macht, M., & Simons, G. (2000). Emotions and eating in everyday life. *Appetite, 35*(1), 65–71.

Maniam, J., & Morris, M.J. (2012). The link between stress and feeding behaviour. *Neuropharmacology, 63*(1), 97–110.

Marvin, R., Cooper, G., Hoffman, K., & Powell, B. (2002). The Circle of Security project: Attachment-based intervention with caregiver-pre-school child dyads. *Attachment & Human Development, 4*(1), 107–124.

McEwen, B.S. (2007). Physiology and neurobiology of stress and adaptation: Central role of the brain. *Physiological Reviews, 87*(3), 873–904.

Oliver, G., & Wardle, J. (1999). Perceived effects of stress on food choice. *Physiology & Behavior, 66*(3), 511–515.

Ortony, A., & Turner, T.J. (1990). What's basic about basic emotions? *Psychological Review, 97*(3), 315.

Osdoba, K.E., Mann, T., Redden, J.P., & Vickers, Z. (2015). Using food to reduce stress: Effects of choosing meal components and preparing a meal. *Food Quality and Preference, 39*, 241–250.

Oskis, A., Smyth, N., Flynn, M., & Clow, A. (2019). Repressors exhibit lower cortisol reactivity to group psychosocial stress. *Psychoneuroendocrinology, 103*, 33–40.

Pliner, P., & Hobden, K. (1992). Development of a scale to measure the trait of food neophobia in humans. *Appetite, 19*(2), 105–120.

Privitera, G.J., Welling, D., Tejada, G., Sweazy, N., Cuifolo, K.N., King-Shepard, Q.W., & Doraiswamy, P.M. (2018). No calorie comfort: Viewing and drawing "comfort foods" similarly augment positive mood for those with depression. *Journal of Health Psychology, 23*(4), 598–607.

Rimé, B., Philippot, P., & Cisamolo, D. (1990). Social schemata of peripheral changes in emotion. *Journal of Personality and Social Psychology, 59*(1), 38.

Rozin, P. (1977). The significance of learning mechanisms in food selection: Some biology, psychology, and sociology of science. *Mechanisms in Food Selection*, 557–592.

Rozin, P. (1987). Psychobiological perspectives on food preferences and avoidances. In M. Harris (Ed.), *Food and Evolution: Toward a Theory of Human Food Habits* (pp. 181–206). Philadelphia: Temple University Press.

Russell, J.A. (2008). In defense of a psychological constructionist account of emotion: Reply to Zachar. *Journal of Theoretical and Philosophical Psychology, 28*(2), 423–429.

Sbarra, D.A., & Borelli, J.L. (2019). Attachment reorganization following divorce: Normative processes and individual differences. *Current Opinion in Psychology, 25*, 71–75.

Selye, H. (1956). *The Stress of Life*. New York: McGraw-Hill.

Selye, H. (1975). Confusion and controversy in the stress field. *Journal of Human Stress, 1*(2), 37–44.

Simpson, J.A., & Rholes, W.S. (2017). Adult attachment, stress, and romantic relationships. *Current Opinion in Psychology, 13*, 19–24.

Smyth, N., Thorn, L., Oskis, A., Hucklebridge, F., Evans, P., & Clow, A. (2015). Anxious attachment style predicts an enhanced cortisol response to group psychosocial stress. *Stress, 18*(2), 143–148.

Spence, C. (2017). Comfort food: A review. *International Journal of Gastronomy and Food Science, 9*, 105–109.

Symons, M. (2003). *A History of Cooks and Cooking*. Champaign, IL: University of Illinois Press.

Taylor, S.E. (2006). Tend and befriend: Biobehavioral bases of affiliation under stress. *Current Directions in Psychological Science, 15*(6), 273–277.

Tomiyama, A.J., Dallman, M.F., & Epel, E.S. (2011). Comfort food is comforting to those most stressed: Evidence of the chronic stress response network in high stress women. *Psychoneuroendocrinology, 36*(10), 1513–1519.

Tomiyama, A.J., Finch, L.E., & Cummings, J.R. (2015). Did that brownie do its job? Stress, eating, and the biobehavioral effects of comfort food. In *Emerging Trends in the Social and Behavioral Sciences: An Interdisciplinary, Searchable, and Linkable Resource* (pp. 1–15). New Jersey, NJ: John Wiley & Sons, Inc.

Troisi, J.D., & Gabriel, S. (2011). Chicken soup really is good for the soul: "Comfort food" fulfils the need to belong. *Psychological Science, 22*(6), 747–753.

Troisi, J.D., Gabriel, S., Derrick, J.L., & Geisler, A. (2015). Threatened belonging and preference for comfort food among the securely attached. *Appetite, 90*, 58–64.

Tryon, M.S., DeCant, R., & Laugero, K.D. (2013). Having your cake and eating it too: A habit of comfort food may link chronic social stress exposure and acute stress-induced cortisol hyporesponsiveness. *Physiology & Behavior, 114*, 32–37.

Tryon, M.S., Stanhope, K.L., Epel, E.S., Mason, A.E., Brown, R., Medici, V., Havel, P.J., & Laugero, K.D. (2015). Excessive sugar consumption may be a difficult habit to break: A view from the brain and body. *The Journal of Clinical Endocrinology & Metabolism, 100*(6), 2239–2247.

Ulrich-Lai, Y.M., Fulton, S., Wilson, M., Petrovich, G., & Rinaman, L. (2015). Stress exposure, food intake and emotional state. *Stress, 18*(4), 381–399.

Wagner, H.S., Ahlstrom, B., Redden, J.P., Vickers, Z., & Mann, T. (2014). The myth of comfort food. *Health Psychology, 33*(12), 1552.

Waters, H.S., & Waters, E. (2006). The attachment working models concept: Among other things, we build script-like representations of secure base experiences. *Attachment & Human Development, 8*(3), 185–197.

Williamson, D.F., Thompson, T.J., Anda, R.F., Dietz, W.H., & Felitti, V. (2002). Body weight and obesity in adults and self-reported abuse in childhood. *International Journal of Obesity, 26*(8), 1075–1082.

Winnicott, D.W. (1965). *The Maturational Processes and the Facilitating Environment: Studies in the Theory of Emotional Development*. New York: International Universities Press.

Wood, P., & Vogen, B.D. (1998). Feeding the anorectic client: Comfort foods and happy hour. *Geriatric Nursing, 19*(4), 192–194.

Chapter 4

"Let food be thy medicine"
The impact of nutrition on mental well-being

Julie Friend

One cannot think well, love well, sleep well, if one has not dined well.

(Virginia Woolf, 1929)

Food and mood

Developing effective ways to better understand and improve poor mental health is crucial in today's climate. In 2014, around one in six people in England met the criteria for a common mental disorder (CMD) such as anxiety, depression, panic disorder, phobia and obsessive-compulsive disorder: reducing the prevalence of CMDs has been recognised as a major public health challenge (McManus et al., 2016). In their "Mental Health Action Plan: 2013–2020," the World Health Organisation state:

> People with mental disorders experience disproportionately higher rates of disability and mortality. For example, persons with major depression and schizophrenia have a 40% to 60% greater chance of dying prematurely than the general population, owing to physical health problems that are often left unattended (such as cancers, cardiovascular diseases, diabetes and HIV infection) and suicide. Suicide is the second most common cause of death among young people worldwide.
>
> (WHO, 2013, p. 7)

There is an abundance of evidence-based advice and excellent resources surrounding the maintenance of good emotional health. Mind, the mental health charity, recommends adopting "Five Ways to Wellbeing" in order to look after our emotional happiness: connection, activity, taking notice, learning and giving. It is also widely recognised that an integrative mind-body approach to tackling the distress caused by psychological difficulties and trauma is critical to an individual's recovery (Ogden, 2006; Rothschild, 2017; van der Kolk, 2015). But more recently we have seen a growing body of evidence relating to the direct association between what we eat and drink and how we feel, think and behave – nutrition and diet are being increasingly recognised as a cornerstone of the mind-body approach to mental well-being (Watts, 2014). Perhaps instead of just five ways to well-being we need six, with the addition of good diet and nutrition?

The Mental Health Foundation (2017) state:

> One of the most obvious yet under recognised factors in the development of mental health is nutrition. Just like the heart, stomach and liver, the brain is an organ that requires different amounts of complex carbohydrates, essential fatty acids, amino acids, vitamins, minerals and water to remain healthy.

To an increasing extent, organisations such as the NHS, Mind and WHO are including on their websites guidance regarding the impact of what we eat on psychological health, and a burgeoning body of health professionals are focusing on improving diet for those with mental ill health (Watts, 2014). The route to psychological resilience via nutrition is a two-pronged approach: not only is it vital to understand which foods can actively improve mental health (protective factors), but equally it is necessary to understand that unhealthy diet and feeding habits can, in effect, fuel or maintain poor mental health (risk factors).

Protective factors for mental health

Neurotransmitters are our chemical messengers, transporting neurological information from one cell to another. They can affect a wide variety of both physical and psychological functions including heart rate, sleep, appetite and mood. A well-stocked brain "fed" with sufficient amounts of water, essential fatty acids, complex carbohydrates, amino acids, vitamins and minerals can support healthy neurotransmitter activity (Mental Health Foundation, 2017). Certain nutritional elements also offer protection to the brain from the effects of oxidants, which have been shown to impact negatively on state of mind (U.S. Department of Agriculture, Food & Nutrition, 1999). A number of published studies have demonstrated the essential function of good nutrition on children's brains – enhanced academic performance and increased ability to concentrate have been linked with nutrition (Food for the Brain Foundation, 2007; Meyers et al., 1989). Conversely, children's behaviour and levels of school absenteeism are impacted negatively when they are hungry (Murphy et al., 1998). Some schools organise breakfast clubs to ensure all pupils are adequately fed in order to concentrate and learn.

While it is beyond the remit of this chapter to examine in any detail the effects of all of the nutrients which have been found to benefit the brain and mood, it is worth mentioning some of the key elements which have been shown to impact on mental health and brain health. The most convincing evidence relates to omega-3 fatty acids (Stokes, 2014). A diet high in omega-3 fatty acids has a protective effect on brain function, delaying memory loss and other cognitive problems and helping to prevent plaque forming in the brain (Gómez-Pinilla, 2008). Studies have also shown how intake of omega-3 can help to relieve depression, reduce anxiety and significantly improve mood and ability to cope with stress (Kiecolt-Glaser et al., 2011; Marangell et al., 2003). The British Nutrition Foundation recommends that we consume two portions of fish per week, of which one should be an oily fish, particularly high in omega-3. Other good sources of omega-3 fatty acids, particularly for vegetarians, are flaxseeds and walnuts.

Strong evidence also exists for B vitamins, often described as the anti-stress and energy-giving vitamins (Glenville, 2016) and which play a key role in balancing blood sugar, in synthesising serotonin (the neurotransmitter which contributes to mood regulation) and in nervous system support. In particular, folic acid (vitamin B9) has been shown to improve symptoms of depression (Abou-Saleh & Coppen, 2006). Where certain vitamin B's are lacking, reports show that symptoms of depression are more likely to occur (Williams et al., 2005). Other significant nutrients with an important role in mental health disorders include the amino acid tryptophan (Levitan et al., 2000), zinc (Nowak et al., 2005) and chromium and selenium (Davidson et al., 2003; Rayman, 2002). The benefits too of vitamin D are becoming more evident. From a psychological point of view vitamin D has been shown to impact positively on sleep, depression, mood, anxiety, sense of well-being and seasonal affective disorder (Vieth et al., 2004). A meta-analysis published in the *British Journal of Psychiatry* (Anglin et al., 2013) showed a link between vitamin D deficiency and depression: participants with the lowest vitamin D levels were the most depressed, and those with the highest levels of vitamin D were much less likely to show any depressive symptom.

Risk factors for mental health

The flipside to nutrients which are beneficial to psychological health are foods which actively maintain or even stimulate poor mental health such as processed foods, refined foods and saturated fats. Processed food has been altered in some way during preparation: not all processed food is "bad" – milk, for example, undergoes a pasteurisation process which is necessary to prevent bacteria. However, it is true to say that many processed foods do have added sugar, salt and fats – often incorporated to make texture and flavour more palatable. Since the industrial revolution, our dietary habits have changed quite dramatically, particularly in terms of the increased consumption of refined grains and sugars (Neil, 2014). During the refining process a large number of nutrients are lost (for example fibre, B vitamins, zinc, chromium and magnesium) that help to regulate blood sugar levels. Over-indulging in sugary foods (including honey and maple syrup) and refined carbohydrates (white flour, white rice, white pasta) creates a vicious cycle within the body. Although glucose is a necessary fuel for cells, in particular brain cells, when sugar and refined foods are consumed, glucose enters the body very quickly, leading to rapid spikes in blood sugar levels which then sharply drop away (Scott, 2011). This is a bit like an internal roller-coaster ride for the body and the brain, and the drop (hypoglycaemia) can result not only in physical symptoms such as palpitations, headaches and fatigue but also to changes in mood such as anxiety, irritability, feeling overwhelmed and depression – the so-called blood sugar blues. In studies conducted with psychiatric patients, a link has been established between violent and criminal behaviour and hypoglycaemia (Neil, 2014).

Research has shown that poorer quality diets which are high in sugar, saturated fats, processed foods and refined carbohydrates are associated with poor mental health in children and adolescents and with individuals with a diagnosis of bipolar disorder (Beyer & Payne, 2016; O'Neil et al., 2014). A review examining the mental health of people living in the Arctic and subarctic regions suggests that high levels of mental disturbance, depression and suicide in this population can be linked not only to factors such as extremes of climate but also to changes in traditional diets. Historically, the circumpolar diet was seasonal and rich in protein, omega-3 fatty acids and antioxidants and low in carbohydrates. Decline in mental health has, the authors conclude, occurred alongside the growing consumption of a more "Western" diet, high in carbohydrates, saturated fat and processed foods (McGrath-Hanna et al., 2003).

Food deficiency and poor mental health: a stark illustration

In World War Two, 19.5 million military personnel died in conflicts across the globe. Yet in those same years, more than 20 million died from starvation and malnutrition (Collingham, 2013). During the latter years of the Second World War, conscientious objectors participated in a study led by Ancel Keys and his colleagues at the University of Minnesota. The Minnesota Starvation Experiment was designed to gain insight into not only the physiological but also the psychological effects of semi-starvation and to address the issue of how best to refeed people who had starved during the war.

Thirty-six men participated in the experiment, all of whom were deemed to be physically and mentally healthy. The format of the study was as follows: three months of a control period where the men were observed, given regular exercise and put through batteries of tests to gather data. At this stage they were fed 3,200 calories of food daily. During the following six months their calorie intake was halved, but they continued with the same levels of exercise. Keys designed the meals to be carbohydrate rich and protein poor to mimic the diet that people during the war were generally eating, such as potatoes, cabbage, bread and macaroni. During the last three months of the experiment, the men were gradually re-fed.

The ramifications of this meagre diet soon became evident. Physically, and not unexpectedly, they became skeletally thin, lost strength and energy and were constantly fatigued. They also reported dizziness, tinnitus and felt cold all of the time. As for behaviour and mood, Keys and his team were struck by the depth of the psychological strain experienced by the participants. They began to lie and cheat in order to obtain more food, and they were prone to hoarding. Preoccupation with food surpassed other important matters in their lives, including their politics and social opinions, personal hygiene, and their relationships. They became depressed, anxious, apathetic, humourless and prickly. One participant broke down and reported disturbing dreams of cannibalism – he was sent to the psychiatric ward of the university hospital where, once re-fed, he fully recovered.

Following the experiment, Keys proposed that in order to rehabilitate an adult man who has been in a state of semi-starvation, approximately 4,000 calories daily for several months was necessary to allow tissues to be rebuilt. In their paper which reflects on the experiment, Kalm and Semba (2005) emphasise the wider significance of the work carried out by Keys and his colleagues:

> Keys also stressed the dramatic effect that starvation had on mental attitude and personality, and argued that democracy and nation building would not be possible in a population that did not have access to sufficient food. Information from the experiment was shared with various national and international organizations and the military as they worked to develop a post-war relief plan.

The "bread and butter" of the consulting room: the therapeutic relationship

> It makes sense in a profound way that everything concerning feeding and weight gain is loaded with import and emotion. After all, a baby's continued survival depends on making sure she's growing.
>
> (Daniel Stern, 1998, p. 100)

On reviewing the literature, it is clear that the links between good nutrition and good mental health are significant: in all likelihood the research to date is just the tip of the iceberg in terms of what we may learn in the future. But the "science bit" is all very well. The big question for clinicians is how do we usefully employ this knowledge in the consulting room, and more specifically, how can we make use of discussions around food and feeding to inform and aid our work with clients from the perspective of attachment theory?

Attachment theory and feeding

The importance of food and feeding is nothing new in the field of attachment theory. Bowlby's view was that while some infants can experience feeding as an intrinsic source of consistent comfort and gratification, others may have an experience of inconsistency, leading to frustration and anguish (Bowlby, 1969). Many a new mother will focus concern on the feeding of her baby, worrying about sufficient milk production, difficulties attuning to her baby's feeding needs and communications, anxieties over possible allergies to her milk and so on (Stern, 1998). The act of feeding itself can mediate the mother's response to stress, reducing anxious feelings and creating a greater sense of calm in both mother and baby.

When feeding is a satisfying and pleasurable experience for both, the baby's brain becomes more efficient in switching off cortisol (a stress hormone) when no longer needed and therefore can return to a state of homeostasis much more quickly. However, if the feeding experience is neither nurturing nor consistent, then the infant's stress response can be activated and the brain becomes flooded with cortisol, setting up a "reactive stress response" which can lead to future mental health disturbances (Gerhardt, 2015). In adults, early attachment disturbances have been linked with maladaptive eating behaviours. Research has shown that more than 80 percent of all eating disorder patients manifest insecure adult attachment styles (Dakanalis et al., 2014).

In the consulting room: assessment

The literature regarding assessment in counselling and psychotherapy is interesting given how much food forms part of our daily lives. Clinicians are generally guided to ask clients at first meeting about topics such as childhood experiences, past and current relationships, possible traumatic events and what triggered the need for therapy. Encouraging therapists to show curiosity regarding clients' relationship with food (unless this forms part of the presenting issue itself) is rare. Questions such as how and what clients feed themselves, how much/little they eat, when and where they eat and with whom are conspicuous by their absence. We may be quite likely as therapists to ask a client what a typical day involves for them, in the hope of gaining insight into their daily routine, available resources, relationships, level of activity and extent of solitude. However, questions regarding daily feeding habits usually only extend to enquiries about general appetite.

As a therapist it can feel quite uncomfortable to enter into conversations about a client's diet, as most of us are not qualified nutritionists and some may find this kind of questioning at odds with their therapeutic orientation. It is vital of course to always act in accordance with the ethical guidelines of our professional bodies and to ensure that clients are fully aware that our role is not one of nutritional expert but that we are able to explore and signpost as necessary (Terry, 2014). Interestingly, research has shown that therapists' own attitudes towards diet, health and exercise will impact on their likeliness to engage with such issues in the consulting room (Burks & Keeley, 1989).

By engaging sensitively and ethically in discussions around a client's feeding habits we may be able to shed some light on what "protective" foods and vitamins might be lacking or perhaps where diet might potentially be exacerbating mental health issues through over-consumption of less healthy options. Thinking jointly about nutrition and relationship with food can become a way of encouraging clients' self-curiosity and spur an interest in their own self-care. Some clients will welcome this perspective on their mental health and can develop a greater interest in their feeding habits and nutrition, "eating" everything up that the therapist proffers. Others, however, will be much less willing to take on board or "digest" what the therapist is offering and may reject any attempts to address such issues.

Importantly, how clients react to interest and discussion about self-feeding can provide therapists with an insight into attachment styles, relationship with self and the transference relationship.

One of the aims of attachment-based psychotherapy is to encourage clients to mentalise – in other words to be able to self-reflect and to reflect on others' minds, or as Holmes (2010) puts it, "The ability to see oneself from the outside and others from the inside." Another aim is to help clients develop self-compassion and to internalise the therapist as a new, good object who is supportive, gently challenging and curious and who can delight in the client's successes (Cundy, 2017, 2019). This can be achieved in many ways throughout the course of the therapy, but one inroad can be through discussions around food and self-feeding. By cultivating self-observation in our clients and encouraging them to notice and to challenge the punishing or neglecting parts of the self which emerge in their relationships with food, clients can begin to develop a new, healthier internal object whose voice is compassionate, kind and nurturing.

In the consulting room: the therapeutic relationship

In order to demonstrate how conversations around feeding habits can prove therapeutically rich and informative, I present here two clinical vignettes: one focused on a client (Liz) who exhibited a principally preoccupied (anxious-ambivalent) attachment style and one client with a predominantly dismissing (anxious-avoidant) attachment style (Andy). Both clients have been anonymised and disguised in order to maintain confidentiality.

"I couldn't bear to take it all in": Andy

Avoidant or dismissing individuals are "masters in the art of defence" (Cundy, 2019). They are experts at shielding themselves against feelings, desires, memories and their own disavowed neediness. By and large they have been raised in environments where displays of affection and emotion were most likely met with anger, hostility, disapproval or criticism. Parents of avoidant people often struggle to manage their own feelings and thus find them hard to witness and to endure in their offspring. The child therefore quickly learns to repress any unwelcome feelings, in effect to "protect" his parent(s). Avoidant children may appear quite unaffected by what would ordinarily be thought of as upsetting event, such as when their mother is out of sight in an unfamiliar environment – in Ainsworth's Strange Situation Test, such children don't cry when their mother leaves the room and appear to ignore her when she returns. As they grow they may become self-contained, acquiescent and inhibited children who don't cause "a fuss." van der Kolk describes avoidant children as "dealing but not feeling" (2015, p. 118). Nevertheless, research has shown that while from the outside they will often appear fairly tranquil and unaffected, internally their heart rate is soaring and their stress response systems are in a state of hyperarousal (Gerhardt, 2015).

As adults, characteristics of an avoidant personality are likely to include high levels of self-control, self-blame, self-reliance, a strong work ethic, difficulty in expressing emotions and being cognitively organised (Baim & Morrison, 2011; Cundy, 2019). In the therapeutic relationship one of the central challenges of working with a dismissing patient is to "enable the patient to allow the therapist to matter" (Wallin, 2015, p. 212). A dismissing client will be prone to diminishing the importance of therapy, often undermining the work and indeed the person of the therapist, who may end up feeling criticised and deskilled. In terms of relationship to food, the literature shows that, broadly speaking, people who severely restrict their eating habits, such as anorectic patients, show a predominantly dismissing attachment style (Elgin & Pritchard, 2006; Ringer & Crittenden, 2007; Zachrisson & Skårderud, 2010).

Andy was a very bright 34-year-old man who arrived in my consulting room on the first day armed with a large notepad and pen and essentially "interviewed" me for the job of therapist. He was forthright in telling me that he only needed six therapy sessions in order to tackle a feeling of low mood which he felt had "come out of the blue" and that he expected a verbal "progress report" at the beginning of each session so that he could monitor any improvements in his situation. He was keen to know from the outset what my "plan of action" was to be regarding the therapy. He wanted a practical approach to the therapy – "tools and techniques" to "get myself out of this mood." Initially, the relationship between myself and Andy operated in a joint, goal-oriented mode (Liotti, 2007). I have often found that this relational style can provide a safe opportunity for the more dismissing/avoidant client to begin gaining trust in the therapy/therapist. It allows for the development of a solid working alliance before moving on to more exploratory, attachment-based work where the focus on the therapeutic relationship can feel exposing and, for some, frightening.

With Andy's current mood in mind, as part of the initial assessment I asked about his nutrition and feeding habits. This was met with a good helping of annoyance, disbelief and eye-rolling. He found this to be irrelevant and somewhat irritating. I reflected this reaction back to him – this was equally distasteful to him. The assessment period proved to be quite challenging, as I became increasingly aware that Andy routinely resisted "taking in" any talk of self-feeding and self-care, and as for any exploration of childhood, the message was clear from Andy that this had no bearing whatsoever on his current state. Wallin (2015) suggests that in order to understand a dismissing patient's communications, we need to attune to the subtleties in our own psychobiological states. In the countertransference I increasingly felt as if everything I offered to him by way of interpretation, comment or reflection was in effect "regurgitated" back at me in the space between us. More often than not I was left feeling undermined and constrained.

While for Andy my curiosity regarding his feeding habits and self-care seemed completely irrelevant, our interactions were priceless for me clinically, as they enabled me to better understand his predominant attachment style. I was not only listening on one level to Andy's words but simultaneously to the underlying music of what he was telling me, tuning in to the way he responded to my questions about his diet and self-care as opposed purely to the content. The Adult Attachment Interview, a tool devised to ascertain attachment styles (Main et al., 2008), focuses on people's narrative style rather than the content of their stories. Individuals who are deemed "dismissing" are people who minimise life events and who tend to give sparse and emotionally barren accounts. As Andy talked I was aware of feeling I was being fed "tidbits" of information, and our conversations felt stilted, controlled and restrictive. His narrative felt impoverished in terms of detail about his history and his relationships, and I didn't feel even close to being able to see the full picture.

While initially Andy essentially batted back to me any curiosity which I showed in how he cared for himself, a process ensued which led to therapy of a different flavour. He did begin to gradually open up, and we were able to have "light" conversations about his daily routine and eating habits. This revealed that his food intake was, similar to our conversations, quite restrictive and controlled and seemingly lacking in some important nutrients which could potentially be having an impact on his mood. Andy began to see some value in thinking about general self-care and the link to his mood and became quite interested in nutrition as a whole, reading resources that I had recommended. Importantly, these "shallow" discussions allowed the therapeutic alliance to develop and for Andy to begin to develop more trust in me – I was beginning to "matter."

As Andy's defences loosened he began, tentatively, to engage in discussions around his childhood. It became apparent that his parents were both quite self-obsessed and critical characters who appeared unable to empathise with their children. While not totally unloving, their care was experienced by Andy as "perfunctory." They placed great emphasis on academic excellence and little on the emotional lives of their offspring. Andy's maternal aunt had died tragically when she was in her twenties, and Andy remembered this time clearly – he had never seen his mother grieve. She possessed a "grin and bear it" attitude towards any upset or adversity, and feelings were rarely expressed.

Therefore, discussions around food had several advantages in this particular case. First, they provided a platform on which the therapeutic relationship could begin to develop and trust begin to build. They also offered insight into actual diet and nutrition, which seemed to be lacking, and this could therefore be addressed practically, which suited Andy's solution-focused style. But most importantly perhaps these exchanges allowed the therapeutic relationship to shift from a working alliance through to a deeper therapeutic attachment relationship: eventually Andy was able to acknowledge (somewhat excruciatingly I must add) that there was an "us." For dismissing clients, dependency on others can be frightening and is often to be avoided at all costs – it will, in their minds, result in rejection. For Andy, therefore, this was a crucial step. He was able ultimately to express to me that my initial curiosity about his eating habits, diet and self-care in general had felt too much, and that my enquiries seemed to shine a light on him which felt deeply uncomfortable and foreign. He had felt as if he couldn't quite digest my care and attention: "I couldn't bear to take it all in."

"Are you eating properly, love?": Liz

The preoccupied or anxious-ambivalent individual can be broadly characterised as having been on the receiving end of inconsistent and/or anxious parental attention, whereby the early attachment figure cannot be relied on or trusted and is often someone who deals with their own emotional states by needing to be needed by others (Wallin, 2015). This pattern is characterised by exaggerated attachment-seeking behaviours and enmeshed and intense relationships which can make the individual hypersensitive to abandonment. As children, preoccupied people tend to keep their feelings close to the surface and will wait vigilantly for any opportunity to get their caregiver's attention (Fonagy, 2004). They can therefore often present as clingy and needy. In terms of relationships to food, broadly speaking, bulimic/binge-eating patients are often found to have a preoccupied attachment style (Gander et al., 2015).

Liz was a 40-year-old woman who came to see me initially for issues around her relationships at work. She presented as fretful, "hard done by," overly ruminating and full of angry resentment. She felt that her work colleagues were jealous of her and were constantly trying to sabotage her position. She felt victimised by them and had regularly throughout her career been involved in various work disputes and complaints – some initiated by her and other complaints initiated by colleagues towards her. From day one when we first met, Liz "spewed" her vitriol about these people into the space between us, and I noticed that I was very silent during our sessions, with little room for reflection.

I observed a pattern in Liz whereby she would enter into very close and intense relationships with new members of staff very quickly and would idolise people very readily. Within weeks, however, these "friends" would inevitably disappoint Liz in some way: usually the sense would be that they hadn't completely given her their full attention and devotion, for example not responding to texts immediately or not taking her side in a dispute with another colleague. In Liz's mind these firm friends quickly morphed into enemies, and her raging about them was caustic and unrelenting. Her world, it seemed, was populated with nemeses. This is quite typical of the preoccupied client, where "actual relationships with real people in the real world are often conflictual enough to guarantee that they continue to exist in other peoples' minds" (Cundy, 2017, p. 9). Better to be present in someone's mind in a negative form than not to be held in mind at all. Listening to Liz's rantings, my internal alarm bells rang. How long would it be before I too became the enemy?

During one of our sessions, a rare opportunity arose where I was able to interject and comment on something I had noticed about Liz's attitude to self-care. I said that I had noticed that when Liz spoke of her working day she often talked about how she frequently skipped breakfast and lunch, "running on empty" throughout the day, but would indulge in huge take-away meals at the end of the day, rounded off by lots of sugary snacks and treats. I reflected back to her, gently, that it seemed as if she neglected herself in terms of lack of food during the day and consuming lots of unhealthy food in the evening and wondered aloud about her levels of self-care. Liz went unusually quiet, put her head in her hands and burst into tears. What ensued proved to be quite a pivotal moment in the therapy. It transpired that the mere fact that I had "noticed" her eating habits and self-neglect and appeared somewhat concerned was experienced by Liz as "maternal." She free-associated to her university days, when she had noticed that her friends' mothers would routinely ask their offspring: "Are you eating properly, love?" Liz remembered feeling excruciating jealousy because her own mother rarely made enquiries about how she was feeding or looking after herself.

Conversations henceforth moved from workplace grievances to Liz's relationship with her mother. During Liz's childhood her mother's behaviour had been erratic and inconsistent: at times she was emotionally and physically unavailable, often disappearing for an afternoon or a whole day without telling anyone in the family where she was going. Liz found these times enormously anxiety provoking, describing the "dark cloud" which settled over her father and her siblings as they waited "on tenterhooks" for mother to return. When her mother did return she was more often than not in a really jolly mood (which Liz suspected was linked to alcohol) and would be "over the top" in her desire to cuddle her children and play games with them,

> making us all dance about the living room with her, which felt really weird and none of us wanted to, but we just played along so as not to upset her. She just seemed like a big kid and I hated it – I wanted her to be a normal mum.

Liz and I were able to begin to see links between her daily eating habits – feast or famine – and her mother's behaviour and her inconsistent demonstrations of love. Liz and her siblings were either "starved" of their mother's love and presence or "overfed" on her unrestrained and intrusive behaviour. Liz's feeding habits seemed to reflect this pattern. I hypothesised that in order to gain mastery over her own emotional world, which her mother was unable to mirror or to help her regulate, Liz would turn to fatty foods and sweets treats in order to soothe herself. It seemed to me that as a child Liz was unable to find enough psychic space to attune to her own needs, wishes and desires, as they were in effect "eaten up" by her mother's own dominant needs and Liz's need to be vigilant. It also occurred to me that Liz's poor self-feeding might well have been a communication to her unreliable mother that she was in deep need of her attention.

The impact of my curiosity around Liz's eating habits began to take shape within the therapeutic attachment relationship. In the transference, I became a "normal mum," showing a maternal interest in her health and well-being, just like her university friends' mothers. Liz felt as if I was attuning to her needs: feeding, as has been discussed, is a crucial matter of attunement. As a therapist I was able to offer the much-craved consistency that Liz had lacked in earlier life and, importantly, able to show interest in her without intrusion. I began to perceive in her a sense of "earned" security (Hesse, 2008), whereby she was able to, at least in part, internalise me as a "good object" (Winnicott, 1969).

I must confess, however, that this development within the therapy and within the therapeutic attachment relationship was not all plain-sailing. While this vignette can only offer a relevant and brief glimpse of our work together, it is important to acknowledge that at times I did, as predicted, become Liz's "enemy." Sessions were often peppered with resentment, anger and bitterness towards me as, in Liz's mind, I became a less idealised mother. This was often sparked by my unavailability, such as my holidays or breaks in the therapy, or where Liz realised that I did not belong uniquely to her. Cundy (2017, p. 12) states that "Despite the hungry devouring, these clients so rarely feel nourished by what they consume." Throughout her therapy, although Liz did address her tricky relationships and her issues around self-care and began to explore her childhood experiences at greater depth, what I had to offer her in terms of consistency and care ultimately was never quite enough.

Secure attachment/earned security

I think it is worth mentioning, by way of contrast to the above vignettes, that someone with a principally secure attachment style or even someone with "earned" security (which can arise from healthy attachments formed in later life, such as with teachers, psychotherapists and close relationships) would likely respond very differently to matters of self-care and self-feeding. The chances are that their relationship to food will be nurturing and adaptive. Food will equate with love, safety and comfort and may symbolise a cherished attachment figure, the smell and taste of certain foods evoking fond memories and warm feelings. A secure individual would be less likely to engage in emotional eating in order to regulate uncomfortable feelings due to a capacity to tolerate and talk about their emotions. Secure individuals are also more likely to have good self-esteem and a healthy, stable body image. The act of eating will be reflective, mindful and attuned to the body's needs and desires.

Conclusion

The daily act of eating (for those of us who are fortunate enough to be able to take this for granted) is crucial to our survival, but it is more than just fuel for the fire. As can be seen from the literature, the impact of nutrition and diet on our health, well-being and on our minds is worthy of our attention. Food really does impact mood. It is also tied up with our self-image, self-esteem and self-care. And it can, in certain circumstances, be a very useful way of understanding people and their relationship to self and others, including within the therapeutic relationship. I wonder if, as therapists, we might need to reflect more on how we feel about engaging in conversations around food in the consulting room. Or perhaps we have an aversion to doing so? Might it be useful to examine in greater depth our own attitudes to food, feeding and self-nurture? After all, if indeed "food be thy medicine," then perhaps the old adage "Physician, heal thyself" might well apply?

References

Abou-Saleh, M.T., & Coppen, A. (2006). Folic acid and the treatment of depression. *Journal of Psychosomatic Research*, *61*(3), 285–287.

Anglin, R.E.S., Samaan, Z., Walter, S.D., & McDonald, S.D. (2013). Vitamin D deficiency and depression in adults: Systematic review and meta-analysis. *British Journal of Psychiatry*, *202*(2), 100–107.

Baim, C., & Morrison, T. (2011). *Attachment-based Practice with Adults: Understanding Strategies and Promoting Positive Change: A New Practice Model and Interactive Resource for Assessment, Intervention and Supervision*. Hove: Pavilion Publishing and Media Ltd.

Beyer, J.L., & Payne, M.E. (2016). Nutrition and bipolar depression. *Psychiatric Clinics of North America*, *39*(1), 75–86.

Bowlby, J. (1969). *Attachment and Loss, Volume 1: Attachment*. London: Hogarth Press.

Burks, R., & Keeley, S. (1989). Exercise and diet therapy: Psychotherapists' beliefs and practices. *Professional Psychology: Research and Practice*, *20*(1), 62–64.

Collingham, L. (2013). *Taste of War: World War II and the Battle for Food*. London: Penguin Books.

Cundy, L. (2017). Fear of abandonment and angry protest: Understanding and working with anxiously attached clients. In L. Cundy (Ed.), *Anxiously Attached: Understanding and Working with Preoccupied Attachment* (pp. 1–30). London: Karnac.

Cundy, L. (2019). Masters in the art of defence: Shame and defences against intimacy. In L. Cundy (Ed.), *Attachment and the Defence Against Intimacy: Understanding and Working with Avoidant Attachment, Self-Hatred and Shame* (pp. 69–108). Oxen: Routledge.

Dakanalis, A., Timko, C.A., Zanetti, M.A., Rinaldi, L., Prunas, A., Carrà, G., Riva, G., & Clerici, M. (2014). Attachment insecurities, maladaptive perfectionism, and eating disorder symptoms: A latent mediated and moderated structural equation modelling analysis across diagnostic groups. *Psychiatry Research*, *215*(1), 176–184.

Davidson, J.R., Abrahams, K., Connor, K.M., & McLeod, M. (2003). Effectiveness of chromium in atypical depression: A placebo-controlled trial. *Biological Psychiatry*, *53*(3), 261–264.

Elgin, J., & Pritchard, M. (2006). Adult attachment and disordered eating in undergraduate men and women. *Journal of College Student Psychotherapy*, *21*(2), 25–40.

Fonagy, P. (2004). *Attachment Theory and Psychoanalysis*. London: Karnac.

Food for the Brain Foundation. (2007). *Food for the Brain: Child Survey*. www.foodforthebrain.org/media/229763/fftb.pdf.

Gander, M., Sevecke, K., & Buchheim, A. (2015). Eating disorders in adolescence: Attachment issues from a developmental perspective. *Frontiers in Psychology*, *6*, 1136.

Gerhardt, S. (2015). *Why Love Matters: How Affection Shapes Baby's Brain*. Hove: Routledge.

Glenville, M. (2016). *Natural Alternatives to Sugar*. Tunbridge Wells: Lifestyle Press.

Gómez-Pinilla, F. (2008). Brain foods: The effects of nutrients on brain function. *Nature Reviews Neuroscience*, *9*(7), 568–578.

Hesse, E. (2008). The adult attachment interview: Protocol, method of analysis, and empirical studies. In J. Cassidy & P.R. Shaver (Eds.), *Handbook of Attachment: Theory, Research, and Clinical Applications* (pp. 552–598). New York: The Guilford Press.

Holmes, J. (2010). *Exploring in Security: Towards an Attachment Informed Psychoanalytic Psychotherapy*. London: Routledge.

Kalm, L.M., & Semba, R.D. (2005). They starved so that others be better fed: Remembering Ancel Keys and the Minnesota Experiment. *The Journal of Nutrition, 135*(6), 1347–1352.

Kiecolt-Glaser, J.K., Belury, M.A., Andridge, R., Malarkey, W.B., & Glaser, R. (2011). Omega-3 supplementation lowers inflammation and anxiety in medical students: A randomized controlled trial. *Brain Behavior and Immunity, 25*(8), 1725–1734.

Levitan, R.D., Shen, J.H., Jindal, R., Driver, H.S., Kennedy, H.S., & Shapiro, C.M. (2000). Preliminary randomized double-blind placebo-controlled trial of tryptophan combined with fluoxetine to treat major depressive disorder: Antidepressant and hypnotic effects. *Journal of Psychiatry and Neuroscience, 25*(4), 337–346.

Liotti, G. (2007). Internal working models of attachment in the therapeutic relationship. In P. Gilbert & R.L. Leahy (Eds.), *The Therapeutic Relationship in the Cognitive Behavioural Therapies* (pp. 143–61). New York: Routledge.

Main, M., Hesse, E., & Goldwyn, R. (2008). Studying difference in language usage in recounting attachment history: An introduction to the AAI. In H. Steele & M. Steele (Eds.), *Clinical Applications of the Adult Attachment Interview* (pp. 31–68). New York: The Guilford Press.

Marangell, L.B., Martinez, J.M., Zboyan, H.A., Kertz, B., Florence, H., Kim, S., & Puryear, L.J. (2003). A double-blind, placebo-controlled study of the omega-3 fatty acid docosahexaenoic acid in the treatment of major depression. *American Journal of Psychiatry, 160*(5), 996–998.

McGrath-Hanna, N.K., Greene, D.M., Tavernier, R.J., & Bulto, A. (2003). Diet and mental health in the Arctic: Is diet an important risk factor for mental health in circumpolar peoples? A review. *International Journal of Circumpolar Health, 62*(3), 228–241.

McManus, S., Bebbington, P., Jenkins, R., & Brugha, T. (2016) *Mental Health and Wellbeing in England: Adult Psychiatric Morbidity Survey 2014.* https://assets.publishing. service.gov.uk/government/uploads/system/uploads/attachment_data/file/556596/apms-2014-full-rpt.pdf.

Mental Health Foundation. (2017). *Food for Thought: Mental Health and Nutrition Briefing.* www.mentalhealth.org.uk/sites/default/files/food-for-thought-mental-health-nutrition-briefing-march-2017.pdf.

Meyers, A.F., Sampson, A.E., Weitzman, M., Rogers, B.L., & Kayne, H. (1989). School breakfast program and school performance. *American Journal of Diseases of Children, 143*(10), 1234–1239.

Murphy, J.M., Pagano, M.E., Nachmani, J., Sperling, P., Kane, S., & Kleinmann, R.E. (1998). The relationship of school breakfast to psychosocial and academic functioning: Cross-sectional and longitudinal observations in an inner-city school sample. *Archives of Paediatric and Adolescent Medicine, 152*(9), 899–907.

Neil, K. (2014). Blood sugar blues. In M. Watts (Ed.), *Nutrition and Mental Health: A Handbook* (pp. 115–125). Hove: Pavilion Publishing & Media.

Nowak, G., Szewczyk, B., & Pilc, A. (2005). Zinc and depression. An update. *Pharmacological Reports, 57*(6), 713–718.

Ogden, P. (2006). *Trauma and the Body: A Sensorimotor Approach to Psychotherapy.* New York: W.W. Norton.

O'Neil, A., Quirk, S.E., Housden, S., Brennan, S.L., Williams, L.J., Pasco, J.A., & Jacka, F.N. (2014). Relationship between diet and mental health in children and adolescents: A systematic review. *American Journal of Public Health, 10*(4), 31–42.

Rayman, M.P. (2002). The importance of selenium to human health. *The Lancet, 356*, 233–241.

Ringer, F., & Crittenden, P.M. (2007). Eating disorders and attachment: The effects of hidden family processes on eating disorders. *European Eating Disorders Review, 15*(2), 119–130.

Rothschild, B. (2017). *The Body Remembers: Volume 2: Revolutionizing Trauma Treatment*. London: W.W. Norton.

Scott, T. (2011). *The Anti-Anxiety Food Solution: How the Foods You Eat Can Help You Calm Your Anxious Mind, Improve Your Mood, and End Cravings*. Oakland, CA: New Harbinger Publications.

Stern, D. (1998). *The Birth of a Mother: How the Experience of Motherhood Changes You Forever*. New York: Basic Books.

Stokes, C. (2014). Eat yourself happy: Nutritional therapy in practice. In M. Watts (Ed.), *Nutrition and Mental Health: A Handbook* (pp. 143–152). Hove: Pavilion Publishing & Media.

Terry, N. (2014). Food and mood. *Therapy Today, 25*(1), 14–18.

U.S. Department of Agriculture, Food & Nutrition. (1999). *Can Foods Forestall Aging?* https://agresearchmag.ars.usda.gov/1999/feb/aging.

van der Kolk, B. (2015). *The Body Keeps the Score. Brain, Mind and Body in the Healing of Trauma*. London: Penguin.

Vieth, R., Kimball, S., Hu, A., & Walfish, P.G. (2004). Randomized comparison of the effects of the vitamin D3 adequate intake versus 100 mcg (4000 IU) per day on biochemical responses and the wellbeing of patients. *Nutrition Journal, 3*(8), 1475–2891.

Wallin, D.J. (2015). *Attachment in Psychotherapy*. New York: Guilford Press.

Watts, M. (2014). *Nutrition and Mental Health: A Handbook*. Hove: Pavilion Publishing & Media.

Williams, A.L., Cotter, A., Sabina, A., Girard, C., Goodman, J., & Katz, D.L. (2005). The role of vitamin B6 as treatment for depression: A systematic review. *Family Practice, 22*(5), 532–537.

Winnicott, D.W. (1969). The use of an object. *The International Journal of Psychoanalysis, 50*, 711–716.

Woolf, V. (1929). *A Room of One's Own*. London: Hogarth Press.

World Health Organisation. (2013). *Mental Health Action Plan: 2013–2020*. Geneva: WHO Press.

Zachrisson, H.D., & Skårderud, F. (2010). Feelings of insecurity: Review of attachment and eating disorders. *European Eating Disorders Review, 18*(2), 97–106.

Chapter 5

Overcoats, burning buildings and planks of wood

An integrated attachment-based approach to working with eating disorders

Penny Forster

Introduction

There is a truism among medics in psychiatric services about working with eating disorders – either you find it endlessly fascinating, even though the work is also endlessly frustrating and often very difficult, or you can't stand it and wouldn't go within a million miles of working in an eating disorder unit. I have turned out to be one of the former, and when I discovered attachment theory I knew I had found a shaft of light that would add immeasurably to my original training in integrative psychotherapy. Since then I have done a lot more training in attachment theory, and it continues to illuminate and inform my work with this patient group.

I am an attachment-based integrative psychotherapist working exclusively with people with moderate to severe eating disorders. I have been doing this for a quarter of a century and have accumulated over 18,000 hours of supervised clinical experience with individual patients and in groups. I work in a private outpatient medical practice in Central London in a partnership with two consultant psychiatrists and two dietitians. My colleagues and I each have over 25 years' experience, and we have previously worked together in various eating disorder units in National Health Service and private hospitals. We work very closely as a team. I see my patients weekly, either until they reach recovery or drop out of treatment (which is uncommon), or they need to be admitted to hospital or a rehabilitation unit. If this is necessary, they usually come back to us to continue their outpatient treatment.

I am very lucky to be able to work with skilled and experienced colleagues in such a contained environment. In attachment terms, this collaborative approach already puts me on a positive footing; it is very containing for us, and also for our patients. We let them know that we communicate frequently between ourselves and that we are aware of what happens in one another's sessions, and this helps to prevent splitting (patients' resistance to giving up their eating disorders may take the form of attempts to undermine the professionals treating them, setting us up against each other).

By the time people have found their way to us, they have usually been seriously unwell for several years. I see adults, mostly women aged from late teens to late fifties, most of whom have been unwell since adolescence. I also run a weekly recovery group for patients who are now at normal weight and getting back into normal life. They may originally have seen me for individual therapy or they may not; there is a mixture of diagnoses, but there are non-negotiable ground rules in place. One of these is that they have to be at or near their healthy BMI, and if they start to lose weight significantly they have to leave the group. The group gives an opportunity to raise all sorts of issues that arise when members have to start negotiating the outside world without falling back on their ED (eating disordered) behaviours. These can be as varied as what to do about a strong impulse to binge after colleagues at work brought in a cake for someone's birthday; how to manage pregnancy, breastfeeding and the post-birth body (there have been five babies produced over the years by group members); or how to navigate the dating scene and the intricacies of starting a relationship, including physical touching and sex, if they still have a problem with their body image. There is a WhatsApp group for members to communicate between themselves for any day-to-day issues that arise, and they use this also with certain ground rules in place. It is an open group, and some members have been attending for several years. They find it a valuable resource to stabilise and maintain their recovery, and strongly positive relationships have been formed over time.

What are eating disorders, and why do people develop them?

Eating disorders are complex, severe psychological illnesses which also encompass many serious physiological problems. Fundamentally, they are disorders of eating behaviour that develop to deal with problems in areas of emotional life, most commonly to do with self-esteem, shame, fear and the complexities of relationships. They have very little to do with food, just as fear of flying has little to do with the actual risk of aeroplanes; they are strategies discovered and employed to deal with distressing emotions and conflicts, many of which have their origins in problematic attachment experiences.

The more familiar EDs are:

> **Anorexia nervosa:** persistent restriction of energy intake, leading to significantly low body weight. An intense fear of gaining weight or becoming fat. Disturbance in the way body weight or shape is experienced and undue influence of body shape and weight on self-evaluation. Persistent lack of recognition of the seriousness of current low body weight.
>
> *Subtypes:* Restricting type, binge-eating purging type
>
> **Bulimia nervosa:** recurrent episodes of binge-eating with recurrent inappropriate compensatory behaviour in order to prevent weight-gain, for example, self-induced vomiting, misuse of laxatives or diuretics or other

medications, fasting and excessive exercise. Self-evaluation is unduly influenced by body weight and shape.

Binge-eating disorder: recurrent episodes of binge-eating and a sense of lack of control over eating. Eating until uncomfortably full when not hungry, feeling disgusted with oneself and depressed afterwards. Marked distress regarding binge-eating.

Other specified feeding or eating disorder (OSFED): feeding or eating behaviours that cause clinically significant distress and impairment in areas of functioning, but do not meet the full criteria for the other eating disorder diagnoses, for example, purging disorder or night eating syndrome.

(The full list can be found in the *Diagnostic and Statistical Manual of Mental Disorders Edition 5*)

Note here that "restrictive" and "binge-eating" mean restriction of food to the point of starvation, and bingeing and purging behaviour so prolific it can continue for several hours in a ritualised way, entailing the consumption of enormous amounts of food interrupted by equally prolific purging either by vomiting, use of laxatives or obsessive and incessant exercise. It is the extreme nature of these behaviours around food that signify an eating *disorder* rather than disordered eating or dieting, as we might know these terms.

There is often a lot of overlap between the different eating disorder diagnoses. A typical situation is where a person has been anorectic, restricting her food for several years, but later starts bingeing and vomiting while continuing to restrict food between binges. This is her nightmare scenario; her body has demanded more and more urgently that she must eat and so, as she sees it, she has "broken down and given in"; control has vanished, and often at that point she has become desperate enough to seek treatment.

Physiology of eating disorders

Eating disorders cause serious harm and may be fatal – anorexia has the highest mortality rate of all mental illnesses. People die either from heart failure caused by starvation or from suicide. The physiological harms that come with severe eating disorders can affect almost every part of the body, including:

- Brain – brain function is affected by shrinkage due to starvation, also due to the chaos of bingeing and purging. This causes impaired cognitive function and cerebral atrophy.
- Impairment of heart function due to cardiac stress caused by starvation.
- Bowel and digestive system – irritable bowel syndrome and other bowel disorders are very common due to restriction of food, vomiting, laxative abuse or a combination of all three.
- Liver dysfunction.
- Hair loss due to restriction, starvation and/or purging.

- Skin conditions, for example, eczema linked to restriction or picking at skin.
- Tooth decay due to prolific bingeing and vomiting.
- Bone density loss, leading to osteopenia and osteoporosis due to early menopause triggered by menstruation ceasing at a low BMI (the rate differs individually).
- Loss of fertility due to the previous.
- Feeling cold all the time due to lack of insulating body fat.
- If obsessive over-exercising features, stress fractures and muscle and ligament problems are frequently present.

Almost all these conditions are reversible, however, and most return to normal functioning once the person has returned to normal weight, has stopped exercising excessively and is eating a balanced diet. This often seems miraculous when someone has been severely unwell for a long time.

However, the outstanding fact we must never forget when seeing patients with an eating disorder is that the basis of all this is *feelings*; trying and failing to control unbearable feelings that fill them with shame and humiliation, fear of rejection, and guilt. The behaviours around food and exercise, while potentially deadly, are a desperate attempt at affect regulation, pushing away these intolerable thoughts and feelings by replacing them with obsessional ruminations about food and body image. Self-starvation, or bingeing on huge amounts of food and then getting rid of it by vomiting or using laxatives, are very effective ways of obscuring these unbearable thoughts and feelings because they are replaced by other all-consuming, self-punishing preoccupations; *how many calories, how much can I avoid, how can I get away with throwing away my lunch, how much do I want that Pret brownie but I'm NOT HAVING IT – Oh God I'm such a vile, lame, pathetic bitch now I'll have to find somewhere to throw it up . . .* – what one of my patients called "sick F.M." They are wracked by constant indecision about what, when and whether to eat. It is common for them to spend several hours in supermarkets pacing up and down the aisles picking up and putting back items of food, unable to decide whether they can bear to buy. They berate themselves for their perceived weakness and inability to follow the rules in their heads about food and calories in a particularly cruel, sadistic way.

As a therapist treating someone with an eating disorder, the first task is to understand the *meaning* of the behaviour for each individual rather than to focus on behaviour change. There is always a reason for the use of bingeing, purging, restriction or obsessive exercise. That reason will be to do with repeatedly trying and failing to achieve some sort of affect regulation around emotions that they find both unbearable and unspeakable.

Who gets an eating disorder?

What factors have to be in place to flick the switch in someone's brain for an eating disorder to set in? A combination of factors come together to make it more likely.

When patients come to us they often present with a dual diagnosis of anxiety or depressive illness, or attention deficit disorder, bipolar disorder or borderline/emotionally unstable PD, and they mostly have a sensitive, perfectionist and shame-prone personality. However, there are other features that I have noticed are often present and have involved some form of humiliation and shame at a very sensitive time in adolescence, when their bodies were changing in a way that was completely outside of their control and sexuality started to become active.

This list is from observations gained from my clinical experience:

Dyslexia or attention deficit disorder, where the person has difficulties focusing on academic work and has therefore been judged and bullied at school as being "stupid." They have processed this as their internal working model. Their perfectionist personality drives them toward something they can use to feel in control, which their peer group will notice and admire them for. They go on a diet and lose some weight, and their friends tell them they are looking good. This is rocket fuel for their self-esteem; suddenly they feel better about themselves, and it is a short step to becoming convinced that staying thin is absolutely the way forward for them.

Early experience of their body being judged for a specific purpose, for example, ballet, gymnastics or other sports such as diving, tennis or rowing. Any weight gain or "fatness" is forbidden and the person loses their place in the team, in front of their peers, in a manner they find humiliating. There is growing evidence that abusive body shaming is carried out in these environments by some coaches and trainers.

Acne: I began to realise some time ago that acne might be a particular issue for our patients. Now I routinely ask whether they had acne as teenagers, and time after time they tell me that yes, they did. When I thought about it I could see there are various consequences of having acne that might contribute to developing an eating disorder: deep shame about feeling ugly, often involving bullying and rejection by one's peer group. Doctors are likely to recommend a diet which involves restricting fats, chocolate and sugar. The young person diets; the acne may not be much better, but she loses weight and people start congratulating her on looking "better" and thinner, and even envying her. This is incredibly powerful for a teenager who has had bad skin, with all the cruelty, rejection and feeling hideous which goes with it. In the recovery group I run, seven out of eight of the current group members suffered from acne as teenagers. Perhaps there is also an underlying difficulty relating to psychic skin (Bick, 1968), uncertainty for the individual about her own boundaries and sense of self, what is inside and what is outside, and this may be heightened during the physical upheavals and sensitivities of adolescence, where the body can feel alien and the actual skin is under attack from hormonal changes.

Money: I have noticed an issue about the way money is managed among people with eating disorders which corresponds with their diagnosis and becomes part of their illness. Anorectic patients have great difficulty in spending money on themselves. They will spend generously on other people, but for themselves they typically purchase clothes from charity shops, never buying anything new. Sometimes they have difficulty in turning on the heating in winter, despite feeling profoundly cold all the time. There seems to be a parallel perception involved in the way they think about food, so that buying anything for themselves to give comfort or enjoyment is seen as a "soft" indulgence that is forbidden.

People with bulimia and binge-eating disorder, on the other hand, can sometimes become multi-impulsive, and as well as developing drug and alcohol addictions, they may form an over-spending habit, buying clothes and make-up in shops or online, bringing them home and often leaving them unpacked and never worn. When put together with the money spent on binge food, financial problems often ensue. Deep, burning shame is involved in this.

There is often a *family history of disparagement of the body*, with mothers or fathers themselves having a history of eating disorders of some kind, and either parent often being absent figures in childhood, but when present are seen to be highly critical of "fat women," ridiculing them in the street or on television. Fathers have a special influence in mirroring their daughters' feelings about what is an acceptable body image in women. Also, anorectic girls are more likely to develop a dismissive/avoidant attachment pattern if this is present in the father (Neuberg & Andersson, 2017). If there is a family history of eating disorders, there will always have been anxiety around food and eating, involving fear or disgust or shame. These tensions in the parents will have been absorbed by the child, feeding into her own relationship with her body and herself.

And attachment difficulties are always present. More about this later.

I have had many patients with one or more of these issues present in their early lives and for whom gaining a sense of control of their bodies by dieting or vomiting and using laxatives has seemed a kind of salvation at first. But soon enough the biological effect of starvation of the brain, or the chaos of bulimia, has tipped the balance into developing a serious eating disorder.

A word about the biological effects of malnourishment on the brain. A major study was carried out in the United States just after the Second World War by Ancel Keys, called the Minnesota Starvation Study (Keys et al., 1950). The purpose was to monitor thirty-six healthy men who volunteered to undergo experimental semi-starvation to help prepare the United States to take care of returning prisoners of war. The impact of their weight loss and limited food availability was profound. The thinking and behaviour of the men, including their preoccupation with food, mirrored what we now see in people with restrictive eating disorders. Many features of anorexia are actually symptoms of starvation, including starvation of the brain. The Keys study showed that prolonged semi-starvation produced increases in severe emotional distress, including depression and self-mutilation.

There was a constant preoccupation with food, loss of libido, social withdrawal and isolation, and a decline in concentration and judgment capabilities. These effects are all experienced in a range of eating disorders, and the study led to a crucial understanding in treating restrictive eating disorders that recovery depends on physical refeeding, together with psychological treatment.

The neurological effects on the brain in anorexia nervosa lead to impaired cognitive function caused by abnormal white matter in the brain during periods of marked weight loss, with some reduction in grey matter. Some studies show this may just reflect malnourishment and can be reversed with weight restoration, though it is not yet clear whether there are permanent cognitive deficits in anorexia nervosa (Mehler & Andersen, 2017). "Anorexic thinking," however, forms part of the psychological effects of the illness, where thoughts about body image are delusional and distorted and the patient's self-esteem is unduly based on the control of weight, body shape and food. This can be reversed when healthy weight is achieved and stabilised. This also applies to other diagnoses, for example, bulimia nervosa.

So when we look at what makes someone vulnerable to developing an eating disorder, we see

- a combination of a sensitive and perfectionist personality and early attachment difficulties,
- a tendency towards anxiety and depression,
- external factors that caused profound guilt and shame about appearance or body image during childhood and adolescence, and
- then, once the person starts restricting food and using exercise excessively or starts bingeing and purging using vomiting or laxative abuse, these behaviours entrench the illness.

Many other factors are present, including early emotional or physical neglect, self-harming behaviours and abuse of various kinds, often sexual; and these can leave a legacy of unresolved trauma which inevitably causes attachment problems in adulthood. It is not possible to have an intimate, mutual relationship with someone whose primary preoccupation is their relationship with food. Sex and sexuality have a particular significance for this group of patients; the behaviours around food and body image all serve to cut off any sexual desire, and in anorexia the female body reverts back to preadolescence. In recovery we do a lot of work around regaining female sexuality, when menstruation restarts and libido returns with the prospect of becoming close to someone sexually, including touching the body, becoming emotionally intimate and with it the possibility of rejection, abandonment and shame. This is a tall mountain to climb for our patients after already scaling the foothills of regaining normal weight and finding some control over the behaviours they have been using. One function of an eating disorder is the regulation of intimacy, keeping other people at a "safe" emotional distance; as such, they are attachment disorders.

Men and eating disorders

In our clinics we see mostly girls and women, but some boys and men too; currently in the United Kingdom, the Eating Disorder Association (Beat) estimate that "approximately 1.25 million people in the United Kingdom have an eating disorder, and around 25% of those affected are male." There is general agreement that boys and men with eating disorders are under-diagnosed and there is a great level of unmet need in the community for both males and females with eating disorders.

Men in general seem to seek different body image-related goals. Compared with women, who mostly desire thinness, men want varying body shapes, from thin to lean muscular torsos, like Premier League footballers or Game of Thrones and Marvel movie actors, through to the extreme big-muscled "bodybuilder" shape. There is a perception that gay men develop eating disorders more commonly, and this appears to be because there is an increased value given to a thin muscular shape among gay men. Bulimia and binge-eating disorder are much more usual in men than anorexia; some studies in the United States suggest these disorders are now as common in the community among men as among women (Andersen, 2017). It is interesting to note as our Western culture increasingly values lean muscularity in men as displayed so prominently in magazines, social media, sports, TV and film, that men who may be predisposed to emotional distress are increasingly drawn into the web of eating disordered behaviours.

Andrew "Freddie" Flintoff is an English sporting hero, a one-time world-class cricket all-rounder and captain of the national cricket team. Retiring from that team sport he first became a heavyweight boxer and is now a popular television presenter best known for his work on Top Gear, the self-proclaimed "lad's" programme about cars. He has been secretly bulimic for twenty years. His eating disorder evolved as a young man in response to body shaming, ridicule and blaming in the press that heightened his sensitivity to body shape and weight. He quickly lost three stones in weight (around 19 kilos) and received many compliments for this. In a television documentary he discloses for the first time his long "addiction" to vomiting after meals, and extreme exercising (Freddie Flintoff: Living with Bulimia, 2020). "A lot of people in the gym want to get bigger. I want to get lighter and smaller." It is as if he is still haunted by the traumatic taunts from his past, despite his dramatic weight loss and changed body shape. He feels guilty when he eats, and explains that, as a man, he feels extra shame at his eating disorder, which he thinks of as a "girl's thing." Because of this shame he has never sought treatment for it. "I recognise two sides of my personality. There's Freddie who's that person who's out on the cricket field or driving fast cars. Then there's Andrew, the bloke who worries about a lot of things and has a lot of insecurities."

My own experience of seeing male patients has been limited. I have worked with some young men with bulimia or binge-eating disorder, and the underlying reasons for their illnesses have been very similar to those of the women I have seen – all arrived with a comorbid diagnosis of depression and most had experienced ruptured attachments in childhood and being bullied or excluded by their peers as adolescents. As a result, they found forming adult emotional relationships difficult. So an attempt at affect regulation was the trigger to the onset of their illness in the same way as my female patients, and the way out of their illness similarly involved coming to terms with their emotional distress so that they could address their eating disordered behaviours and, in turn, their depression. I have only ever worked with one young man with typical anorexia nervosa, who was an inpatient when I worked in a hospital eating disorders unit.

My colleagues do not know for sure why few males are referred to us, or why we see few men and boys being referred to other outpatient teams that we know. There is anecdotal evidence that boys and men do not seek medical help for reasons of shame or denial that there is anything really wrong; if they go to their GP either they do not refer to their eating disorder at all or the GP does not recognise it; they hide it well from their friends and families, who do not recognise eating or body image problems in men in the same way as they may suspect something is wrong in a woman; also that there is less concern and more approval around males frequently going to the gym in order to "gain muscle definition" or "bulk up" with protein shakes as food replacements. Arnold Andersen sums it up thus:

> Males, compared with females, develop eating disorders within a different social learning experience regarding ideal body weight and shape, have a different hormonal milieu, value different goals in sports, diet for different and more personal reasons, may have different comorbid disorders, and will be returning to a different gender role in society. For all these reasons, in diagnosis and treatment, it is of great importance for the clinician to recognise and treat males with eating disorders while respecting the male-specific components.
>
> (Andersen, pp. 251–252 in Mehler & Andersen, 2017)

Working with attachment and eating disorders

When assessing a patient for indications of dismissing, preoccupied and disorganised/unresolved attachment styles, it is tempting to think that this group of patients can neatly be fitted into:

Anorectic – Dismissing/avoidant
Bulimic – Preoccupied
Binge-eaters – Preoccupied/disorganised

But it is not as easy as that, of course. Very often we see patients who go through different stages of illness, starting with anorexia, then tipping over into a particularly self-loathing combination of restriction combined with bingeing, purging and over-exercising – or becoming bulimic after losing a lot of weight from an original binge-eating disorder. In my assessment at the beginning of my work with patients, I regularly find emotional or physical neglect combined with disrupted or broken attachment that has been catastrophic and has contributed in a major way to the development of their illnesses. This has started at a very young age, and so from early childhood their defences have started to build from an internal working model based on their own perceived badness, failure or weakness. As noted earlier, people who are predisposed to becoming eating disordered tend to be both perfectionist and highly sensitive, and these negative self-evaluations are hard to bear.

Attachment theory is particularly suited to these patients, providing a framework to make sense of experiences and self-states that they avoid knowing and cannot articulate. All insight is obscured by their behaviours around food and eating, and they find it impossible to reflect on or verbalise how they feel or why they are doing these "unspeakable" things. These patients are often very articulate in general, so their inability to verbalise their feelings is frightening. They lose any capacity to make sense of themselves or other people and are overwhelmed by the need to get through each day following their self-imposed eating disordered "rules." There is an enormous need for emptiness or desire to be filled by food that prevents self-awareness.

A large part of what I do with these patients involves working on mentalisation, helping them develop their ability to recognise, understand and reflect upon their own state of mind and to understand and verbalise what they are feeling and why. They can then go on to understand and empathise with others. This allows them to develop compassion, both for themselves and the significant other people in their lives, and in turn helps to dissipate anger and blame (toward themselves or their attachment figures).

Bearing the previously mentioned caveat in mind, there is some evidence for an association between particular eating disorders and certain patterns of attachment. The clinical vignettes that follow either have been disguised or permission has been given for use.

Binge-eating disorder and preoccupied/unresolved attachment

Attachment patterns develop from early childhood in response to the kind of caregiving received. In preoccupied attachment the core anxiety is of being abandoned, and the patterns of defence set up are all aimed at preventing separation. However, these defences often have the opposite effect – the desperation of attracting and needing to hold on to the care and attention of others, especially when they show signs of leaving, are counterproductive. Coercive helplessness, angry protest and indeed illness are sometimes found to be effective in preventing desertion. The panic involved in all this makes it difficult for preoccupied individuals to think or reflect on their feelings. A great deal of repressed blame and anger is often in the picture, and there is always deep shame and fear combined with a struggle to manage and regulate intense affect.

Patients with binge-eating disorder often have enmeshed relationships; in other words they get very mixed-up about boundaries in relationships and cannot easily make appropriate boundaries between themselves and others. Others may experience them as overwhelming, demanding and intrusive. As a result, they are often lonely, and a few patients I have seen have become agoraphobic. The world outside feels hostile to them. They are subject to a great deal of shaming by people they encounter in their day-to-day lives because of their size – at work, travelling on public transport, and especially in shops when buying food, or if they ever eat in public. They have often had no psychological treatment for their illness, being offered only invasive bariatric surgery as the sole intervention. Longstanding undiagnosed anxiety disorders and depression are common, and they all have extremely low self-esteem.

Many of these patients have described to me the need to make their bodies into an "overcoat." By this they mean that they use their bodies both to cover up and also to contain and insulate themselves against unbearable feelings they cannot allow to spill out.

Some patients I have seen with binge-eating disorder have also shown signs of a disorganised or unresolved attachment style. When abuse or other major traumatic experiences occur in early life, memories may have been repressed and "forgotten," and during therapy these memories can start to return or be rationalised as normal childhood events experienced by "lots of people." In these circumstances great care has to be taken to allow the patient to go at their own pace and not to rush, nor replace the patient's words with the therapist's version of events. The effects of this developmental rupture can manifest in many different ways in adulthood, from panic attacks to hypervigilance and complex post-traumatic stress disorder (Herman, 1994). Very often it turns into severe depression, and these are the patients we see with longstanding eating disorders.

An example was patient "P," who arrived with an original diagnosis of binge-eating disorder, now with a diagnosis of OSFED (or atypical ED). She was in her late forties and had been unwell since she was a child. P had been sexually abused by a family member for most of her childhood and adolescence. She had not allowed herself to open her mind to her fear or shame, preferring to "blame and be angry with everyone" around her. She was often tearful during our sessions, needing a great deal of holding and containing. Some excellent family therapy provided by a family therapist with experience of eating disorders and P's close working relationship with my dietitian colleague were both invaluable here. The cognitive strategies referred to later in the chapter were particularly effective with P in enabling her to develop insight into her feelings. In doing so, she came to recognise that she needed to take courage and move forward into her future life without using the behaviours around food she had relied on for so many years.

Working with anorexia and dismissing or avoidant attachment

In the dismissing or avoidant attachment style, a different set of defensive strategies has been built up. This group of people avoid intimacy and back away from any perceived "neediness" or becoming "clingy." As with the preoccupied pattern, the underlying fears and anxieties have their origins in childhood relational experiences, but this time the child may have been punished or shamed for needing comfort and so learned to distort, repress and hide from others – and from themselves – their need for security, comfort and love.

This attachment style is very familiar to me from working with many anorectic and depressed patients, though it can also reveal itself with other diagnoses. When I start to work with dismissing anorectic patients I often get a strong sense that the person in front of me is frozen, with all her senses inert. As the work goes on and they begin to get better, it feels like watching a long, slow thawing out process, with little tendrils of emotion and awareness emerging.

It is important to remind ourselves that the thoughts anorectic patients have about their bodies are completely delusional, a manifestation of their psychological illness. It can be oddly easy to forget this, as in other ways they are perfectly rational and often highly intelligent, well-educated people. Yet when addressing body image, they sit in front of me in the room looking completely emaciated and talk with utter disgust of their "fat, fleshy bodies," insisting that they feel the fat growing on them as they eat anything from the long list in their heads of forbidden foods.

I want to say a bit more about softness and hardness here. I have come to the conclusion that anorexia is only about thinness in a secondary, ancillary way. The primary goal for the anorectic person is to acquire a *hard* body and to get rid of all soft bodily flesh. They often reserve a particularly visceral hatred for their stomachs, which naturally change and get fuller and softer if they have eaten, and in digesting their food their stomachs swell. When a person with anorexia has gained weight, with great reluctance but with an understanding that it is necessary to get better, their body may only be acceptable to them is if it is *toned*, and to do this they must use exercise to make it as hard as possible. I was fascinated when, as part of my post-graduate diploma course, we watched a recording of Mary Ainsworth's Strange Situation test (Ainsworth et al., 1978). In the film, infants aged 15 to 18 months who were already displaying signs of avoidant attachment did not protest when their mothers left the room but seemed to hold on to hard toys made of wood or metal as if to contain themselves, rejecting all the soft "comforting" toys.

Like women, men with eating disorders despise soft "flab" and wish to develop hard bodies. They do this by working obsessively on developing a muscular physique. I have heard many of my female anorectic patients talk to me longingly of wanting their bodies to be "just like a plank of wood; thin, hard and with absolutely no curves." There are strong implications here too of a complete rejection of sexuality, as anorexia renders a woman into a non-sexual being, with no sex hormones present and fertility suppressed. A plank of wood indeed.

Although they are shut down emotionally and find verbal communication difficult (especially regarding their emotions), these patients communicate very powerfully with their bodies. Their thin, hard bodies demonstrate the process Gianna Williams describes in her "no-entry system of defence." She says:

For some years I have been interested in work with patients who are difficult to reach, and patients with eating disorders do often belong to this category. In many of them I have experienced a quality of *'do not trespass'* that has brought me to formulate the hypothesis of a "no-entry" system of defences.

(Williams, 1997, p. 115)

Mary Levens describes a similar process:

The anorectic is fighting her body because she considers it to be, first, the concrete manifestation of the unacceptable part of herself . . . and second, the territory or base of an all-powerful, alien invader. The battle is likely to be re-enacted within the therapeutic relationship because the patient has developed a survival 'tactic', which depends upon her not giving in (or giving up control). To accept from another person anything which threatens this posture is to lose the battle for her own sense of self.

(Levens, 1995, p. 101)

Anorectics hate to be touched, in any way or by anyone. A sure sign of recovery when we have our ending session, sometimes after years of therapy, is when I ask if I can give them a hug. It is the first time we would have had any kind of physical contact. Their permission to let me touch their bodies and for us to communicate softness and warmth to each other represents an enormous achievement for them, and an indicator of how far they have come in their recovery.

Working with bulimia and avoidant attachment

As previously noted, specific eating disorders are not necessarily paired with particular patterns of attachment. I have met patients with a diagnosis of bulimia nervosa who appear to have an avoidant/dismissing attachment style. When I first meet a patient like this, they appear cold and aloof and show polite contempt at my pathetic attempts to understand them. I immediately recognise that dismissing attachment is in the room. I also recognise that shame, self-loathing and longing are there.

Someone I worked with who showed this attachment pattern was "S." I began working with S when she was 20, and she arrived with a diagnosis of bulimia nervosa and depression. She had previously been anorectic, having restricted her food intake from the age of about 11. S was brought up in a religious family, and we found that shame had formed a large part of her internal working model. I saw her for three years, and during that time we made a great deal of progress that enabled S to gain insight, change her self-perception and get rid of the behaviours that had troubled her so much.

S memorably invented the term "the burning building feeling." By this she meant the panic she felt when she approached a feeling of emotional closeness with a man. She had been quite multi-impulsive, going through a period of over-use of alcohol and drugs, risky behaviour and one-night stands or very brief sexual relationships. She would only have sex when she was drunk, and was unable to be emotionally connected. She described to me a time when she had sex in this way and was still in bed with the young man in the morning. He turned to her and was affectionate, cuddling her and saying loving things to her; she could not bear this. She said, "It felt like the building was burning and I just had to get out of there. I got dressed in a blind panic and ran out of the house, like it was on fire." In subsequent sessions this term became a kind of shorthand to describe her feelings when she felt panicked by getting too closely connected emotionally. Yet on other occasions she expressed a craving, a yearning to be close to a man, and said she couldn't bear to feel alone. She made a connection between this feeling and her bingeing, and recognised that the craving for emotional connection quickly turned into a craving to feel physically full, "stuffed" with sweet or creamy food.

My supervisor was very struck by S's "burning building" feeling when being held or cuddled, connecting it to very early experiences of mothering and S's body being caressed in a loving way. She thought I may have offered her an acceptable form of that connection in our therapeutic relationship.

Working with bulimia and preoccupied attachment

In contrast with patient S, many of my bulimic patients have a preoccupied attachment style, and I sometimes find it a struggle to keep going in the face of the anxiety and craving of contact that can feel disabling, as if the person wants to gobble me up and spit me out. Unlike a dismissing patient, where the problem seems to be that I am useless and cannot do anything to help them, here there is a sense that I cannot possibly do or be enough.

A young woman patient, B, now in her early thirties, comes to mind to illustrate how I worked with this type of attachment style and diagnosis. I saw her for almost three years, with a six-month gap when she "spat me out." She came back after a crisis and eventually stopped seeing me individually after a planned ending as her symptoms receded and she felt much happier and in control of her life. She is now settled with her partner in a long-term relationship.

B had a diagnosis of binge-eating disorder and depression, with a history since the age of ten of restriction and body-checking and an obsession with exercise, rather than vomiting, to compensate for the calories consumed in her binge-eating. I remember the first time I went to find B in the waiting-room; I almost did a double-take as the person sitting there, whom I had I assumed from her appearance to be a young man, stood up and said hello. B is a gay woman, and she later spoke to me with great insight about her sexuality, saying she had always felt different and "other" but had come to terms with herself and her sexuality quite comfortably. However, her sexuality did have a bearing on her body image and her relationship with her family.

In common with many of my patients, B had acne as an adolescent. She carried enormous shame about this and did not look into a mirror for many years. Her acne was a very important part of the development of her illness, both the depression and the eating disorder, in that it had set up an internal working model of very low self-esteem manifested in a concrete way; the inner "badness" perceived about herself was shown on the outside to the extent that she thought others recoiled at her appearance. There was also a family script about fatness being bad (her mother had a history of anorexia, and her father belittled "fat women"). It was a short step to the realisation that at least there was *something* she could do to control one of the unacceptable aspects of herself, and that was to stop being (as she saw herself) "fat" and become thin.

As is common in therapy with preoccupied individuals, boundaries were an issue in our sessions (Cundy, 2017): B always wanted to stay longer, and I had to be firm about ending times. She emailed between sessions and found ways of trying to engage me with amusing pictures, memes or Internet links she thought would interest me. I had to be careful not to respond until I saw her in the session and tried to find links between her behaviour with me and with other relationships in her life.

I worked with B to create a breathing space and to enable her to see the bigger picture; what she was missing by continuing to be stuck in her blaming, angry state. I found a way of engaging with her left brain which B could relate to – she was a very organised person and liked evidence, so I used some more active strategies, including a Feelings Diary, to help her make sense of her own feelings in a different context.

Anorexia, bulimia and disorganised attachment

We sometimes see severely unwell patients who may have been diagnosed with, or display aspects of borderline personality disorder or bipolar disorder. They often have chaotic family histories that include emotional neglect, sexual abuse or other trauma. Family relationships are enmeshed and angry, and in these circumstances they have developed a pattern of unresolved or disorganised attachment. They can often function well as adults in some areas of life, for example, work, but fall apart in close relationships. Kernberg et al. (2002) suggest their inner worlds are fragmented and they cannot experience themselves or others as whole, or held together, and this is terrifying for them. In their relationships with others they often provoke extreme responses, and so they feel persecuted and misunderstood. Kernberg also suggests that extreme envy is a feature of the "borderline" inner world, and envy is often a response when having to share what minimal emotional resources were available in childhood. Negative comparisons and extreme envy (always concerning others' bodies, which are perceived to be thinner) are a feature of people with eating disorders.

Outlining her theory of complex post-traumatic stress disorder, Herman writes that "disturbance in identity and relationship is most prominent in borderline personality disorders" (Herman, 1994, p. 126), and the varied symptoms in adult survivors of childhood sexual abuse include depression, anxiety, sexual difficulties, anger, dissociation, self-mutilation, addictions and suicidal impulses.

The eating disorder quickly takes hold in these circumstances, and in our practice we see this pattern most often in our patients who are multi-impulsive bulimics or severely restrictive anorectics.

A patient comes to mind as an example. D had been anorectic since she was a teenager. She was very thin, and she combined restriction with prolific bingeing and vomiting. She had been sexually abused by her brother as a child and had an enmeshed relationship with her mother.

As her treatment progressed, D was able to give up bingeing and vomiting. However, her restriction remained, and she began to lose more weight. She was astonished about this; an important thing to know about anorexia is how strong the denial of illness can be. Unlike bulimia, where there is a great deal of shame, guilt and secrecy about the behaviours around food, in anorexia patients are proud of their perceived "strength" in controlling their longing to eat and are profoundly afraid of the control breaking down. Denial of illness is one of the main symptoms of anorexia and is similar to the delusional thinking about body image. Patients insist nothing is really wrong and resist any interference from us in getting on with the essential job of obeying the loud, insistent anorectic voice telling them to eat less food and lose more weight. For D, her belief was that she had balanced her bingeing and vomiting perfectly, so that she mistakenly thought she was getting rid of all the calories in the food she had eaten in her very prolific binges. It is clear that in attempting to manage her calorie intake and expulsion, D was actually trying to regulate some very intense and painful feelings.

Some practical strategies for therapists working with eating disorders

The complex nature of working with people with eating disorders means a clear focus is necessary for effective intervention. I have found that a good understanding of attachment theory provides this and has underpinned all my work. It enables a warm approach, where I explain what I am doing and how I am thinking as I go along so that my patient is always kept in the loop. Importantly, it also models a boundaried yet attached relationship, often the first they have experienced. Therapists need to be prepared to use some active strategies when working with this client group because they believe they have already found a strategy that they cling to and are terrified of letting go; as the therapist you must have something new and different that they can be encouraged to try.

Mentalisation is very helpful here in gently challenging perceptions that are clearly distorted and to help them reflect and explore ideas about their own experiences, think about the outcomes and gradually develop some empathy and compassion for themselves and others around them. This creates some space for thoughts and feelings to emerge without becoming overwhelmed by intense fear or anxiety. Being able to make sense of their own minds and impulses and having the courage to confront the distress underlying their symptoms gives patients an invaluable resource.

I have found using an integrated approach with some cognitive tools very help-ful, and these can be utilised in the therapeutic work easily and seamlessly. They are not new as cognitive strategies but they need to be used with insight into the individual pathways of how eating disorders work for patients. In addictions to drugs or alcohol it is possible, though extremely difficult, to banish the addictive substance from your life. In contrast, food is cheap, legal, freely available – and essential in order to stay alive.

I The Feelings Diary

I was introduced to this way of working in the 1990s by Professor Hubert Lacey at the Roehampton Priory Eating Disorders Unit. He had conducted a long-term out-come study at Springfield Hospital in bulimia nervosa, binge-eating and psycho-genic vomiting (Lacey, 1983), and introduced an integrated outpatient programme in 1994 based on this study (the findings were later written up by Murphy et al. (2005)). The treatment was focal, insight-oriented and combined psychodynamic and behavioural techniques to bring structure to the chaotic eating pattern expe-rienced by the patients taking part. The programme was based on clinical experi-ence of working with patients with increasingly complex symptoms and with the need to treat the needs of patients with binge-eating disorder, bulimia and less chronic anorectic patients.

The weekly food and emotion diary was introduced together with the estab-lishment of a stable eating plan and formed the starting point for behavioural changes. The Feelings Diary was pivotal in forming a crucial understanding of the link that exists between distressing or unbearable feelings caused by a thought or an event or a relationship, followed by an immediate impulse to use disordered behaviours around food – whether bingeing or restricting. The distressed feelings are instantly replaced by a preoccupation with the behaviour and how to carry it out. It is a very effective defence against reflecting on or thinking about what is truly distressing or unbearable in the person's life, preventing mentalising. But it comes with a terrible sting in the tail – an inevitable strengthening of the power with which the eating disorder takes over the person's life.

I continue to make use of the Feelings Diary with many of my patients. I have to think carefully about when to introduce it, usually after the assessment and once I have made the initial formulation about their internal working model and how best to work with them. I explain its use and purpose in some detail, and show them the little blue book I have had printed with instructions for how to use it – a new book for every week. There is a page for each day, with the time, behaviour used or thought/trigger about a behaviour – then on the opposite page, space for a description of the situation involved, with the thoughts and feelings associated with using the behaviour. I emphasise that I am not bothered about the quality or neatness of the writing or spelling (as previously noted, many of my patients are dyslexic and/or perfectionists), and if they prefer, they can write on their phone or laptop and email it to me. I use the diary as part of my work to help them develop an increased awareness of the emotional meaning of their behaviours, which we can then address in therapy, and to build insight into the function and symbolic nature of their actions, especially around difficulties in differentiation of self, and in relationships with others.

The diary becomes an invaluable tool for many of them, and some like to continue to use it so that it becomes a record of their recovery. One of my patients did this and used it as part of a book she later published (Jones, 2016). There is another important role for the diary in forming a symbolic link between patient and therapist as a transitional object (Winnicott, 1971). Its use is a commitment to recovery by keeping the patient engaged in therapeutic activity between sessions. I remember Professor Lacey suggesting I gave it to the patient "with gravity and respect, like a Japanese tea ceremony," and I have taken that advice ever since.

2 Getting better or staying stuck

Another approach involves the patient writing two letters: (a) a letter to a friend in five years' time with your illness still in place, together with (b) another to a friend in five years' time having recovered from your illness. I was introduced to this device for working with anorectic patients by the team at the Eating Disorders Unit at Roehampton Priory Hospital in the 1990s. It can be a very powerful tool to pierce the denial of illness that all patients with anorexia display, which is a key aspect of the symptomatology and often difficult to work with. Anorectics have a delusional and distorted view of their bodies as "fat," which they despise, and their minds are full of guilt and shame as well as terror at the idea of being "made" to gain weight; their belief is that being thin and hard is the only thing that keeps them under control and stops them falling apart. It can be useful for bulimic patients as well, but care should be taken not to amplify the guilt and shame they already perceive about having ruined their future by being unable to give up using their behaviours around food.

This tool is helpful toward the beginning of therapy, just as cracks are beginning to show in the patient's apparent steely denial. It can be introduced as homework between sessions or, if the patient is very unwell, it is better to do it in the room as part of the session, as they will need support in thinking of all the ramifications implied in each letter.

I start by asking them how old they will be in five years, then encourage them to think about:

- **Where will I be living, and who with?** – at home with parents; independently with friends; with their husband/wife/boyfriend/girlfriend; on their own; as a long-term hospital patient.
- **What work will I be doing?** – student (first degree or master's, etc); in a job they enjoy; in a job they hate; unemployed; unable to work as too unwell.
- **Relationships** – family, friends, sexual relationships, working relationships. What will be the *quality* of these relationships?

- **Will there be children?** – anorexia stops menstruation and puts young women into early menopause, causing infertility. This is reversed with recovery.
- **What will my quality of life be like?** – interests, travel, sports, hobbies, activities, pets, etc. If anorexia persists there will likely be none of these.

This exercise usually highlights in grim detail the emptiness of adult life with anorexia still in place, contrasted with the prospect of a full, productive and *relational* life when recovered. However, it will also highlight the fears that may exist of taking part in a full life, with its expectations of success and managing relationships, including sexual relationships and children. It is useful to explore these fears and recognise that holding on to anorexia will mean never having to confront them.

3 Friend or enemy?

This very useful tool is an adaptation of one devised by Janet Treasure and Lucy Serpell as part of their treatment programme at the Maudsley Hospital, London (Serpell et al., 1999). The client is asked to write one letter to their illness as her friend, and another where the illness is addressed as enemy. The purpose is to highlight the ambivalence about recovery that is always present in any eating disorder diagnosis. There is a longing for recovery and to regain a life, feel "normal," lose the continual churning of eating disordered thoughts, to stop lying, stop the shame of secretive bingeing and purging, stop the physical pain they often feel with profound coldness and sparsely covered bones crunching on beds and chairs, or the painful symptoms of irritable bowel syndrome – yet there is also a need to cling to their illness and the "control" they seek but never find to their satisfaction. The illness is indeed a hard task-master, but to let it go feels terrifying. This can be used for anorexia, bulimia or binge-eating disorder.

Here is a recent example, written by an anorectic medical student:

My friend anorexia . . .

- I like the feeling of lightness you give me and not feeling full.
- I like seeing/feeling my hip bones and collar bones.
- I like my clothes being baggy.
- I like feeling cold.
- I like having you to focus on/as a distraction.*
- I like feeling smaller.
- I like how you make me feel less ugly and gross.*

My enemy anorexia . . .

- I hate how you occupy my thoughts.
- I hate how tired you make me.
- I hate how you make me study the menus of restaurants I eat out at.
- I hate how much time you make me spend in supermarkets.

- I hate the secrecy you come with.
- I hate how you constantly make me calculate calories consumed.
- I'm tired of justifying every "bad" thing I eat.
- I hate how you affect my relationships and work.

This made the start of a useful exploration of what her anorexia was doing for her in everyday life and to notice that five out of seven points on her "friend" list were undeniable confirmations that her anorexia was present. The other two (asterisked) made for fruitful discussion over several sessions, together with all the points in her "enemy" column, which listed all the consequences of having her illness so firmly in place – and led to a discussion of how she might begin to let it go.

Working with distorted body image

This is one of the most difficult aspects of working with an eating disordered patient. Their own image of their bodies is always distorted, this is one of the most prominent features of having an eating disorder. People with bulimia have great difficulty with body image as well as those with anorexia nervosa. I have found it is counterproductive at first to comment directly on what is obvious in the room – that the person in front of me is deeply distressed about something that is not there. Patients believe implicitly they can feel and see something profoundly disgusting about themselves that they find unbearable – the "fat" on their bodies that does not exist. I do gently remind them that this is a *psychological* illness they have – that's why they are here having psychotherapy and seeing a psychiatrist – and that the beliefs and feelings they have about their bodies are delusional, a symptom of the illness in their brain. They find this difficult to accept. Body dysmorphia varies quite a lot in its intensity between patients, and some experience it more powerfully than others. It is very difficult to shift, but working away at it while never minimising their distress and accepting and working with their profound but misplaced feelings of disgust about themselves are the best place to start.

There are distressing aspects of this that all patients experience, women and men. They have a particular dread of photographs. I have had a few patients who avoided their own wedding because they could not do something that would involve them being photographed as the centre of attention. In the same way, they hate mirrors or any reflective surface, like shop windows or shiny cars, yet they can't stop looking and negatively judging themselves in all these things which they use as a form of compulsive self-harm. There is a great deal of magical thinking involved in this, a belief that parts of their bodies literally grow in size as they obsessively scrutinise and check them.

It is helpful to acknowledge this with them and make a *contract* that while they are in treatment they will cover up or get rid of any full-length mirrors in their bedroom or bathroom. They will not compulsively look at photographs of themselves at their thinnest/fattest either on their phone or on paper. They will delete apps like Instagram or any eating disorder-related app. You can ask them to do this in the room with you there to support them, as it will be very difficult for them. You can make a list with them of all the ways in which they body check, scrutinising the parts of their bodies they particularly detest in minute detail, including touching their knees, thighs, collarbones, faces or wrists to check they are the same size. Some people use a pair of tight-fitting jeans or a belt to check the fit is the same. Some people weigh themselves many times in a day. They should notice when and why they do these things. Ask them what they thought the body checking would do for them – and how they actually felt, having done it. Sometimes you will notice their hand unconsciously going to their collarbone or wrist in the room with you, if something is raised that makes them distressed or anxious – it is helpful to point out this unconscious body checking in a non-judgmental way and ask them why they needed to do it at that moment. It will usually be done as a form of reassurance or self-soothing, to check the bones still protrude, as they will have experienced a wave of feeling fatter linked to the wave of distress. The Feelings Diary is useful to include here as a way of recording how, when and where they started to body check and to notice when the need to do it started to feel compulsive. There are some useful techniques and further information about body dysmorphia and other common compulsive behaviours including skin-picking and trichotillomania (compulsive hair-pulling) in David Veale's book, *Overcoming Body Image Problems*.

Working in a multidisciplinary team and working in private practice

I am very lucky to be working in a partnership with two psychiatrists and two dietitians, all highly skilled and experienced clinicians. We wanted to set up and work together in a similar practice, as we had experienced working in outpatient departments within hospital eating disorder units.

If you work as a sole practitioner, before you consider accepting a patient with a known eating disorder, you will need to assess how serious their illness is and ask direct, specific questions about how it affects his or her behaviour, thoughts and feelings. You should make a full and detailed risk assessment, including enquiring about any physical self-harming (bear in mind s/he may not tell the whole truth). Then consider how you and your supervisor feel about taking them on – you will need the experienced support of your supervisor. Given the potential severity of eating disorders and often the dual diagnoses, these are vital ethical considerations; it is essential to work within our level of competence with all clients.

Once you have made your assessment and you feel sure you can manage the risks involved, you would need to be sure you can make a connection with that person. If you are unsure, or if over time your patient reveals more about the severity of their illness, then make clear that your intention is to refer them on to a specialist setting where their needs will be met more appropriately than you can offer as a sole practitioner. And finally, if you have had eating problems yourself in the past, then do think carefully about whether to take on a patient with an eating disorder. You may find it both upsetting and triggering, and it may get in the way of the work you are able to do together.

It will be very important always to share information with the patient's GP, and this should be made clear in the contract. The physical harms of these illnesses are profound, as noted previously, and they must be monitored. If possible, you will also need to involve a dietitian with experience of eating disorders. I cannot emphasise enough how helpful this will be, both for the overall treatment of your patient but also for your own peace of mind. Our two dietitians are skilled at working with patients' bodies and weight, food and nutrition, and all aspects of over-activity and physiological health. They combine this with years of experience and insight into how their patients' minds work within all this. This leaves me free in my sessions to explore all the psychological aspects of their illness, although we do overlap sometimes over body image and perceptions of weight and meaning of the food and behaviours. The consultant psychiatrists assess, diagnose and monitor each patient, prescribing medication where necessary and taking overall clinical responsibility for their care. Our contained environment means we can pass on this sense of containment to our patients. However, we do work with very unwell people, so if you feel confident about working with your patient's level of illness, you will need to consider important things such as how to handle monitoring weight (you or the GP? If you weigh the patient, how will that affect your sessions? If the GP, how will you communicate?), and what to do about meal plans and dietetic advice.

Conclusion

To conclude, I would like to repeat something Linda said to me about contributing to this book. We are both of a certain age, and the prospect of retirement is starting to come over the horizon and is gaining focus. Linda told me she often feels a bit like a matriarch elephant, passing on the knowledge she has acquired over so many years to the younger ones in the herd. I thought that was a particularly apt description, and I am glad to have been given this chance to pass on the knowledge I have gained over the years through my experience in this field. I hope it will be useful for those practitioners who, like me, find working with eating disorders inevitably challenging but also fascinating and ultimately very fulfilling.

I would like to take this opportunity to thank all the clinicians I have worked with, especially consultant psychiatrists Dr Adrienne Key and Dr Barbara Rooney and dietitians Jane Thompson and Carol Bowyer, my partners in our practice. I also owe a great deal to my long-term supervisor Patricia Marsden, who has always been a tower of strength, skill and experience. I have benefited and learned greatly from all the expert work I have witnessed. Most especially, however, I would like to express my gratitude to all the patients in the room with me over the years, who have given so much of themselves in our sessions and from whom I have learned so much. I have been absorbed, astonished, sometimes amused, and always so grateful for the trust they have shown in me and their courage to set aside their fears, go for recovery and regain their lives. I am particularly grateful to those who gave permission for me to write about their stories, and I hope these will be of help directly or indirectly to others who suffer with an eating disorder.

References

Ainsworth, M., Blehar, M., Waters, E., & Wall, S. (1978). *Patterns of Attachment Assessed in the Strange Situation Test and at Home*. Hillsdale, NJ: Erlbaum.

American Psychiatric Association. (2013). *Diagnostic and Statistical Manual of Mental Disorders* (5th ed.). Washington, DC: APA Publishing.

Andersen, A.E. (2017). Males with eating disorders. In P.S. Mehler, & A.E. Andersen (Eds.), *Eating Disorders: A Guide to Medical Care and Complications* (3rd ed., pp. 240–265). Baltimore, MD: Johns Hopkins University Press.

Bick, E. (1968). The experience of the skin in early object- relations. *International Journal of Psycho-Analysis, 49*, 484–486 [reprinted in Raphael-Leff, J. (Ed.). (2003). *Parent-Infant Psychodynamics: Wild Things, Mirrors and Ghosts*. London: Whurr].

Cundy, L. (2017). Fear of abandonment and angry protest. In L. Cundy (Ed.), *Anxiously Attached: Understanding and Working with Preoccupied Attachment* (pp. 1–30). London: Karnac.

Freddie Flintoff: Living with Bulimia. (2020). BBC One, Television 28 September 2000.

Herman, J.L. (1994). *Trauma and Recovery: From Domestic Abuse to Political Terror*. London: Pandora.

Jones, C. (2016). *The Spaces in Between: A Memoir*. London: Constable.

Kernberg, O.F., Yeomans, F.E., & Clarkin, J.F. (2002). *A Primer of Transference-Focused Psychotherapy for the Borderline Patient*. Northvale, NJ: Jason Aronson.

Keys, A. et al. (1950). *The Biology of Human Starvation* (2 vols.). St Paul, MN: University of Minnesota.

Lacey, H. (1983). Bulimia nervosa, binge-eating and psychogenic vomiting: A controlled treatment study and long-term outcome. *British Medical Journal, 286*, 1611–1613.

Levens, M. (1995). *Eating Disorders and Magical Control of the Body*. London: Routledge.

Murphy, S., Russell, L., & Waller, G. (2005). Integrated psychodynamic therapy for bulimia nervosa and binge eating disorder: Theory, practice and preliminary findings. *European Eating Disorders Review, 13*, 383–391.

Neuberg, E.B., & Andersson, G. (2017). The anorectic girl and her father: The interpersonal and intrapsychic meaning to the girl. *Universal Journal of Psychology, 5*(4), 204–209.

Serpell, L., Treasure, J., Teasdale, J., & Sullivan, V. (1999). Anorexia nervosa: Friend or foe? *International Journal of Eating Disorders, 25*, 177–186.

Veale, D., Willson, R., & Clarke, A. (2009). *Overcoming Body Image Problems Including Body Dysmorphic Disorder: A Self-Help Guide using Cognitive Behavioural Techniques*. London: Robinson.

Williams, G. (1997). *Internal Landscapes and Foreign Bodies: Eating Disorders and Other Pathologies*. London: Karnac.

Winnicott, D.W. (1971). *Playing and Reality*. London: Tavistock.

Chapter 6

Dysfunctional eating in recovering addicts

A therapist's shift to an attachment-focused approach

Sarah Pennock

Introduction

After twenty-one years of friendship, my dearest friend collapsed following a spell of breathlessness. She had suffered a series of heart attacks. One week later, with no evidence of brain activity, her family made the heart wrenching decision to turn off her life support. She was 39 years old. I gained some comfort knowing she had been released from a life-long battle with food; it had been her comfort, her reward, her passion, her distraction, her enemy and the place she returned to manage any and all her feelings.

Following a diagnosis of diabetes aged 14, she had rarely given her body the nutrition it needed, instead bingeing on sugar and refined carbohydrates most days, often abusing her insulin to rapidly lose weight through intentionally poor blood sugar control. By signing up to the latest diet plan, she repeatedly attempted to regain control but consistently returned to the familiar yet harmful food behaviours. Our university years were marked with sudden but preventable distress as she suffered regular hypoglycaemic episodes where her blood glucose level dropped dramatically through poor management of her condition.

For much of her adult life, her weight fluctuated and her diabetic body suffered. Her health, so often sacrificed for her appearance, and her food, recruited to change her mood, brought grim consequences to every layer of her life. She developed diabetic retinopathy, cataracts, deep vein thrombosis and eventually kidney failure. She struggled with increasing anxiety, bouts of depression and a whole spectrum of eating disorder traits. Her final year of life was largely spent in and out of hospital. Neuropathy meant minor injuries quickly progressed to more serious medical problems, her wounds failing to heal due to poor blood circulation. One very distressing admission for diabetic foot ulcers had barely avoided foot amputation. She began dialysis and waited for a double (kidney and pancreas) transplant. When the call finally came the organs were unsuitable. It was devastating news.

Her premature death became increasingly likely day by day. Despite this, she continued with destructive behaviour. The diabetic complications couldn't be undone. She seemed defeated. I recall the moment shortly after discharge from yet another gloomy hospital visit, she repeated the doctor's morbid warning about the increased probability of her early passing, most likely before we could celebrate our fiftieth birthdays. I have often wondered if, in that moment, she shared my fear her life would end far sooner; in fact, she died only a few months short of her fortieth.

Six months after my friend passed away, following a period of personal therapy and a significant midlife appraisal, I left a twenty-year career in television and decided to retrain as an addiction therapist. It felt like the right time to embark on a more meaningful vocation, one which would provoke uncomfortable self-exploration, multiple turning points and deeply rewarding work.

Ten years later I find myself identifying as an attachment-based therapist specialising in addiction and dependency, resulting from an integration of two very distinct models of therapy: an abstinence-based addiction model and psychotherapy informed by attachment theory. Tragically, the nutritional-based interventions alone could not reach my beloved friend. As my clinical work continues to provoke memories of her struggles, I wonder if awareness of her attachment insecurity could have provided an alternative insight to her dysfunctional eating that might have extended her life.

Outline

This chapter will describe a therapist's shift from an addiction model of treatment to an integrated attachment-based framework for understanding and working with recovering addicts whose dysfunctional food behaviour is maladaptive and not dissimilar in process or motivation to substance misuse or alcoholism. Focusing on a single case study, a female binge drinker and compulsive over-eater, I aim to share the challenges and small triumphs in helping her surrender patterns of self-harm while explaining why the mere avoidance of particular foods or cessation of damaging food behaviour were simply not enough to bring about lasting change. I aim to highlight why, in my experience, the use of behavioural therapy within an addiction model of recovery has enhanced capacity to heal and repair when considered alongside the client's attachment functioning. In sharing a fragment of my work with this very specific clinical population I hope to demonstrate the link between attachment insecurity and relapsing behaviour and between a poor working model of self and reluctance to pursue more constructive behavioural coping strategies. I will also demonstrate why, in my experience, the client will struggle to make the best use of therapy and a recovery community as a source of soothing and support if they have little or no awareness of their attachment style. Additionally, I will illustrate why an absence of behavioural skills training within addiction-focused attachment-based work will limit clients' learning, restrict their capacity for positive change, and therefore impede their progress towards earning security. By sharing Ava's therapeutic process, I hope to demonstrate why, for me, this integrative approach is both valid and effective when working with recovering addicts and the complexities of their obsessive and compulsive food behaviour.

Definitions of addiction terms

I think it important to share the psychological definitions which framed my clinical work referenced in this chapter. Throughout the last forty years, theories of "addiction" have developed to accommodate new perspectives beyond the morality model of the early twentieth century, such as the self-efficacy theory (Bandura, 1977), the disease model (McLellan, 2000), and the self-medication model (Khantzian, 2003). Following my master's training, I recruited the bio-psycho-social model, a catch-all way to understanding addictive behaviour, characterised by "the inability to consistently abstain, impairment in behavioural control, craving, diminished recognition of significant problems with one's behaviours and interpersonal relationships, and a dysfunctional response to emotions" (American Society of Addiction Medicine, 2011) as embraced by the addiction treatment programmes in which I had trained.

The 12-step philosophy refers to a specific abstinence-based addiction treatment approach. Twelve-step fellowships such as Alcoholics Anonymous (AA) emphasise the importance of accepting addiction as a disease that can be arrested but never eliminated, enhancing individual maturity and spiritual growth, minimising self-centredness and providing help to other addicted individuals. The 12 steps, first published in 1939, are a set of guiding principles outlining a course of action for recovery from addiction, compulsion or other behavioural problems. This method has been adapted to become the foundation of many other 12-step programmes, such as Overeaters Anonymous (OA), a voluntary fellowship for compulsive eaters.

Historically, the addiction field has failed to achieve consensus around defining the term "recovery" (Laudet, 2008). Some promote voluntarily maintained control over substance use, resulting in an abstinent life, free from negative consequences of substance use, which actively fosters greater life satisfaction and well-being (Heather, 1998). Several clinical studies refer to recovery as "transformational change" (White, 2004) and "a process and not an event" (Ibid.). One 2006 review framed recovery as a "stage-dependent developmental process" (White & Kurtz, 2006), reinforcing the stages of change model (Prochaska & DiClemente, 1983), which outlines progress from pre-contemplation of abstinence through to maintenance. This chapter will define addiction recovery as "continuing behavioural growth and change" (Kelly et al., 2010, p. 121) that redefines personal identity and interpersonal relationships and alters the pattern of behaviour or use.

Last, let us consider the term "relapse." Like other chronic diseases, the American Society of Addiction Medicine suggest addiction often involves cycles of relapse and remission (2011). Substance relapse will be defined as a pursuit of the substance, resulting in breaking one's abstinence. Behavioural relapse (such as over-eating) is less black and white, involving counterproductive behaviour, where the urge to complete a behaviour and discomfort if prevented from this resemble the craving and withdrawal symptoms of substance abusers. Therefore, behavioural relapse will be defined as difficulty in managing responses to environmental cues or emotional triggers during ongoing attempts to recover, which result in a return to self-defeating behaviour.

Having completed several clinical placements in addiction treatment programmes necessary to gain my master's, post-graduation I joined the clinical team of a 12-step treatment centre as an addiction therapist in their outpatient programme, where we admitted Ava. While this felt like the right fit for my training, my final year research on the link between developmental trauma and relapse in female recovering alcoholics had provoked further curiosity about how attachment insecurity might result in dependency issues, and crucially how attachment disruption might impact a client's response to addiction-targeted treatment. Alongside my new role, I began a three-year post-graduate diploma in attachment-based psychotherapy, hungry for greater understanding of how our earliest attachments can significantly influence our emotional and social lives and, crucially, our responses to life's stressors. As I continued to observe recovering alcoholics and addicts, I noted that their often-fragmented family dynamics and inharmonious relationships were triggers for relapsing behaviour. For Ava, this resulted in both binge drinking and overeating.

While attempting to demonstrate Ava's attachment insecurity alongside maintaining her uniqueness, I have changed any identifiable details to protect her confidentiality and anonymity. I want to thank Ava for sharing her deeply personal revelations, for the privilege of exploring her struggles together over several years, and for her consent to publish aspects of her story and our work together.

Case study: Ava

I first met 28-year old Ava when she presented for help at an outpatient addiction programme, stating her drinking and overeating were out of control and she was "done with being fat." She described her mood as "sad and anxious for as long as I can remember," with occasional panic attacks. She felt her long term "long-suffering boyfriend" of eight years was a victim of "false advertising," having met her when she was "a young and thin trainee doctor," but who now found himself with a "failed obese care assistant."

She was under the care of a psychiatrist, in her fourth year of taking prescribed medication for depression and anxiety. She had attended weekly (psychodynamic) psychotherapy for the past two years and was able to offer some understanding of the impact her childhood had on her adult choices. She listed the many weight loss plans she had recruited since early adolescence, only to regain the lost pounds and more with each attempt. Despite significant financial and emotional investment throughout her adulthood, she had not been able to overcome the destructive behaviour around food and alcohol which now dominated her life. Desperation had delivered her to an addiction treatment centre.

At our initial meeting Ava wore a loose black shift dress which she continually tugged past her knees, informing me that this "uniform," worn daily, was taken from her collection of exact replicas. These were purchased to remove any morning battles with tight clothing and draw attention away from her overweight body, because even a hint of shame provoked an automatic response to eat. Each surge of shame led to further bingeing, weight gain and body shame, and so the cycle continued.

Ava struggled to make extended eye contact with me. Her narrative peppered with self-whipping humour, she detailed her tortuous love–hate relationship with food and alcohol. I instantly warmed to her. I recognised her comedy, created from decades of discomfort and shame, that barely veiled her insecurities. I wondered how many times she had sought connection through self-deprecation and recalled this skill of exposing shortcomings to present a fictitious ease with oneself to mask low self-esteem. I felt maternal in the face of such vulnerability, alongside hope that together we could ease her emotional pain and create small steps towards positive change.

We agreed to admit her to the fourteen-week addiction treatment programme, and she agreed to attend four weekly sessions: a mixture of group and individual therapy, including a food focus group, alongside fortnightly sessions with a dietician specialising in dysfunctional eating. Within this addiction model Ava would be guided through stages of treatment, each requiring the completion of written and behavioural tasks. It was a prescriptive therapeutic approach, one not dissimilar to cognitive behavioural therapy (CBT), with distinct and formulaic goals.

Early stage of treatment

Step one in a 12-step programme such as AA states that the person is powerless over alcohol and the alcohol abuse-related behaviour; therefore, AA promotes sobriety. Hence our primary goal was to break through any denial Ava might have held regarding her compulsion to drink alcohol and the lack of control once she had consumed the first drink. Ava easily recalled significant evidence to demonstrate her difficulty moderating alcohol, multiple stories of regrettable and risky behaviour resulting in black-out, which had been normalised in her friendship circle yet which consistently resulted in heightened anxiety and shame.

Clearly Ava was a binge drinker, both socially but also alone at home. Yet she immediately recruited this neat and clear boundary regarding abstention from alcohol. Despite an occasional desire to drink, mostly triggered by irritation in the company of her intoxicated friends outside the programme or guilt regarding her boyfriend, who frequently vocalised the loss "of his wing-woman," Ava was able to surrender alcohol from day one with few wobbles. In my experience it was unusual to so easily put down an addictive behaviour.

Understandably Ava questioned if she still qualified for an addiction recovery programme. While counting sober days gave her a sense of shared achievement with her programme peers, it also provoked disappointment that minimal change had occurred within her food behaviour. In fact, letting go of alcohol seemed to inflame her desire to overeat. She quickly identified alcohol was not her primary prop to manage her feelings. That badge was unquestionably awarded to food.

Ava: *The first time I had the urge to binge that I remember I was about eight years old. I crept downstairs when I should have been in bed – it must have been after a birthday party as I remember thinking about all the sweets downstairs. I filled my pants with mini chocolate bars, pulled my nightie down and ran upstairs. I was hiding the bounty under my bed when my mum, who had heard me running around, came into my room and found me. She made me show her what I was hiding then she took the sweets away, and I was told off for being greedy and stealing. I felt utterly ashamed. Another time soon after, I took four or five packets of crisps, I flattened them and slid them into the gap between my mattress and the wall. I was caught mid-gorge. I was smacked this time and my crisps were confiscated. Again, the whoosh of shame washed over me alongside the despair that I had not finished eating and did not yet feel better.*

Ava could track her compulsive eating back to early childhood. I suggested it might be useful to better understand why 8-year-old Ava sought this additional food and how it might have served her young self.

Ava: *I was around seven when I started to show signs of anxiety. I remember the first episode very clearly. I was at my grandparents' house and suddenly a feeling of terror engulfed me like a big wave. I suddenly thought that if I couldn't see my mum and dad, perhaps something bad had happened to them and they may be dead. I lay on the floor and couldn't catch my breath. I was pale and sweating. My granny put me on her lap and cuddled me but no matter what she said, I didn't feel well until my parents returned. The anxiety returned again strongly when my sister went to secondary school. She would always walk home via her friend's house and I would pace up and down until I could bear it no longer, then phone their house to check that she was there. I used to get told off for this, but strangely no one questioned my behaviour.*

We wondered why young Ava felt anxious her parents might not return. She recalled her childhood when her father was largely absent from the home (long hours at work) and her mother often seemed rejecting, favouring her younger sisters, who were praised "for being good and thin." She recalled the unpredictability of her mother's mood swings and violent outbursts (later realised to be symptoms of severe premenstrual tension) which would target Ava, the "bad fat daughter." She would fail to dodge slaps and punches, while heeding a familiar and repeated message: "I hate you, you've ruined my life, I'm leaving."

Ava: *I would run upstairs and hide under my duvet, breathless. My heart would pound, the sound of blood would whoosh past my ears. After her outbursts she would cry and cuddle me and ask if she was forgiven. I always said yes. I hated to see her cry and felt immense guilt and relief that I was loved again. She would say that everything was OK now. I was able to go from distraught back to "normal" within minutes, I learned to push the bad stuff down, eat then carry on with a smile.*

As we explored Ava's early experiences with her mother, I recognised the signs of her insecure attachment and a tendency to move into an anxious state when her attachment system was activated. Attachment theory suggests when a child feels consistently safe, seen and soothed by their parent, she is able to form a secure attachment to that parent. However, when a parent is attuned at times and insensitive or intrusive at others, the child is more likely to develop an anxious attachment pattern. Ava was acutely aware of her childhood anxiety and desire to cling to her mother or grandparents to get her security needs met. She remembered feeling distressed by separations from her family members and yet her struggle to feel soothed when reunited. Ava had many more examples of her mother's misattunement, when she failed to act sensitively to young Ava's needs in the moment. According to attachment theory, our close relationship style can evolve over time, to become more secure or less secure depending on the relationship experiences we encounter and co-create in our lives. So I was sensitive to the different defences she may recruit depending on how secure she felt in her interactions with her programme peers and with me in our therapeutic work. I was mindful of the strong association between intense feelings and her dysfunctional eating and how, inevitably, Ava's coping strategies would be triggered throughout her participation in this fourteen-week programme.

While for me it felt relevant and meaningful to make sense of Ava's historical dependency on food, she was clear that her primary goal of this treatment was positive behavioural change. Her desired outcome was weight loss alongside acquiring the skills to maintain a "right size body." This meant mastering new skills to enable different responses to food cravings, but fundamentally we agreed to explore what might provoke the cravings and why none of the food management or slimming programmes had given her the long-term weight loss she yearned for. If recovery was simply skills training, why had Ava not managed the change to which she desperately aspired?

Initially her individual sessions were dominated by a download of thoughts and disruptive feelings piqued by her current and historical relationships. Ruminating in painful detail only created further agitation, with little thinking space to consider new skills that might support the change we both hoped for. Due to the time limits of the programme, I felt pressure to direct the focus towards psychoeducation (understanding dependency) and skills training, but this focus meant limiting acknowledgement of Ava's intense feelings. Noticeably, if my response to Ava's upset was felt as inadequate or dismissive, it seemed to exaggerate her hurt and frustration, and rational thinking would be a struggle. This presented me with a dilemma. The programme's prescriptive brief – new skills equals behavioural change equals addiction recovery – would neglect any attachment focus and for me felt incongruous. Better would be dividing her individual session time between behavioural skills and unpacking her distressing history, so together we could make sense of what was seemingly being replayed in her adult life and preventing change. I appealed to the clinical director for a second weekly individual session to focus on Ava's history of eating. In using one session to focus on techniques to minimise current defeating behaviour and improve affect regulation, I hoped we might make use of the second to consider the root causes of her overeating. This parallel approach had to be facilitated with transparency so Ava might appreciate the value of a dual cognitive (behavioural) and emotional (attachment) approach.

Affect regulation

Not only essential to addiction recovery, the ability to flexibly regulate emotions in a context-appropriate manner, and to recover from the primary emotional response with the ever-changing environment is a distinct trait of secure attachment. Together we noticed how Ava might recruit different emotional regulation strategies in different situations such as self-blame, tolerance, criticism, rumination, obsession, shame, binge drinking or emotional eating. Of course, affect regulation and distress tolerance skills could rarely be neatly assigned to a particular point in a particular session. There was a need for flexibility and spontaneity from both myself and Ava when she began to dysregulate. To prevent her rapid slide into an unhelpful emotionally negative place (which would inevitably result in overeating), I would appeal for a pause – "Can we apply the brakes," "We've stopped thinking" or "Let's hit pause" – and draw her towards a more cognitive state. We would frequently wonder if the detail she felt so intent to share was serving her emotional stability or rather risked trapping her in unsteadying rumination. We both recognised that anything unsettling would precede overeating; hence, slowing down the session to create a break in that cycle was appealing. These opportunities were recruited to coach Ava into consciously activating her parasympathetic nervous system (the calming restoring part) to dissipate intense feelings rather than (automatically) reaching for food to numb, escape or sedate herself until the feelings passed.

Group skills training presented Ava with new techniques to help her adapt emotional responses to stressful situations. The simplest to master were three calming techniques to modulate her emotional responses, using breath, touch and movement. Box breathing was initially practiced: drawing in breath for four beats, holding the breath for four beats, breathing out for four beats, and holding out for four. Using touch, Ava was taught to place her right hand on her heart in a moment of upset or distress, and talk to herself in a benign manner (for example: *right now I'm going to be kind to myself, offer myself compassion, think reasonably and rationally, and create a moment to make a wise decision without impulse*). Third, Ava was coached to make a tight fist with both hands and hold for seven beats, then release for fifteen to lessen tension in her body. When appropriate, we reinforced these skills in her individual sessions, recruiting them for at least two to three minutes, when Ava reported feeling notably calmer. Each week we agreed a task of applying and sharpening these techniques several times outside of the programme. Yet Ava noticed her motivation would quickly dissolve out of session, away from my direct guidance. I wondered why, in day to day practice, these simple techniques were so often disregarded.

Lacking self-efficacy

Bowlby developed the concept of an "internal working model" (IWM): a set of expectations and beliefs about the self, other people and the relationship between the self and others. Our IWM is a set of expectations and beliefs about our own and others' behaviour – whether or not I am loveable, whether or not others are available and interested to support me, my level of self-esteem and my belief in my ability to succeed.

Ava: *I feel hopeful and inspired sitting here with you . . . but then I leave and it's like the first thing to upset or frustrate or disappoint me, and I'm in the food almost without thinking.*

Sarah: It's like you're learning to swim in open water, and alongside my support boat you feel you can make it to the beach. You know I'm watching and cheerleading, you know I have a life jacket in my hand ready to cast if you need. But if you lose sight of my boat and see I've left you to swim alone, with no life jacket on hand, no supportive gaze, you flounder, and the beach line seems an impossible distance.

Ava: *Yes! That's exactly it! It's like I just don't believe I can do it on my own . . . and so I don't even try, and when I fail, I tell myself of course you failed. How stupid to think this might be different. You'll never get recovery from overeating. You'll always be a fat failure – and then of course, I binge.*

Some of my colleagues reported a similar bias among Ava's fellow participants in the food group. In a goal-orientated recovery programme, this felt significant. It helped me understand why a number of the addicted clinical population struggle to make daily use of new behavioural skills. They lack confidence in their capacity to exert control over their motivation, behaviour and social environment, and therefore achieve their goals. Attachment theory attributes this to a critical parent or significant other (a nanny or teacher, for example) in childhood, resulting in a lack of self-confidence, self-esteem and self-belief. Hence another vital link between attachment insecurity and behavioural change was repeatedly demonstrated by the programme participants. It had to be addressed if we might break their cycle of anticipated failure. To foster Ava's self-efficacy we consistently revisited her thought processes, her motivation, her emotional states and patterns of behaviour. We amplified and celebrated the small behavioural triumphs to demonstrate to Ava she could indeed exert control over her choices each day, even away from the direct support of therapy.

Additionally, we realised that Ava's response to defining herself as a food "addict" or sugar "addict" reinforced a belief that her impulse to overeat was uncontrollable, making it less likely that she might achieve food recovery. Attributing chocolate cravings to "chocoholism" (like alcoholism) reduced her motivation and inflated her old belief that she lacked the capacity to moderate sugar intake. Ava was not alone in this thinking. In identifying the unhelpful implications of "addict" labels used within addiction treatment, I made a conscious choice to shift my language in session, moving away from the stigmatising permanency of the word "addict" toward a more affirming narrative, one which did not define Ava as powerless but instead a person who had historically recruited unhelpful coping strategies and who might now, with support, view challenges as achievable tasks rather than inevitable failings.

Thinking about thinking

Ava often attended her sessions with multiple examples of feeling wronged by those in her life: her mother, her boyfriend, her boss, her friends, a random "rude" barista, a "grumpy" shopkeeper etc. All scenarios provided rich material to challenge Ava's rigid and very negative view of what was in others' minds. It is within the primary attachment relationship that mentalising first develops and may flourish. But we know that insecure attachment can undermine mental development and skew the understanding of another's perspective.

Ava consistently demonstrated a low awareness of what might be going on in others' minds: their thoughts, beliefs, feelings and intentions. We explored alternative perspectives to the malicious motives she was certain other people held. Was it possible that their unreliability, thoughtlessness or lack of response might really be about *them* and their lives, demands, anxieties or responsibilities, rather than something negative about her?

Ava: *Can you believe she would do that to me. Wouldn't you be upset if someone had dropped you at the last minute without any thought of how it might impact you?*

My typical response to Ava's expressions of hurt and frustration was primarily to acknowledge and empathise before facilitating thinking space so we might consider the other person's motivation for their behaviour towards Ava.

Sarah: I can hear this has really upset you, her cancellation was shocking and thoughtless. I can see it's difficult to think while feeling hurt. It might ease the hurt If we can pause for a moment and wonder why she might have cancelled.

Ava: *There is no good reason and I have no idea why you are asking me that. She does it all the time and it's not OK. In fact the more I think about it the more I've no interest in her friendship.*

Ava's perception was that I did not hold her in mind while enquiring about the others' motivations, and this needed to be explored. Experience had taught Ava that she would not be kept in mind, that she would need to fight for acknowledgement and would most likely be misunderstood. We tracked this back to her childhood years. With deep sadness Ava reflected on the absence of a reassuring parent. Instead she had experienced a mother who consistently denied young Ava's feelings, either minimising or dismissing her needs. And Ava had repeatedly found solace in food. She had come to expect my next prompt.

Sarah: Can you name five reasons why your friend might not have answered your call to her . . . and all five have to be entirely about her.

Together we would identify more than five possibilities and Ava would reluctantly concede that her rejection of these alternative explanations was simply her negative perception (born from her early life experience), and no longer useful. Over weeks of developing mentalising skills, Ava began to rationalise others' behaviour in a way that didn't leave her feeling that the world was against her. It was a delight to observe her more secure state playfully tease her insecure self. Increasingly in session, she eye rolled, smiled, even laughed at her irrational responses, before easily redirecting her thinking. This laughter was no longer the self-deprecating defensive laughter from our early work, rather it was knowing laughter, a significant measure of Ava's progress. To more rationally reflect on another's mind was a huge step forward in attachment functioning for Ava, bringing relief and, crucially, a temporary break in the overeating cycle.

Considering abstinence within food recovery

Within group therapy and 12-step recovery meetings, Ava was repeatedly exposed to the concept of abstinence, which this treatment programme and her recovery peers (from alcoholism or drug addiction) endorsed. For them it delivered relief, freedom and milestones to be celebrated. Applying the same approach used in AA (the abstinence model) to food recovery, Ava identified certain problematic foods which might be removed to better regulate her blood sugar and cravings in-between meals. But the idea of limiting her food or removing specific binge foods from her diet (for example, sugar) only served to resuscitate childhood frustration and shame when her mother enforced food restrictions, spawning heightened preoccupation with sugar. And that provoked regressive behaviour – specifically, defiant overeating. Abstaining from certain foods clearly provoked intense feelings, and these intense feelings provoked overeating, which resulted in weight gain, shame and a sense of failure. Disappointingly for Ava, she felt unable to create an abstinence free from resentment or a sense of deprivation.

The idea of abstinence within a treatment model for dysfunctional eating or eating disorders continues to stir debate among eating disorder clinicians, addiction therapists and psychotherapists. A minority group of practitioners believe that recruiting clear unambiguous food boundaries acknowledges an individual's susceptibility to addictive behaviour, rewires the brain's neural pathways and removes cravings, bringing an end to "that constant, exhausting, soul-sucking loop in your head about food and calories" (Thompson, 2017, p. 21). Different clinical approaches alongside an abundance of contradicting literature has left many of those struggling with food behaviour, including Ava, highly confused. We agreed that the technique successfully applied to alcohol was, for her, not as straightforward with food. If sugar and other "binge foods" were to remain in her daily meals, then Ava needed to practice countering her cravings to prevent repeated visits to the fridge and cupboards. Her dietitian introduced Ava to various behavioural techniques to better manage her food choices, while I continued to work with the impulsive behaviour and cravings.

Food craving interventions

To help Ava minimise impulsive food choices, her dietitian consistently encouraged grocery planning, food preparation and better-managed scenarios where Ava might allow herself to enjoy food spontaneity, such as ordering food in a restaurant or accepting hospitality in someone's home. No food or food group was removed, everything was allowed, including planned and moderated sugary snacks. This initially provoked fear in Ava, that an all-inclusive food plan would limit weight loss. Yet several weeks and months of food planning and preparation resulted in less anxiety around her food choices, reduced feelings of deprivation, and less preoccupation with her weight and body image. Her eating became less impulsive, episodes of bingeing decreased, and her weight started to stabilise. Ava was blind-weighed by her dietician on each visit; neither wanted to focus on the number, instead maintaining a focus on the skills. Last, and most provoking for Ava, her dietician insisted she take photographs of everything she ate. These images were posted (confidentially) on the dietician's app and discussed at their follow-up sessions. Exposing the reality of Ava's daily food choices was often triggering, but by sharing her shame and vulnerability with her dietician and myself, we could re-frame the "bad" food as unhelpful choices on a journey of learning and identify the food which best worked for Ava's mood, energy, body shape and general well-being. Similarly, destructive behaviours could be consistently challenged and replaced with constructive ones which helped Ava move towards recovery.

The addiction model posits "automaticity," when the addictive behaviour occurs quickly and without conscious thought. Like a driver who arrives at a location with little conscious memory of the route, Ava could identify examples of robotic behaviour when she had little recollection of reaching for food. There exists a growing body of evidence suggesting that cravings can be downregulated using cognitive techniques (Giuliani et al., 2013, 2014). So taking reference points from her week, we forensically unpacked scenarios which had provoked cravings to eat, starting with her mood state, her thoughts and feelings about her body, how connected or not she had felt that day and what food choices she had made from her first bite after waking, before providing new cognitive techniques to modulate her emotional responses.

Ava: *I met my mum for a walk on Saturday, and she continually made comments on my weight, the lack of effort she thought I had made in getting dressed, and how she'd heard of a new diet that might work for me. I asked her not to talk about my weight and tried to change the subject several times. I felt furious with her, and burning shame about my food and my appearance, but instead of telling her how I felt . . . I just withdrew. All I could think about was the food I was going to buy on the way home.*

Sarah: I can hear how hurtful her comments felt. You often describe a link between becoming upset or angry with your mother, and then binge-eating. Part of our work together will involve helping you to become more aware when that happens in the moment and to help you express your emotions in a manageable way, or soothe them internally, so that you won't need to binge as a way of getting relief from feeling angry, hurt or overwhelmed.

Ava: *It's like Groundhog Day Sarah. And I cannot seem to catch a break. There is always something that throws me off, even if I manage half a day, I always seem to end up back in the food.*

I compared her feelings to a wave on a surf beach and identified the peak of intensity, just before the wave collapsed and crashed, as the moment she would impulsively eat. Once the impulse had passed, self-criticism would dominate, and Ava would inevitably feel shameful.

Sarah: If you can practice riding each wave (of intense emotion), distract yourself until it peaks, it will pass. Next time this happens, I wonder if you check your watch and make a commitment not to eat for twenty-five minutes. Let's see if that might be enough time to allow the feelings to pass.

I presented Ava with an acronym: DEADS, to help her remember to delay (D) the impulse and distract her attention away from the food (Rodriguez & Mischel, 1987); to escape (E) the place or person that might be causing intense feeling; to accept (A) that this impulsive thought was to be expected for now; to debate (D) with herself and offer valid reasons why it might be less painful to leave the food alone in that moment; and substitute (S) the sugar or carbs or large portion with a substitute momentary pleasure such as a cup of tea or play with her dog, watch thirty minutes of television, focus on a work task or call a friend. We found that focusing on the negative consequences of consuming the food (bloating, fatigue, sugar crash, weight gain) alongside the beneficial consequences of not consuming the food (mood stability, increased self-belief, weight loss) served as powerful ways to reduce food craving through cognitive change.

Recruiting any or all of these techniques would take emotional commitment. If Ava could repeat new thoughts and behaviours she would create new habits, inviting her brain to reject the disused old trails and instead stimulate new neural pathways. The bottom line was: distract and steady yourself, or call up a buddy and ask for support. Alternatively, call up a buddy, and if they're not available then return to these new internal resources. With practice Ava was able to increasingly recruit helpful behavioural techniques to lessen the impact of cravings before her feelings peaked and she acted impulsively. She was learning how to regulate her feelings in a way that had never been modelled by her parents and never managed throughout her 28 years; learning how to delay immediate pleasure for a bigger purpose, hugely crucial in addiction recovery and a trait of secure attachment. Following her dietician's guidance, when the food cravings hit, Ava would reassure herself she could indeed have that food when planned, just not right now. Food planning and preparation was continually reinforced, vital in countering impulsivity. Progress was slow. Ava needed reminding and re-engaging with the techniques. But energised by my support, the possibility of longer-term food recovery was rallying.

Building shame resilience

Insecurely attached clients who struggle with issues of dependency and addiction often describe growing up in an environment of shame. In dysfunctional families, children often see themselves as unloved, unworthy and inferior. It is not their actions but their whole being they view as the cause of their shame. Constant belittling, criticism and neglect all stoke a sense of inadequacy that becomes a central part of their self-view. This deep and ongoing shame causes isolation, which often results in secret drinking, drug-taking, over-eating, compulsive shopping etc as a form of self-soothing or self-medication. Additionally, the addictive cycle creates further feelings of shame and low self-esteem, which contributes to a belief that one is unable to cope.

People who feel unworthy of being helped or fear asking for help rarely seek professional services on their own, and when they do arrive in treatment or therapy it has taken a huge amount of courage to temporarily break through the shame to ask for support. And Ava was no different. Her thoughts were mostly self-critical, her behaviours were "wrong" and a reflection of her "unworthiness." Shame had to be addressed.

A starting point was encouraging Ava to share her story with me. Unadulterated. Exposing as much forensic detail as she could manage. And I consistently met her with respect, empathy, understanding and acceptance. To counter the debilitating impact of shame, Ava was encouraged to expose the secrets, and in that painfully vulnerable place I would challenge her highly judgmental and critical narrative so we could begin to diminish the shame. Together we sought an antidote to shame. Primarily, we recruited self-compassion. Ava began to see she was human, with shortcomings like everyone else, and this was acceptable.

Like a secure parent with a small child, I offered mentorship and a place to lick her wounds when she stumbled. I had become a maternal figure from whom Ava sought reassurance in her twice weekly emotional "exhale." However, it was increasingly evident that, no matter how reassuring or empathic I could be, without behavioural skills there would be no change; attunement was not enough. Yet without emotional acknowledgement, Ava was non-receptive to new skills. Explicit and consistent reassurance created an openness in Ava, a willingness to consciously lower her defences so I could access her mind, draw her out of an overwhelming feeling state and into a thinking state, one which was rational and open to learning. Additionally, we realised that my attunement would never be adequate compensation for the many years it had been lacking.

Mourning the absence of consistent mothering

Chronic anxiety in childhood meant Ava had struggled and failed to develop an internal sense of security. She was starting to make sense of her relentless and unsatisfying search for safety in food. A mourning process needed to begin for the maternal attunement and childhood security she had yearned for but never received, and this was something I held in mind as we moved through the time-limited programme. Each time Ava felt let down after another disappointing inter-action with her mother and a shameful return to overeating, I reminded her that unrealistic expectations of love or soothing from either her mother or food was an old fantasy, one that she might begin to surrender. This would be neither a quick nor a linear grieving process. Repeatedly, with renewed hope (and denial) Ava would return to her mum and excessive food consumption in search of soothing.

In order to forgive her mother and surrender any expectations, it felt appropriate to make sense of her mother's abusive and sometimes violent behaviour in

Ava's childhood. Ava shared glimpses of her mother's own difficult and painful early years, when her morbidly obese mother (Ava's grandmother) would shame and beat her for overeating and being unacceptably overweight. A mother's own unresolved trauma may interfere with her ability to sensitively respond to her child, affecting their development of secure attachment and potentially contributing to the intergenerational transmission of trauma. Ava knew that being slim and in control of one's food was revered in her family, and to be out of control was shameful. Appearance and body image were particular triggers for shame in Ava's family. As an adult, Ava often reported feeling scrutinised by her mother, sensing her disapproval as she ate. Continuing to overeat was an act of rebellion, an expression of anger at her mother's judgment and attempt to control Ava's food. Overeating in her mother's presence was an indirect communication of her autonomy. We observed a similar pattern with her boyfriend when Ava felt dismissed or her needs denied. How could Ava protect herself emotionally from their hurtful judgments, not reach for excess food, and still manage openness, warmth and empathy in relationship with them? This was an ongoing and deeply uncomfortable piece of work for Ava, to assert and maintain a separateness (with boundaries) by expressing her feelings and needs verbally rather than in defiant regressive behaviour and by recruiting internal sources of comfort as an alternative to overeating that was not an assault on her body.

Insecure attachment and support seeking

A mandatory aspect of this treatment programme was thrice weekly attendance at 12-step fellowship meetings (such as AA and OA), where Ava was encouraged to seek support from others working an abstinence-based addiction recovery programme. Evidence demonstrates this community extends therapeutic support and provides a secure base to return to each week, to identify and share recovery experiences. When planning a binge and unable to access internal resources to manage the craving, Ava was encouraged to reach out to a fellowship peer who might resonate, empathise and help her to mentalise, or remind her to recruit the calming techniques. When Ava was infused with agitation or sinking in sadness, a peer might be hopeful. When Ava felt wobbly, a peer might steady her. These reciprocal reinforcements would be mutually reassuring. But inevitably Ava experienced days when others were unavailable, unreliable or failed to provide the stability she needed in that moment, triggering historical responses to misattunement that resulted in ambivalence about attending these meetings.

Ava: *I called five people, left voicemails for all of them, not one person called me back. Not even a text. That made me more angry, more lonely, and I just thought what's the point, no one cares, why should I try, so I binged.*

Again we practiced mentalisation by exploring how Ava's peers might be self-absorbed, distracted, tired or simply not able to receive a phone call, and how this would often upset Ava, perceiving their radio silence as personal, triggering feelings of unworthiness resulting in overeating.

Ava: *They obviously didn't want to talk to me. They don't care about me, I'm not important. No one has time for me. You see, people can't be trusted. You just can't lean on anyone – you'll just be disappointed. You see Sarah, food IS my only friend.*

Ava had a tendency to focus on what was missing and block any nourishing interventions. It was noticeably jarring for me when, in these moments, I was unable to penetrate her wall of disillusionment and defence. It often left me feeling frustrated and inadequate. I wondered if others felt this when attempting to support her. Ava's negative bias and mistrust of others threatened her connection with members of the 12-step community and therefore threatened another layer of support in her recovery journey. Experience demonstrated that clients with traits of avoidant attachment found the 12-step meetings deeply uncomfortable as they witnessed others emotional honesty. And those with a more anxious style, like Ava, demonstrated a greater desire to attend but often reported feeling unsettled and preoccupied with relationship dynamics within the community. Clients were labelled lazy or arrogant or rebellious if they chose not to attend. Attachment theory suggests their withdrawal from the meetings or relational anxiety was an expression of their insecure attachment. A greater understanding of my clients' attachment functioning allowed us to make sense of, anticipate and counter their emotional responses provoked within these meetings – a fear of either intimacy or rejection.

While attendance at these meetings was indeed provocative, the interpersonal challenges provided an abundance of opportunity to practice mentalising skills, emotion regulation skills and social skills (honest communication, tolerance and reliability). Put simply, this recovery community presented ongoing experiential learning where clients might try out new "secure" ways of thinking and behaving.

Limitations of working within just one therapeutic model

Following completion of my second year of attachment-based training, I felt increasing dissonance between the pure addiction model and my broadening attachment-based perspective. My experience highlighted the limitations in treating addictive symptoms as one disorder. If attachment insecurity was still active and untreated, it would interfere with the successful treatment of addiction and issues of dependency.

Without doubt, working solely within an addiction model, a task-focused time-limited approach, had delivered results. Not least it prevented loss of life for those clients whose alcoholism or drug use had been a dangerous flirtation with overdose or death through misadventure, and for many more it prevented further immediate misery. In theory, it provided behavioural techniques to better manage affect, access to a support community and, for most, a significant shift in personal responsibility and therefore a positive reworking of their narrative.

Yet in my first few years of clinical practice working purely within an addiction model, I observed multiple episodes of substance and behavioural relapse.

I witnessed many clients lose their sobriety or abstinence and return to the programme for a second, third, fourth treatment episode (the revolving door). While distressing and disheartening for my clients, I also felt frustrated, confused and questioning. Why was this happening, and how might I better support my clients in their bid to break their dependencies? Despite busting denial, developing motivation and teaching new skills, their reluctance to consistently recruit these skills when in need was baffling. Hearing an addicted client labelled as resistant, reluctant, defiant or a hopeless case in clinical discussions deeply frustrated me and did not make sense. Why would they seek admission to an expensive addiction treatment programme, invest time, step away from their daily lives, then reject the step-by-step behavioural treatment being offered? I began to question whether a therapeutic model of addiction alone could offer long-term rehabilitation as well as short-term restoration.

Attachment-based training provided the missing piece of the addiction treatment puzzle. Clients' lack of self-efficacy (due to their IWMs), their pervasive sense of inadequacy and their shame in finding themselves an "addict" all had to be addressed in order to positively impact behavioural change. Therefore, attachment functioning could not be neglected, primarily because attachment insecurity would hinder the recruitment of new skills and second because attachment insecurity would negatively impact support seeking.

Additionally, I felt increasing concern at the expectation created among clients and family members that enduring symptom remission might be achieved from a single episode of addiction treatment when the reality for most was multiple episodes of relapse. When clients were discharged for exhibiting addictive behaviour such as an inability to abstain or a loss of control over substance use or destructive food behaviour, the outcome was unsettling. My clients would describe a sense of abandonment, feeling berated, vilified or misunderstood for failing to utilise recovery skills. In a programme which celebrated abstinence milestones, they lost their clean days, their count returned to zero, resulting in further loss and failure. If relapse occurred more than once this might be grounds for denial of treatment admission and an indicator of poor prognosis rather than a need for a different clinical approach.

My experience repeatedly demonstrated that recovering addicts had less potential for long-term recovery if they lacked the techniques or skills to change. Ava needed to work closely with her dietician, to educate herself in nutrition, to plan and prepare her weekly food and to gain the coping skills to better navigate food-based social events. Additionally, she needed the skills to better manage her cravings and regulate her emotions. All of these were vital for long term recovery.

Behavioural change is undeniably reformist and if practiced repeatedly undoubtedly accelerates change. But engaging in an addiction treatment programme is only the beginning of recovery. If clients are curious and willing to engage in longer term psychotherapy they can begin to understand the root causes of their dysfunctional behaviours and, with that awareness, further the process of change. Without awareness of their attachment history, a maladaptive aspect of themselves is left active, serving only to hinder their recovery process.

Moving into an attachment-based framework

I yearned to offer my clients greater flexibility in the pace and length of the treatment to explore attachment history and attachment functioning in greater depth, with a focus on how this might be impacting their dependency issues and capacity to recover. So after several years working in addiction treatment centres, it felt time to step away and create a private practice in which I could integrate both models of training, specialising in addiction and dependency. I continued to work with Ava in weekly face-to-face sessions.

Increasingly, I recruited attachment theory to assess clients, to frame their early developmental experiences, to make sense of their lifelong thinking and behaviour, particularly when under stress, and I used this theory to gain a fresh perspective on my relating style in the consulting room. Reviewing a client's attachment history in an extended assessment allowed me to somewhat foresee the level of care an individual might demand, depending on their attachment functioning, and therefore consider if I had the availability and emotional capacity at that point to support his or her needs or instead make a referral to an organisation better suited, resulting in better care for the client and a conscious maintenance of my professional resilience. It was liberating and hugely enhanced my clinical work. Attachment theory had become a theoretical anchor, a base camp for clinical exploration. I began to gain the confidence to present myself as an attachment-based therapist.

Conclusion

Many of us can relate to Ava, myself included, where unnecessary food is scouted to alter mood, to ease the impact of unwanted news, to reward, to compensate, to rebel, to cajole, to indulge with friends when creating connection. Without doubt food indulgence was a pleasurable activity shared with my diabetic friend, our relishable retreat from a confronting life. It's culturally accepted to give and receive food to celebrate, to sympathise, as an expression of thoughtfulness. We all need to eat, and while for some there is a mild to moderate temptation to overindulge, for others – like my friend and Ava – a dependent relationship with food is shamefully destructive, a symptom of something far more complex than bad habits or gluttony.

Why did Ava have such a hard time following through her desire to change? Because this change required far more than breaking a habit. This change required significant attachment-focused work to support Ava in shifting her thinking, building self-belief, nurturing self-compassion and learning to navigate her feelings without resorting to overeating. This change required the capacity to make sense of others' behaviour, to challenge her expectations of others, to surrender an old coping strategy that no longer served her and – crucially – to forgive and grieve an unyielding mother so Ava might no longer seek reassurance from someone who did not have the capacity to provide it. This change meant enlisting her developing internal parent, one that would consistently go easy on the recovering Ava. This change required courage, to drop her guard and expose her vulnerability, when she might turn to supportive relationships rather than salty and sugary foods, when she might seek connection rather than chocolate. It required reconfiguring her internal working model.

For twenty-eight years Ava had recruited food to manage her anxiety, control her fury and soothe her sadness. Food helped minimise her social fears, escape body shame (temporarily) and numb her reality. Clearly for Ava, binge drinking and overeating were symptoms of insecure attachment functioning, substitutes for human support and self-care gone wrong. When her attachment needs were activated, so too was a powerful urge to eat. And in a dysfunctional way, this had helped her survive for almost three decades. For Ava, like all her programme peers, change meant loss and lamenting the old way of living. It was unsettling and slow. The behavioural change was slippery, engaging with the recovery community was fraught with uncertainty, and "acting secure" demanded huge discomfort and risk. The result, not uncommonly, was a vacillation between dependency and recovery, an expression of ambivalence towards change and the journey towards earning security.

Importantly for Ava, her impulsive and compulsive eating began to lessen; her weight initially stabilised, then slowly over months began to diminish. Enlightened, she became more alert to self-harm, both behavioural and relational, to make better informed choices about what she needed and how she might meet those needs, both internally and externally. She began to flourish, with increasingly satisfying human connections rather than disappointing fast food fixes.

Our work together has brought improvement in many aspects of Ava's life, but I cannot fail to share the somewhat predictable regressions over the past three years. Unsurprisingly some of life's stressful events (illness, job change, pregnancy, bereavement, Covid-19) activated her attachment system and old anxious coping strategies triggered extended periods of relapse. Under difficult circumstances Ava returned to overeating, demonstrating that change is not straightforward and feeling "secure" is pivotal in manoeuvring life's inevitable curve balls.

Since I graduated from my attachment diploma, these past five years have brought an abundance of evidence supporting an integrated attachment-based approach when working with addiction and dependency. Awareness of my own relating style has prompted further personal growth and the tools to better manage my attachment responses when activated by a client's defences. Being sensitive to both my client and my own attachment functioning has allowed me to aim therapeutic interventions at key factors that maintain the addictive behaviour and complicate the therapeutic relationship. This dual focus on behavioural change and attachment functioning has significantly improved outcomes in my clinical work. For my clients it has brought a shift from acute short-term treatment to sustained recovery management, and for me, a developing confidence and belief in my ability to help liberate my clients from the despair of dysfunctional eating.

References

American Society of Addiction Medicine. (2011). www.asam.org/Quality-Science/defini tion-of-addiction. Accessed on 18 April 2020.

Bandura, A. (1977). Self-efficacy: Toward a unifying theory of behavioural change. *Psychological Review*, *84*(2), 191–215.

Giuliani, N.R., Calcott, R.D., & Berkman, E.T. (2013). Piece of cake: Cognitive reappraisal of food craving. *Appetite*, *64*, 56–61.

Giuliani, N.R., Mann, T., Tomiyama, A.J., & Berkman, E.T. (2014). Neural systems underlying the reappraisal of personally-craved foods. *Journal of Cognitive Neuroscience*, *26*(7), 1390–1402.

Heather, N. (1998). A conceptual framework for explaining drug addiction. *Journal of Psychopharmacology*, *12*(1), 3–7.

Kelly, J.F., Stout, R.L., Magill, M., & Tonigan, J.S. (2010). The role of Alcoholics Anonymous in mobilising adaptive social network changes: A prospective lagged mediational analysis. *Drug and Alcohol Dependence*, *114*(2–3), 119–126.

Khantzian, E.J. (2003). The self-medication hypothesis revisited: The dually diagnosed patient. *Primary Psychiatry*, *10*(47–48), 53–54.

Laudet, A. (2008). The road to recovery: Where are we going and how do we get there? Empirically driven conclusions and future directions for service development and research. *Substance Use Misuse*, *43*(12–13), 2001–2020.

McLellan, T. (2000). *Addiction is a Chronic Brain Disease*. Archived at the National Institute on Drug Abuse website. Accessed on 13 January 2020.

Prochaska, J.O., & DiClemente, C.C. (1983). Stages and processes of self-change of smoking: Toward an integrative model of change. *Journal of Consulting and Clinical Psychology*, *51*(3), 390–395.

Rodriguez, M.L., & Mischel, W. (1987). Cognitive strategies and delay behaviour in impulsive older children. *Paper presented at the Annual convention of the American Psychological Association*, New York. https://psycnet.apa.org/record/1988-19783-001. Accessed on 5 January 2020.

Thompson, S. (2017). *Bright Line Eating: The Science of Living Happy, Thin and Free*. Carlsbad, CA: Hay House Inc.

White, W.L. (2004). Transformational change: A historical review. *Journal of Clinical Psychology*, *60*(5), 461–470.

White, W.L., & Kurtz, E. (2006). The varieties of recovery experience. *International Journal of Self Help and Self Care*, *3*(1–2), 21–61.

Chapter 7

Kitchen Therapy
Cooking for connection and belonging

Charlotte Hastings

I believe there is nothing that has to be done that cannot be done creatively.
(Winnicott, 1986, p. 51)

[O]ne way of cooking sausages is to look up the exact directions in Mrs Beeton (or Clement Freud on Sundays) and another way is to take some sausages and somehow to cook sausages for the first time ever. The result may be the same on any one occasion, but it is more pleasant to live with the creative cook, even if there is sometimes a disaster or the taste is funny and one suspects the worst. . . . for the cook the two experiences are different: the slavish one who complies gets nothing from the experience except an increase in the feeling of dependence on authority, while the original one feels more real, and surprises herself (or himself) by what turns up in the mind in the course of the act of cooking.

(Ibid.)

Introduction

It is 2011. I have been invited into a primary school to run family cooking workshops, and the offer stirs something in me; I sense my vocation knocking. The chance to teach simple, fun and nurturing cooking ideas and to enhance relational bonding turns out to be exactly what I want to do with my life. My favourite recipes happen in one pot; I use my senses, knowledge and current resources to decide on today's interpretation. This is what it feels like to bring cooking, therapy and community together for me; it incorporates in one pot all the ingredients that life has given me into an organic, fluid and active recipe for living.

This first family cooking workshop was scheduled for Halloween/harvest time. In I went with my exciting Thai-inspired soup. I missed the mark with the recipe, but the idea of bringing people and families together in this community kitchen was stronger than their dislike of the soup. We were there to explore and be with one another; the meal at the end was secondary, although nonetheless vital. Like the left and the right sides of the brain, the process of cooking and edible product go hand in hand, but as Iain McGilchrist (2009) explains, there is a master and an emissary. Kitchen Therapy is about placing the right brain, open receptivity first, with the left brain's definitive productivity second; one cannot work without the other. We come together with the purpose of making a meal, but the community feeling is the lasting sustenance we take away.

I left this first workshop fully alert to the need for a more grounded way of responding to this new community. The opportunity was on my doorstep – November 5 meant burgers and bonfire cake, which I would trial at home. While his dad took charge of the burgers, my 5-year-old son Carl and I took on the cake. I put the components on the kitchen table – chocolate sponge, flame-coloured icing and a variety of chocolate sticks and logs. I didn't show him the picture from a magazine I had seen, not wanting to influence the creative process. Carl adores fires, as many a child does, and was a natural creator – as many a child is. He set to work, fixing the sponge into various log shapes, gluing it together with the icing and scrabbling the chocolate matchwood together in a glorious reverie, as only par-ent-endorsed freedom with sweet chocolate, fires and cakes can stir in a small boy.

For me, the process was hideous! His cake was a chaotic, messy disaster. What was I going to do? For now, I must sit on my hands, sit back and watch, only helping when asked. He was happily in charge. I felt a little sick. There came a moment when he stood back and felt finished. Staring at the cake, I asked what he thought of it, expecting a dispirited answer, despondency that could be compen-sated by eating the chocolate riot. Eyes wide, he told me "It's AMAZING mum, it's the BEST thing I've EVER made!"

I stood back, taking the moment to capture on camera and absorb the lesson. I was reminded of secondary school where I had to make a vegetable-inspired pot-tery piece. It was a sweetcorn – ostensibly. It was a horrible, humiliating, typical disaster. I am cack-handed and rubbish at art; this pot was proof. However, the 1970s newly qualified teacher *loved* it; she found it full of unusual character and held it to be one of the best in the class. I never had the heart to tell her it was in fact a complete mistake. She did not have the picture of perfection I had in my head, she was seeing it with her own fresh, unfettered by expectation eyes, and what she saw was luscious.

I realised as Carl told me that this was the best thing he had ever made, that this is the nature of creativity – that the pleasure is in the process, the product is experienced in the light of that process. I realised this is why I am a good cook – but rubbish at art. When I try to paint, I have the picture I am trying to make clear in my mind, and anything that doesn't match up is disregarded. However, I love food, so I can cook with playful intuition. I have such implicit trust in this process that I allow it to be and become whatever it is, without the judgment or expecta-tion that, as Carl had shown me, would ruin or dismiss so much of life.

I was also taught something, much harder to explain, about the nature of fol-lowing the child – the one both inside and outside that it is our privilege to nurture. My son taught me here about the nature of Kitchen Therapy, that my work is not to create objects of perfection but conjure moments of pleasure, potential and possibility to take into life. It is about developing not only our attachment relationships through working together but also our relationship to ourselves: how we nurture, nudge and follow our own child inside.

Back to the beginning

The idea for what has become Kitchen Therapy began to take shape at the beginning of my psychodynamic therapeutic training. While I was returning to study, I also returned to teaching, but to a new – kitchen – classroom. Training as a therapist fulfilled a long-held ambition and, alongside teaching cooking across the community, I felt a sense of arrival.

The compatibility of cooking and therapy as ways of helping people to connect with their lives quickly became apparent. Early in my training, Pam Howard introduced me to her paper about love and therapy:

> The work of psychoanalysis and its derivative, psychoanalytic psychotherapy, is largely concerned with love. Specifically, it seeks to bring about an exploration of the client's own unique way of loving or, as Sigmund Freud famously stated, "his specific method for conducting his erotic life"
>
> (Howard, 2008, p. 23)

and attachment theory explained how "affection shapes a baby's brain" (Gerhardt, 2004), speaking exactly to my approach when teaching cooking. My favourite class was called "Learn to Love Cooking," in the knowledge that adding your pleasure, not just for the food but for the joy of making, is a good cook's secret ingredient. The idea began to simmer.

The initial ingredient of Kitchen Therapy (KT) was my experience of a community cooking class, sparked by one student in particular. I had brought all the food for students to cook, but Mary tried to give hers away, seeing others' needs as greater than her own. In a class of young men with learning and behavioural difficulties, this middle-aged woman and I shared a certain bond; I liked her a lot. She spoke to me about her anxiety and her ambivalence around cooking – hating it yet knowing she needed good food. I watched as she gingerly stirred her pan, and could see her deference not just to the other students and their needs, but for the wooden spoon itself – her worry that by clunking the edges of the saucepan she might cause offence or just make herself heard. Without thinking, I said to her, "That's how you do life isn't it?" Her eyes encouraged me further: "The way you're holding that spoon is as though you're scared of it, or of causing some problem just by being here, making use of it." She looked at me clearly and talked to me about her life on the edges, trying not to be seen, certainly not to have needs, and the persistent, pervasive anxiety this leaves her with.

This correlation, between how Mary was holding her wooden spoon and how she "did life," took me back to the therapeutic project: to discover our "unique way of loving." Our early relationships form the basis for how we come to relate with the world. Making connections between present and past, becoming "storied selves" (Holmes, 2001), we have the opportunity to rewrite the original script. As we made a simple cheese sauce, Mary's story, her unique way of being and relating to the world, came through. There was an emergent understanding between us. As we continued through this class, and further into the course, I witnessed Mary become increasingly involved, sharing ideas and laughter and happily taking her share of the ingredients home with her. She went on to report a reduction in her anxiety and the beginnings of taking pleasure in both making and eating her own food. She was starting to nourish herself.

Mary helped me lay the foundations for Kitchen Therapy's collaborative basis. Just as cooking a good meal means allowing it to unfold in your care, so a therapeutic journey is led by the client, with therapist as support. Mary's vulnerability led me into this new approach; our conversation helped and changed us both, continuing long after that lesson and into today. KT is not a top-down approach but one that reaches into our unique creative, healing and connecting potential. We all need to eat, but what that process means for us, the how, what and why of food, gives us a mutual individuality.

Working with families, using cooking as a way of bringing people together around the kitchen table, was and is a key focus of my work. I wanted to extend my learning, and the next logical step was to enrol onto a systemic family therapy course. I was inspired by the scope and ripple effect of family work, and excited that Kitchen Therapy could make a contribution. In our early development training, we watched the harrowing Harlow's monkey experiments (1958), providing evidence to support attachment theory. These experiments showed how a stressed monkey would choose the relational place of a soft, warm hug over the unyielding wire food dispenser. It became increasingly clear that Kitchen Therapy would become an attachment-based approach: therapeutic cooking promotes and supports relationships.

During this course, we explored our own family relationships, experiences and influences. It was significant how many different maternal figures I had in my life, all of whom have influenced Kitchen Therapy as it continues to evolve. My grandmother (Gabby) and her mother (Nana) had the time and space to give me, and I am continually grateful for their physical and emotional closeness in my life. I learned to cook alongside Gabby, a housewife, gardener and wonderful cook. Nana was a single parent and retired seamstress and was not overly fond of cooking; however, she LOVED to play cards, and oh my goodness, so did I! She would happily while away an hour or four with me, just as Gabby was more than happy to let me help her chop and sieve in her kitchen. The only thing Nana preferred to cards, and to me it seemed, was her knitting circle. I felt excluded. My creative solution was to offer a tea party to said knitting circle, guided by my grandma's helping hands.

This tea party was a delectable success. There were individualised invites and place mats, and a classic English tea of cucumber sandwiches, scones and home-made strawberry jam tarts was served. Afternoon tea, with me at centre, was my instinctive solution to feeling left out, allowing me a place in the group. I asked for help and everything I needed came my way. The resources were all around me, ready for the asking.

In years to come, I would recognise this as the moment Kitchen Therapy began, with a little girl becoming part of the group by bringing her love of food and cooking to share. A little girl who had, and has, a lot to learn.

KT rationale: nature's classroom

Less palatable but more intrinsic lessons have come from Romanian orphanages discovered in 1989 as communist rule ended. The suffering of the infants housed there highlights the necessity of physical attachment, maternal attention and loving intention for primates to grow. One of my earliest memories of being a mother was my how my baby "explained" breastfeeding to me; while I was feeding her, this would not be the time to chat with friends on the phone, or watch television. No, I would need to be looking deep into her eyes, finding myself in a land that time forgot. In my later training as a therapist I learned that this maternal gaze is responsible, no less, for wiring a baby's brain (Gerhardt, 2004) – a great deal more than "just feeding"!

In order for this essential bonding to be established, the baby is born to teach a prepared and cared-for mother. Sometimes known as the love drug, oxytocin heightens dopamine's motivation and endorphin's relaxant properties, gold stars released in the early feeding experience. This hormonal reward system returns when we later learn to feed ourselves and those around us. As we welcome the baby into the family with the breast, so we later welcome guests with a repast. Preparing food is an essential, profound and specifically human way of expressing our attachment to one another, of communicating our belonging, our trust and our mutuality.

Nature has carefully arranged her first classroom with a recipe combining life's essentials – food and love – in our bonding sequences that we call attachment behaviour. As social creatures, our fundamental need for each other is initially met through the establishment of the "nursing couple" and continues later around the campfire or dining table. Making and sharing food with one another confirms our attachment to the group, assuring our place around the table. Klein (1940) asserts that weaning is our first experience of loss, but it also prepares the way for initiation into the group, from the nursing couple into the arms of our attachment network: good food, time, and creative confidence help the baby grow into his or her family and become part of its social group.

Wrangham (2010) convincingly argues that cooking made us human, physically, cognitively, psychologically, culturally and spiritually. Discovering how to make and manipulate fire was a defining moment for our species. Cooking our food provided more nutrition, freeing up foraging time and creating opportunities for cooperation and creativity. These developments help explain the growth of our human frontal cortex. This large, sophisticated brain region has to be grown outside the womb, with considerable input from other people, and that gives scope not just for idiosyncrasy but also for human error.

Early relationships with our attachment figures, whose feeding abilities and quality of attention are flavoured by their own experience, bitter or sweet, shape who we are to become. That preverbal connection between being fed and being related to – held, delighted in, soothed, or stressed – endures. How we are fed, our psychologically potent experience of nourishment, influences how we later nourish ourselves in terms of our growth, security and well-being,

> The hedonic pleasure experienced by the infant when he or she is being fed, spoken to with a gentle rhythm, or caressed creates intense expectancies in the baby, who later will expect or try to re-experience the same or similar pleasant affects/states.
>
> (Ammaniti & Ferrari, 2013)

Feeding ourselves brings us in touch with our earliest experiences – we may enjoy preparing nourishing fare or food may be little more than necessary sustenance. Bollas (1994) sees the mother's role as a transformer of the baby's affect states: when a fortunate infant is bored, she plays with him; when he is tired, she rocks him; when he is frightened, she soothes him; and when he is hungry, she holds him and satiates his hunger. But not all babies are blessed with a reliable, responsive, attuned caregiver, and this has consequences later. The many insecurities and life struggles we encounter in the therapy room – depression, anxiety, addiction, self-harm, eating disorders and relational difficulties – can often be traced back to the transgenerational transmission of "human error" as it is expressed in the feeding situation.

Food as an aspect of relationships: from merger to dyad to group

How, why and what we eat tells a vital story of how we become ourselves, both as a species and as an individual. Making food for friends and family has been a crucial part of my personal self-actualisation, bringing a sense of satisfaction, belonging and usefulness. The feelings – pleasure and gratitude – of people, especially little ones (pets included), being nurtured by the food I've made helps me feel valued and at home.

However, there comes that moment when the satisfaction of nurturing our children is challenged by the separation injunction, as their need for their attachment figures changes and family dynamics shift. That is often the moment young people need to cook for the family and prove *their* usefulness, to earn their place in the pack and prove their mettle for the world that awaits them, and parents must support this striving. That moment has been reached by teen Carl (he of the bonfire cake). During lockdown he has deepened his love affair with his bed, but compensated by learning to make sourdough (which means getting up early to bake bread for breakfast). He has shown commitment, patience and nurturing ability as he brought the ferment to life.

Carl needs the space to grow into himself that lockdown has diverted into maturing at home. While he can no longer express himself out with friends, he has turned to expressing himself in the kitchen. His bread tastes of practical potential; the boy will not only survive out there, but has something great to offer. He is maturing, and his care-giving capacity is growing.

The smiles on people's faces when they make something that is as simple as it is good, like bread, hummus or pesto perhaps, is invaluable to me as mother/facilitator and to them as creator. The exchange of roles – the one who feeds and the one who is fed – and the process of making food good enough to share affords priceless inner resource. When we express hunger, we communicate our attachment needs for one another, and through feeding others we develop our skills as attachment figures.

Carl instinctively reached into his human roots, researching how to make our daily bread from a ferment he can pass on to his grandchildren. His sourdough marks a momentous developmental step in our species, for me as a mother and for his personal growth as a capable young man. Time and space dissolve in the mixing bowl. It is a rite of passage.

The practice of Kitchen Therapy

Kitchen Therapy can take place in the therapy room as an aspect of traditional "talk therapy," but also in a dedicated kitchen or community kitchen. In the former, we often return to clients' feeding-related stories. Recalling mealtime experiences can help us explore a person's early relational environment and the echoes that continue into the present. For example, a client struggling with jealous rage remembered the kitchen table of his childhood, which shifted from providing comforting dinners for him into a work space for his busy primary school teaching mother, so that other children took her nourishing attention away from him. When we returned to this memory together, he was able to reach his younger self with compassion and release his envious fears of losing his attachment figure.

But when KT takes place by the stove, it is here we might discover our "unique way of loving" (Howard, 2008, p. 23). Deficits and resistances are highlighted. How and what my clients choose to cook offers me both an emotional barometer and an insight into their internal working models. Our relationship with food stretches like dreams across the time and space of self. Although for many of us this can be a site of pain, loss and lack, by connecting with this in the practical, supportive safety of a therapy kitchen, a renewed opportunity can emerge to have our historic and current needs recognised and met by developing self-care.

Winnicott's words at the beginning of this chapter capture the spirit of Kitchen Therapy, which, like art and music therapies, is a creative approach (but with an edible outcome). Good cooking involves tuning into the dish, appreciating its visual qualities and aroma. It is playful. And there is a paradox: like a parent with her infant, the cook is at once firmly invested in the outcome of her labours (a tasty meal) yet without fixed expectations, allowing the dish to become its best self. By the same token, it allows the cook to enjoy an innate satisfaction, not just in the eating but in the making and – especially – in sharing the dish. KT aims to help clients attune, play, take risks, trust themselves, be in touch with their senses and bodily needs and also connect deeply with others.

So how exactly does KT work?

As previously stated, KT is mostly a regular talk-based therapy. However, clients approach me knowing that I am also a cookery teacher and that I offer "in the kitchen" sessions too. At assessment I ask what each individual is looking for, and we start from there. What is different is that food is used as a metaphor, as a way into the client's world, past and present. I am curious to hear what each person is like in his or her kitchen, what senses, memories and associations are triggered when we use the subject of food as a portal, rather like dreams. Sometimes I may suggest that the client makes some food at home and brings it in. We can then discuss the process – rather as an art therapist may work with a drawing the client makes between sessions – and this can highlight unconscious processes. What is different is that we eat the food together; I am nourished by the client's creativity. A client with perfectionist expectations and a critical superego may anticipate my disappointment and find it hard to accept my pleasure at their creation. This shifts the therapy from "talking about" to having real experiences in the here-and-now that we can process. This is a delicate, intimate, meaningful connection with the therapist trusting the client, literally taking in, digesting, what he or she brings to the table.

If the talk therapy feels stuck, as it so often does when working with addiction, moving to the studio kitchen can get things moving. We discuss and negotiate what the client will cook (it must be manageable within a longer session of one and a half to two hours, be realistic in ambition, and with no deep frying!). I send a recipe to the client in advance to buy ingredients. He or she takes ownership by choosing to buy premier brand or supermarket's own, vegan alternatives, organically grown or whatever fits their needs and tastes. I provide the basic store cupboard ingredients but encourage them to bring some of their own equipment, including a knife and a container to take their food home. It is an important feature of KT that the food made in the kitchen is taken home, symbolising the work we have done in therapy. The client takes responsibility for and ownership of this edible transitional object and, once eaten, what was created in the therapy kitchen continues to provide internal sustenance.

In the kitchen setting, my role changes. I work alongside the client, perhaps chopping vegetables, often in greater proximity. My role is to provide a sense of security and confidence while the client prepares ingredients to cook. Like a good-enough mother, I facilitate the process and encourage the client to experiment, play and enjoy the experience. I challenge them to be in the moment, aware of the sensual aspects of food preparation that can then lead to memories and associations. In transference terms, I may represent a critical parent, an expert who gives instruction or a supportive figure. Again, this is highlighted in the kitchen, brought into the room more intensely than sitting and talking about our relationship and what it means. The fact that I'm quite short can affect the power dynamic – this is more obvious when we are both standing and moving around rather than seated.

I do KT in the kitchen with couples and parent–child pairs too, where my role also involves observing the dynamic between them and facilitating them to work in partnership, negotiating tasks and preferences. It is often easier to address tensions in the relationship with the apparent distraction of engaging in an activity. Preparing food together is a bonding task in itself requiring a certain level of mutual trust, promoting clear communication and secure attachment. According to the great food writer, MFK Fisher, "Sharing food with another human being is an intimate act that should not be indulged in lightly" – and that certainly includes sharing the cooking. These practical and cooperative elements distinguish KT from other creative therapies.

So the Kitchen Therapist's role is complex, combining an educative dimension (practical aspects such as good posture, how to use utensils effectively etc, and psychoeducational – the significance of providing good nourishment for oneself), observing the process as the client prepares the dish, commenting on what is observed and engaging the client's curiosity about possible connections (like Mary with her wooden spoon), and encouraging memories and associations throughout the session. We can also address projections and the transference relationship directly.

An example of one-to-one Kitchen Therapy: current and online

Peter has been in traditional talking therapy with me for two and a half years, during which time we have built a strong therapeutic alliance. However, we have noticed two significant factors halting progress. First, the therapy tends to stay in the room; it doesn't seem able to be held in mind or take on life beyond the contact session. Hence the second: despite making changes to his world view and coping strategies, Peter is holding off from tackling the core issue of low self-esteem, as he holds onto his long-term addictive relationship with Benson and Hedges (within which struggle romantic relationships flounder). He comes in the middle of a large, busy family in which it was hard to get a postnatally depressed mother's relaxed attention. Without knowing which comes first, addictive personalities are also often highly sensitive characters. Peter is no exception. Early attachment strivings were frustrated for him, and this led to a turning inward, a self-reliance that defends him from the aching shame of felt rejection.

> In adult life . . . to seek the transformational object is to recollect an early object experience, to remember not cognitively but existentially – through intense affective experience – a relationship which was identified with cumulative transformational experiences of the self.
>
> (Ibid., p. 17)

Through immersing ourselves in the arts, the natural world, spiritual and religious practices, romantic relationships and *food*, we attempt to recreate the particular ambience of our earliest transformational relationship. But we may also recreate unpleasant but familiar affect states – loneliness, unhappiness, shame – and one route back to the distant past is through mood-altering substances, many of which are addictive. Peter's nicotine addiction and his self-neglect hint at early deprivation of playful, lively engagement, the transformative experience of being *enjoyed*. He does not enjoy himself.

We have been discussing how to use cooking in our sessions for some time now as a potentially powerful intervention to work with addiction (viewed in classical psychoanalysis as a disturbance of the oral developmental stage). In the midst of Covid-19's lockdown period, Peter and I agree to embark on our cooking sessions. This was originally, for him, about stirring the courage to hold a dinner party, confronting the social anxiety that comes between him and community. For me, it is about stirring his courage, desire and belief to fully enter into life. For now, we are experimenting with Kitchen Therapy online, and any dinner gathering is postponed till post lockdown.

Ruptures in early care that may manifest in later addiction have two key characteristics. First, the locus of transformation becomes concretised, located in the physical fuel "fix," as opposed to an ongoing sense of emotional sustenance found when we access an internalised "secure mother." Now the source of pleasure and transformation is found *outside* ourselves, lacking the relational content of interpersonal exchange, of intimacy. In contrast, in the context of good enough (secure) attachment, the infant learns that physical and psychological nutrition have a relational quality, and our creative agency and participation are a crucial part of the equation. Making satisfying food for ourselves, food which both feels and tastes good by virtue of our own creative effort, stimulates a lust for life.

Addiction can also be understood as a distortion and stagnation of our appetite for creative connection, a turning away from our need for true intimacy (love) and toward the non-animate, fixed object (alcohol, cocaine, tobacco, food etc). Fearing the repetition of painful relational ruptures, Peter withdraws, self-soothing through addictive behaviours. These initially transform the self-state but ultimately stagnate and, ironically, repeat the dreaded early rupture, thus fortifying a Rapunzel-like isolation. Smoking has been his chosen avenue of self-medication, established in the teen years of awkward bonding, but is now part of his identity and his armour, resistant to the call for growth, change or intimacy.

Peter does not like cooking; neither does he like vegetables, fruit or a wide range of other colourful, healthy, "grown up" foods. Meal choices are dominated by soft, pale-textured foods laden with sugar or salt, thoughtlessly thrown together with as little mess and time as possible. I imagine the meals of his childhood and am reminded of his time-pressed, depressed mother; how fed up she must have felt with Peter's curious infant-self, not yet discouraged from exploration, who once dropped a milk bottle from his bedroom window just to see what happened. What other impulses may have been expressed in that gesture? His food and cooking choices now point to a halting of developmental processes, shielding painful attachment memories that are hidden away under a pallid blanket of smoke and mashed potato. Perhaps he learned to smother his life spark early, to protect himself from the pain and shame of being unable to kindle a similar spark in his mother's eye? Kitchen Therapy aims to create opportunities for both understanding and rewriting our attachment stories.

Doing these sessions online with Peter means that therapy happens in his own home, where it is not so easily lost in transit. It is also significant that he is much more technologically aux fait than me, and this has the potential for him to take greater ownership of the process. We are each in our kitchens preparing the same meal. This demands greater involvement, risk and active responsibility from Peter, where he has the power to affect change for himself. He does not shrink. Except, that is, from celery and mess.

Long distance/online therapy has never been my choice. However, as a human being and committed therapist, I adapt. Going into Peter's kitchen (on screen) is a revelation. I'm in his world, where celery is forgotten and food mess resented. Most significantly, space is taken up by his DIY projects rather than culinary supplies: "do-it-yourself" is a passion for Peter, and I reflect on the self-reliance of the addictive personality, the one who both desires and shies away from connection, harbouring untold fears about what it might bring. DIY is also a means for Peter to be useful to others – on his terms. Once the project is completed he can safely leave, his good deeds remaining behind him. But cooking and food demand more relational space.

For the first KT session Peter chooses to prepare a casserole, and I am given an insight into his internal world as well as his environment. Celery. For me, she's the maternal backbone of many a dish, custard excepted. Like most women, she improves with age, but even in her zealous, raw youth, she's a supportive friend. Cooked, she takes a back seat and simply makes everyone else in the casserole be their personal best. Peter's casserole doesn't know this yet, as celery was forgotten from the shopping list! Our different understanding of and relationship to this vegetable helps me think about Peter's relationship with the maternal object and its availability to nurture him.

When, in another session, we are making a wished-for crumble, there is confusion over the size of the bowl and flour goes all over the floor, leading to a discussion about the mess cooking makes. DIY is one thing, but food doesn't offer enough return (as yet) to earn its clearing-up time. I learn how Peter feels uncomfortable getting his hands so dirty as we make that crumble, and a picture emerges in my mind; the fended off, messy feelings of anger for an adored but busy and doleful mother; of jealousy for too many siblings and fear at his jealous rage being found out. His attitude to celery and mess seem to reflect an uncomfortable attachment trajectory. Peter has not acquired enough courage, desire or belief to accept disowned parts of himself, his Shadow.

In our first talk-based meeting after these kitchen sessions, it becomes clear that strong feelings were stirred in Peter around the cooking process and the ingredients involved. A realisation came to him when we thought about clearing up after the crumble session, that he holds himself back in therapy as he doesn't want to be left with a dilemma to go home (alone) with. He reports a powerful dream: he is in a cave with people he doesn't know but who "have his back."

The cave image struck me as archetypal, connecting with our early human ancestors. Caves are places for fires and the alchemy of cooking. Perhaps Jung would interpret the symbol as representing the womb, or the Subconscious? For Peter, it was not an entirely safe environment ("the roof might fall in"), and caves are also places of darkness and shadows. This dream had the feel of a significant message from Peter's unconscious, triggered by our sessions in the kitchen. Something was starting to come into awareness and shift.

As we continued to cook in our own spaces, connected online, I managed to lose pace with Peter at times, and he pointed out my assumptions about what would be in his store cupboard. By his therapy taking place in his own kitchen, Peter was able to reflect my misstep with his process. Something very important happened here, as I saw him taking charge of the recipes and allowing the meals to develop to suit his tastes. His favourite was the casserole; however, my suggestion that he left the lemon in meant it was an overpowering flavour of something he doesn't like. Next time, he will change that. He realised that on day three, this meal can become a hearty soup, so that not one drop will be wasted. His personal engagement with the process helped him to find an inner resource that enabled change and growth, reflected in the casserole taking on new life to nurture him each day.

The risotto disaster (long story) was resolved by him into a salad lunch. More risotto rice was bought, because this dish would need to be made again, in order to make use of the celery. Yes, he was persuaded in the end to try it – and discovered that he likes it.

[My thanks to "Peter" for his permission to publish these details.]

Campfire con-panis

The transitional space between hunger and satisfaction is the first space in which play, empathy and mentalisation develop. The hungry infant learns to defer gratification, to contain himself. Winnicott refers to the importance of the good-enough mother failing in her adaptation in order for the infant's mind to develop; he comes to trust in others to meet his needs (Winnicott, 1960). The young child taking charge of his spoon desires to join in with the family, to be "one of us" but to make his own choices. In time, he can actively participate in the process of feeding and eventually pass on the skills. The attachment dynamics of dependency, agency and reciprocity constellate in our feeding stories.

Food is a universal language, but with a unique personal and social background. The giving and receiving of food create an edible bridge between the worlds of you and me. Community cooking classes have brought me into contact with many overseas students, and cookery has been the perfect platform for communicating both our cultural differences and our human similarities. So it is with clients, whose stories of cooking and eating reveal to me their cultural roots and inner worlds. In groups, these narratives can elevate the intensely personal into empathic dialogue, where we can meet to work through childhood longings, confusions and loss.

This group approach centres around our word "company," which comes from the Latin *con-panis* – "with bread." When we share a meal together, we are also sharing ourselves and our most basic humanity. We all need to eat, sharing a digestive system along with other living things; so "with bread" means meeting with one another in the most primal of places where we are all linked.

Perhaps you're familiar with that feeling of being around a campfire, feeling connected to those people present and in the ancestral past, sharing this necessary pleasure and maybe eating from the same pot, possibly singing the same tune. It could be argued that sharing food provides the missing link to finding our way back to an experience of a unified "we." Anthropologist Lévy-Bruhl (1985) described "participation mystique" as early man's communion with elements in the outer world. When we create a meal, there is something of this mystical merger, and when we share the experience of eating we are imaginatively connected not only to each other but also to the ingredients. In Esquivel's Mexican tale *Like Water for Chocolate*, anyone eating Tita's food also feels her mood, and this speaks to the notion of participation mystique. Likewise, the ritual sharing of food, symbolised in Holy Communion, suggests the experience of conscious oneness, a return to original wholeness first felt at the breast, expressing our lifelong need for attachment.

KT with groups

This pleasurable experience of being in company around the campfire-cauldron keys into our attachment-wired natures and provides the stepping off point for Kitchen Therapy groups. The emphasis is on the relational aspect of food, the bonding, con-panis experience; not just in terms of how we cook, engaging with and relating to the dish, but also the opportunity to feel welcomed around the table – whatever you have to bring. The stories, tips and issues that arise during the process all go to make this a rich and rewarding meal to take home.

Recently, an organisation that provides food and activities for families in the school holidays asked me to run Cooking for Wellbeing groups. Participants were invited who wanted to learn new culinary skills and who also may want to tackle mental health issues – a gathering where anxiety and depression were specifically welcomed guests at the table. Each group member had their own reasons for being there; some needing to learn how to cook, some wanting to share their knowledge and some to overcome their fear of groups, perhaps encouraged along by a friend and the desire to make food.

Each session was structured into a beginning, a middle and end. We started with tea and chat, introducing the dish of the day. We then cooked the meal together, swapping stories, tips and queries with one another. The session ended with sharing the meal, discussing how it could be made by each of them at home, and any memories or thoughts that had been evoked during the session. This drifted into clearing up and sharing out the leftovers to take away. While the focus was on the joint cooking of a meal, the aim was to explore the importance of making food for our personal and social well-being. By teaching the dish and how it could be adapted at home, a sense of supported agency, resourceful creativity and the healing potential of cooking good food would go home too. The therapist/teacher and the group are internalised in the process and taken away as an internal resource.

What comes across in each session is how much I have to learn, how my cupboard of assumptions needs clearing out and reordering! In this group, Anya had such severe anxiety she could not speak, Sonia could not bear to take her coat off and believe she could stay, while Kate could not even arrive until halfway through the second of a three-session course, a reminder of just how threatening groups can feel, even when they know this to be a safe, welcoming place (they had all taken part in events with this organisation before). By inviting people to introduce themselves, I had already challenged Anya – who could not speak. But later that session, she found her role, becoming the group's photographer and silently recording the session. Despite offering a brilliant tip of keeping the tomato vine in the pasta sauce for extra flavour, Sonia did not return. Kate, on the other hand, arrived on time to session three.

The middle session stands out most clearly. We made a basic mince recipe three ways: bolognaise, chilli and cottage pie. We used red lentils to bulk out the mince, using less/no mince depending on their needs. The group divided themselves to work on each meal, playing with the flavour balance of each variation. This meant accommodating to the group while considering what changes they would make in their own homes. As visitors' noses kept popping round the kitchen door, we knew we were doing well. The atmosphere was focused, fun and energised.

Participants were so pleased to be inviting staff to share the meal, revelling in the subtle but sure differences in each dish. The relaxed confidence around the dining table was a real pleasure to be a part of. Quite a few flavour tips were proffered in this session, but the biggest take home was how well lentils tasted, adding a welcome creaminess. Making nutritious meals on a low budget was a necessity for most. I learned from one group member that porridge oats do a similar but, in her opinion, less tasty bulking job. I also gleaned how this meal would support both a young man's body-building programme (following a severe eating disorder) and his grandmother's diabetic dietary requirements. Our only male, and also the youngest in the group at just 17, was "discovered" as a natural in the kitchen, and the group went on to suggest that he became a cookery leader for family workshops. The smiles spoke clearly of the intrinsic value of cooking good food together and how vital this is for a sustainable community, going above and beyond the food on the plate.

We had aimed to reach as many people as possible within a limited budget, therefore planning two three-session courses with a limit of ten participants on each. However, just three sessions found us ending too soon. Just as a child cannot be hurried into adult time, needing the space to develop at their own pace, so a group cannot be rushed through its developmental process. Given how much each individual took from the sessions, and the group's wish to continue, we planned a follow-up outdoor well-being course, which I now hope to run in the autumn of 2020 (social distancing permitting). These individuals had started to be important to each other, to be a community, having bonded over the chopping of vegetables and the seasoning of sauces. They had shared themselves with each other. This had been so much more than a group cookery lesson; it had been therapeutic for all of us.

The Harlow monkey experiments, watching animal packs, and our own family life tell us that we need comfort from one another as much as we need food in our bellies. Our world has become so focused on the *product*, the *profit*, the *external* value of "food" that our need for the *psychological* nutrition has been taken for granted or lost. Importantly for this low-income group, they were being given access to a therapy that they could take home and develop in a format that also made practical sense for their lives.

Kitchen Therapy is about taking a sustainable approach to cooking and eating, connecting with our need for active self-care, kinship and creative confidence. While the food draws people in, providing nutritional information and culinary tips, what people are really taking home is their sense of achievement. Campfire con-panis builds future resilience, playfulness and a sense of practical resources at their fingertips.

Conclusion

Reciprocity lies at the heart of being human. Speaking of the African philosophy of Ubuntu, Archbishop Desmond Tutu said: "when I have a small piece of bread, it is for my benefit that I share it with you. Because, after all, none of us came into the world on our own. We needed two people to bring us into the world" (Dalai Lama et al., 2016, p. 60). All humanity is connected through a universal bond of sharing. In other words, breaking bread with one another, in the spirit of con-panis, denotes an exchange of our humanity. It is the relational process of cooking, sharing and giving food that Kitchen Therapy centres around.

Our stories of feeding, nutrition, and sometimes poison can have a mythological quality, reaching into the past to illuminate the present, revealing who and how we are; the product of "the transformation of raw experience into selfhood that is the essence of creative living" (Holmes, 2001, p. 86) – an appropriately alchemical metaphor. Understanding our developmental relationship with food enables a new attachment trajectory to emerge.

In Buddhist philosophy, being attached means being unhealthily dependent; we are attached *to* as opposed to *with* – they belong *to* me, rather than I belong *with* them. "Attachment" is addiction. In this sense, we grasp at the immediate fix, the ephemeral, finite object of satisfaction. We hunger for more. We fear its loss, lack or imperfection, finding ourselves on the "hedonic treadmill," always searching for something we don't need. Our increasingly left-brained world focuses on product over process, competition over cooperation, in a culture where the notion of "me" obscures the vision of "we." This brings to mind "food porn," where we focus on the reified beauty and sensual presentation of a dish that lacks relational or contextual associations that actually make food taste good.

In contrast is Holmes's concept of therapeutic non-attachment as "a non-possessive, nonambivalent, autonomous, freely entered into attachment, in which the object is held and cherished but not controlled" (2001, p. 84). This reminds us how much we learn from the child's need for, experience of, and approach to play. Carl's omnipotent creativity that made the "best ever" cake at the beginning of this chapter was unfettered by parentified notions of perfection. When we enjoy, immerse and engage ourselves in the process, the product will be just right.

The word "attachment" embraces our human need for security, for belonging, for food and for love. With meaningful relationships to nourish us, we can access a wellspring of creativity and sustenance. Kitchen Therapy brings our need for physical (food) and psychological (love) nutrition together.

Food journalist Craig Claiborne (1969) sums this up perfectly: "Cooking is at once child's play and adult joy. And cooking done with care is an act of love."

References

Ammaniti, M., & Ferrari, P. (2013). Vitality affects in Daniel Stern's thinking: A psychological and neurobiological perspective. *Infant Mental Health Journal*, *34*(5), 367–375. https://doi.org/10.1002/imhj.21405.

Bollas, C. (1987). *The Shadow of the Object: Psychoanalysis of the Unthought Known*. London: Free Association Books [reprinted 1994].

Claiborne, C. (1969). *Craig Claiborne's Kitchen Primer*. New York: Random House.

Esquivel, L. (1989). *Like Water for Chocolate*. London: Doubleday [Published in English in 1993, translated by Carol Christensen and Thomas Christensen].

Gerhardt, S. (2004). *Why Love Matters: How Affection Shapes a Baby's Brain*. Hove: Brunner-Routledge.

Harlow, H.F. (1958). The nature of love. *American Psychologist*, *13*(12), 673–685.

Holmes, J. (2001). *Search for the Secure Base*. Hove: Brunner-Routledge.

Howard, P. (2008). Psychoanalytic psychotherapy. In S. Haugh & S. Paul (Eds.), *The Therapeutic Relationship: Perspectives and Themes* (pp. 23–35). Ross-on-Wye: PCCS Books.

Klein, M. (1940). Mourning and its relation to manic-depressive states. In (1975) *Melanie Klein: Love, Guilt and Reparation, and Other Works*. London: Vintage.

Lama, Dalai, Tutu, D., & Abrams, D. (2016). *The Book of Joy*. London: Hutchinson.

Lévy-Bruhl, L. (1985). *How Natives Think*. Princeton, NJ: Princeton University Press.

McGilchrist, I. (2009). *The Master and His Emissary: The Divided Brain and the Making of the Western World*. New York: Yale University Press.

Winnicott, D.W. (1960). Ego distortion in terms of true and false self. In D.W. Winnicott (Ed.), *The Maturational Processes and the Facilitating Environment* [1990] (pp.140–152). London: Karnac.

Winnicott, D.W. (1986). *Home Is Where We Start From: Essays by a Psychoanalyst*. London: Penguin.

Wrangham, R. (2010). *Catching Fire: How Cooking Made Us Human*. London: Profile.

Appendix

Making use of KT in your own therapy practice

Kitchen Therapy is an eminently simple, accessible and useful way of working with people. It is an embodied therapeutic approach that connects us not only to individual infancy experiences but connects us with previous generations and right back to the cultural beginnings of humanity. Our stories around food, how it was made and how we make it now take us into the very heart of who we are, have been, and can be tomorrow. It is not necessary to be a trained chef or cookery teacher to use KT principles in therapy with clients. Here are some suggestions for how to bring it into your own work:

First things first: reflect on the memories, thoughts and feelings associated with *your own* experiences of being fed and of feeding yourself.

As part of your assessment process with clients, you might like to find out

- What they know/have been told about their early feeding experience.
- What meal times were like growing up and how these may have changed.
- What priority meal times and food generally, its quality and quantity, was given in their family of origin.
- Whether there were any particular rituals, like Sunday lunch, Christmas, Friday night dinners, birthday parties, or how/if family gatherings might have been managed regarding food.
- Cultural or religious traditions around food and how these may have been expressed in the family.
- What a typical breakfast or dinner might have been and the stories, feelings and memories evoked; this can be a good way into exploring family life and what this meant for your client.
- How they manage, experience and respond to hunger in their lives today; what their food habits are like and how they relate to food, cooking and eating on a daily basis.

As a way into inner work, akin to working with dreams, you might wonder about:

- A really special meal that comes to mind. What about it was special?
- A really awful meal.
- Your own signature dish, something that you love and seems to say something about you – explore.
- What type of cook are you? How do you like to cook? Explore thoughts and feelings emerging and link to underlying process or attachment patterns (see clinical material above for ideas here).
- Foods you love and foods you hate; explore the stories and feelings around these foods.
- What changes to their food habits/relationship do you both notice over time? Does the desire for a quick sugar fix develop into a desire to cook a more substantial meal to enjoy/share?

Food and cooking as an explanatory or exploratory metaphor

- "You can't make an omelette without breaking eggs" – the profound necessity of their mistakes and mess that is welcomed into the therapy room.
- "What is the missing ingredient in your life?"
- "If food was a person in your life, who would they be? What would they be like? What role would they play?"
- The small, seemingly insignificant parts of their functioning are important – just as a bay leaf plays a small part in a dish, it is omnipresent. By noticing how many ingredients go to make a whole meal, we can also consider how interrelated and interdependent we are, despite self-reliance fantasies.

As a connecting principle and vehicle for psychological awareness:

- Role of food in connecting us culturally and in terms of community.
- Emotional and spiritual messages we take in when we feed ourselves.
- Role of food, cooking and eating in our self-care routines.
- The relationship between food and love, expressed in our word company – con-panis.

Guided visualisation

Like fairy tales, our food stories can take us into our inner world, stretching like dreams across the time and space of self. Guided visualisations create a bridge between conscious and unconscious worlds:

You are entering into a place where you know you will receive a special meal. What is the place like? What smells and sounds are in the air? Are people there already, and who might you hope or expect to be there? You find your seat at the table; what does the cutlery and table ware look like? Trays carrying various dishes begin to arrive, and you notice a feeling in your belly which rises into your thought; what might that be? There is one serving dish you are surprised to see; it has your name on it, being just for you. What do you imagine this to be? As you open the lid to see what it is, does it meet, challenge or surpass your expectations?! Can you sense the thoughts and feelings that are emerging, shifting and sifting through your mind and body at once? There is now a surprise guest who arrives who informs you that they have made this feast for you and the other guests here. I wonder who that cook might be? How do you relate to them? How do you now feel about this meal they have made for you? You get to choose one special dish to take home with you that will be made to order. What would it be?

As in our dream interpretations, we can understand every aspect of this visualisation to be an aspect of the self – the food, the atmosphere, the tableware, the guests and perhaps most significantly – the cook.

Chapter 8

Food in the consulting room

Jenny Riddell

Introduction

At the time of writing this, I was also in the process of reducing my clinical practice; this chapter represents the stages in the life cycle of my work as an individual and couples' psychotherapist. During my thirty-two-year career, I have had many, many experiences in the consulting room involving food. Therapy itself can be seen in terms of feeding metaphors, with interpretations offering "food for thought." And there have been plenty of occasions when I have felt fed and nurtured but, at other times, devoured by clients – the therapy room is a place, to paraphrase Shakespeare, "Not where we feed but where we are fed upon" (Hamlet, Act 4, scene 3). Writing this chapter has given me an opportunity to revisit, reflect and digest as part of the process of retiring.

When invited to contribute to this book I began by free associating to "food in the consulting room." Here are my first spontaneous notes, all based on real events that have happened in my therapy room over the years. You may have had similar experiences yourself:

1 **Breast feeding (and bottle feeding) in the consulting room**

In individual or couple therapy. Who is present? Parent/s and gender/s; dyad or triad? Am I the third in the room, or the fourth? What is the transference or countertransference? What are the observers feeling: hungry, envious, jealous, proud, embarrassed, sleepy? What if the mother is confusing the baby's need for comfort with need for food . . . or feeding; and the therapist is observing this misattunement? Is the misattunement causing anxiety, and in which one of the three (or four) of us?

Projectile vomiting; the pain of colic and mutual suffering of the feeder and babe, each unable to satisfy the other. This being observed by the therapist. Does mother/prime carer feel judged? What does that evoke for them?

The infant's loving caress as food is taken in, mirrored by the mother's/carer's gentle stroking. Or ambivalence and confusion; the baby pulling away, or mother exhausted, depressed?

How has the two-year infant observation I experienced influenced my thinking? Is it helpful?

Associations to morning – or mourning – sickness. My memory flashes back to an unintended observation; an anorexic parent feeding a toddler in a café that I watched with new observation skills, having undertaken my MA in infant observation. And then my thoughts move to Steinbeck's *The Grapes of Wrath* (1939), and the passage describing an old dying man being breastfed by a lactating mother. Circularity; the beginning and the end of life.

2   Clients bringing food into the consulting room

Why? What time is it? Is it a defence or a practical necessity? Am I informed or is permission requested? Do I ask? "May I?" versus entitled assumption that it is OK. Is this about power? Am I hungry? Does the arrival of food stir up so many thoughts in me that I am too preoccupied to digest and process what is happening in the session?

Sandwiches verses a hot cooked breakfast (I've had both arrive!): the lingering smell making for more complications than wrappings. My association to packed lunch at school, or the sandwich crammed in between office meetings.

Where do the leftovers/wrappings go? Isn't a therapy room the place to leave your mess? Or a place to dump your waste? Thus, leading to a connection between human waste, physical and psychological, to be interpreted or held.

Drawing the line at alcohol in the therapy room. An alcoholic who arrived with an open can of beer did, gracefully (gratefully?), accept my firm position and left the can on the doorstep. He made his choice to stay – and to leave the can there when he left, his free will liberated.

3   Gifts of food

Gifts of food given to mark the ending of therapy – or holidays. Is it presented at the beginning or the end of the session? What kind of food? And what are the hidden meanings? My confusion and trying to make sense of it all. Psychoanalytic and attachment interpretations – and where do I stand with these?

Here's a memorable example of such a dilemma: a client hands me a box of special chocolates that her partner – who is present in the therapy – had previously given to her. What is the meaning of this? How does her partner feel? Is she in a dissociated state, genuinely unaware of what she is doing? Is it an attack on him? Am I being collusively drawn in against him? Or are they both colluding against me? Is it a test and, if so, of what? How do I understand it? What response will be helpful?!

4   Clients vomiting in the room

This does happen, so how do we react? Is the cause serious, or a manageable illness? And a range of conditions in between? There are practicalities as well as the responsibilities for all concerned. How do we move forward from this event? Just offer tissues and water? How do we make the decision as to urgency? The one time I did ring 999 it was essential. My awareness of the client's fragility. How this event is managed, both in the here and now and in ongoing work; the client's embarrassment, shame, gratitude. . . . Needing to know about health conditions.

5   Tea and coffee, bottles of water, fruit and chewing gum etc

Disposable cups versus reusable; eco-politics acted out in the room. The shopping bought on the way to therapy. The hand dipping into the bag for something to nibble. At what point, and why? What does it mean, and how is it to be worked with? Am I (as I observe this) hungry now? If so, is it empathy, sympathy, envy, jealousy? Or am I just hungry?!

6   Food stories brought to therapy and the insights these give us

What was cooked last night; why, and for whom? What are the associations? Stories from the past; trauma associated with food as a child; the lack of food, or the forcing of it on someone in childhood ("you'll sit there till your plate is empty"). Dreams and fantasies of eating and being eaten; sexuality and food. Exploring all this safely in therapy.

These incidents, like so many others over the span of a career, have required the immediate input of my "internal supervisor" (Casement, 1985).

So where, why, and how did all this thinking and questioning start for me? Some of it was conscious, some unconscious. From my position now, with decades of experience as a therapist of individuals and couples, and recently ending my private clinical practice, the theme of nourishment takes me back to the earliest days of my first training.

It is 6 p.m. on a chilly Friday in 1986; I'm in a large Victorian country house converted from a disused monastery into a residential training centre for a psychotherapy organisation. We are towards the end of our three-year training and on a biannual five-day residential experiential course. There are twenty participants and six trainers.

Upstairs are the bedrooms, and one by one we emerge from them to assemble in the dining room. The training is good; by this I mean thought provoking, challenging, rewarding and just scary enough to help us know we are really learning – not only about the way people are and how they interact but also about ourselves and each other. The day's formal work is ended. As we settle to eat, we represent a wide range of personalities, of culture, age, ethnicity, sexuality, education and so on. We are, in common with every human being, unique. But in the moment we also feel a mixture of emotions, often holding several which are conflicting or confusing, or even frightening. Some may feel triumphant or confident and hold a quality of certainty. Others have a sense of growing understanding, skills developing and intellectual growth. And yet others may feel bewildered, de-skilled and fearful. However, at this stage of training, most of us are getting used to this kaleidoscope of emotions and have adjusted to trying to make sense of them, allowing ourselves to be in a Keatsian state of negative capability:

> I mean *Negative Capability*, that is when a man is capable of being in uncertainties, Mysteries, doubts, without any irritable reaching after fact and reason.
>
> (1973)

The training is experiential, theoretical and practical. We are all in our own individual therapy. Part of the process and the environment, intended or not, is to regress us to unlearned feeling states in order to think about being human from the cradle to the grave. The course follows the chronology of life, in terms of academic and personal learning, from infancy to childhood and adolescence, as well as projecting ourselves into the future, old age and dying and death.

The dining room (and our purpose in the building) carries strong echoes for all of us of education, institution, control, ritual – and hunger. The smell and the layout of the building facilitate this and are familiar; the serviced line of prepared dishes, white enamel with navy blue rims, containing nearly hot-enough contents evoking nostalgia and maybe loneliness; is there someone friendly to sit next to? If the day has been tough, are we famished? Is food comforting, or does the institutional setting increase the sense of isolation? Does the food stick to the roof of the mouth if we feel sad and lonely? If a fellow participant leans over and takes the last potato, does that stir competitiveness and rage from childhood? We eat together and talk and leave the dining room. Later we will call family and friends and touch base with our attachment figures in the world outside. Thirty-three years later, I can close my eyes and smell and see that dining room again.

Some of us have snacks and treats in our room; we may visit each other and share these, along with our experiences. Tomorrow we reconvene in the dining room for breakfast, and then we will return to our real lives, remembering "for there is nothing either good or bad but thinking makes it so" (Shakespeare: Hamlet, Act 2 Sc2 line 249).

Several years pass by; I am now qualified and with experience behind me and far more insight into my own psyche, thanks to my own ongoing therapy. My work is satisfying.

[NB. No clinical examples given here are representative of specific cases or people. Each event described actually happened, but other details are generalised, disguised and conflated from many years of clinical experience. However, I hope that they also communicate a degree of truthfulness as to the human condition and convey a sense of psychological veracity to which the reader can relate.]

Clinical example 1: Donald and Brad

A couple arrive for their therapy session; they knock at the door and as they come in, Donald offers me a takeaway cup of coffee with a pack of sugar balanced on top. His partner, Brad, grins; he's clutching two coffees and says, "We wanted to get you a coffee as well, is that OK?" I hesitate for a moment and then accept the warm and comforting gift on a cold morning with genuine gratitude. We sit down and the session begins, as the three of us sip away. After a few slurps and smiles, Brad begins the session by following up on last week's conversation. There had been tensions between them regarding Donald arranging to meet an ex-partner for a beer after work. Brad is still anxious about this meeting, which is due to happen on the evening of today.

The previous session had ended with Brad feeling OK and reassured by our discussion. Donald had carefully explained the intended purpose of the meeting, and it seemed, at the time, to comfort his partner's fears. As this session progressed, I observe the increase of Brad's anxiety and Donald's confusion and disappointment in not being able to reassure. I wonder what had caused the sense of threat and insecurity to reappear? There is a slight wariness as we all finish our coffees and in rapid succession – harmoniously, one might say, if it were not for the sense of rising anxiety in the room – we place the empty cups in the bin in easy reach of our three chairs.

There follows a long silence. Both men look anxious and avoid eye contact with me and each other, as the clock ticks away. I wait, silence continues. Eventually acknowledging the silence, I ask if either knows what has changed since last week's session. Donald says he thinks the tension is still about tonight's meeting. He hopes it will reassure, not distress Brad when he returns as "the same trustworthy person. Then perhaps one day they could all be friends?" Brad listens to this, looking anxious and embarrassed. Quietly, he says "That's what I want too, but I can't help feeling jealous." There's quite a prolonged silence; I choose to take a risk.

"I know this is coming from left field, but can I ask whose idea it was to buy me a coffee when you stopped at the café?" They look at each other as if I am going nuts and then Donald replies, "Well actually, it was mine and Brad was in agreement. In fact, he wanted to buy you a croissant too, but I said we shouldn't mess up your carpet." We all smile at this.

I say, "What did you think may happen if you just both arrived carrying two coffees and perhaps even two croissants?" His immediate reply was "I thought you might get envious if you didn't have one as well."

Brad looks at both of us in turn with an expression both bewildered and amused, and says, "What *are* you two on about?"

I say I think there is a link between their dilemma about Donald's meeting tonight and the "incident of the coffee cups." They look at me, pause, look at each other, back to me and Brad says, "Well . . . go on then . . . tell us, don't be a tease."

I say, perhaps the dilemma concerns a triangle, a relationship between you two and Donald's ex (I'll call him Colin).

For many of us, it can be challenging managing the tensions in triangles. One person may feel left out. Donald and Colin are meeting up with the intention of normalising and renegotiating a split-up, from an intimate past relationship into a present boundaried friendship. Brad is expressing natural and understandable apprehension about this meeting and may feel a sense of exclusion; he respects Donald's point of view but doesn't know Colin well and can't be sure he trusts him. (And, left unsaid in this conversation, is the fact that we are also in a triangular relationship in the room.)

"You're heading here today for your session and stop for a coffee. Donald is worried about me feeling left out so suggests getting me a coffee too. But a croissant as well is too much and may end up messy; and Donald doesn't want to leave a mess behind, with Brad, or Colin, or me – or, I hope, himself."

There is a pause, they look to each other and smile, and Donald says, "There you go with that psycho-babble again."

"Yeah, but it kind of makes sense as well . . . specially the bit about you!" replies Brad, and they both laugh.

The tension in the room appears to dissipate. We talk about how both are apprehensive about the meeting and the outcome. And that is OK, to feel apprehensive, as long as they know they also trust each other.

This vignette describes part of *my* journey, as well as the progress of the couple and the therapy case in discussion. With experience I have become more secure and able to trust the process. With sufficient feeding – supervision, individual and peer, reading, continuing professional development and, more than anything else, listening to people in the consulting room – I have learnt to be more spontaneous and intuitive. I am also less fearful of the unorthodox or spontaneous thoughts, feelings and acts of freedom which occur in the consulting room. This is not to say I advocate a stream of consciousness to be verbalised aloud. Core conditions of the therapeutic environment continue; the emphasis on boundaries, containment, non-intrusion and containing my own undigested thoughts and judgments are all crucial aspects of our work. And so are freedom of thought and allowing our own fantasies and visceral experiences to invade us. Free associations and fantasy are helpful too, but only as long as we have a critical dialogue with ourselves in internal and external supervision.

This interpretation, offered to Donald and Brad, has come to me in a moment, and with little deliberation; I just say what I say. It is risky but also truthful about what I think and how I believe it relates to the work in the room now, and many other sessions which have led me to know these two people.

The interpretation also relates to the work outside the room. By bringing the coffee into the room, they link the two worlds, but we all know we won't be having coffee together in the outside world. Boundaries are maintained. Classical psychoanalytic thinking may well be critical of both my acceptance of the coffee and my offer of the interpretation. But what may have been the reaction to or impact of my rejection of their gift? Do we sit and watch a cup of coffee go cold? Do they feel embarrassed, or resentful? Will they now feel obliged to bring one every session? Or do we just talk about it, which is what I decided to do. (I wonder how you, the reader would respond or have responded to a client bringing a gift of food or drink to a therapy session for you?)

Of course, in this vignette, like a chess game, each move is calculated on one hand, but it is also instinctive; heart and head are working together. Different possibilities as to which thread to take up are constantly being decided in our three-way conversation. And we never know "the road less travelled" (Frost, 1955).

Feeding the baby

Breastfeeding or bottle feeding a baby in psychotherapy sessions has been long debated, interpreted and discussed. As mentioned earlier, having had the privilege of attending a two-year infant observation and learning not only from what I witnessed but others' observations as well, I see a babe in arms as a natural and helpful addition to the therapeutic encounter, providing all primary carers are consenting. It is attachment in the making.

In each of the cases I have encountered, the tension points of triangles in the room are constantly moving, rarely settling into an equilateral triangle.

Let's start with an example of a mother, baby and therapist. Mother and baby may be locked into a loving dyad, mother "letting down" milk in response to baby's gurgling gratitude as baby strokes mother's breast. Meanwhile, the therapist looks on, her own experiences or lack of experience evoking not only observational reactions but also deep transference and countertransference feelings.

However, there are different kinds of family; there may be a fourth in the room, in couple work, the mother's partner (and we may argue that the partner's presence is felt even in his or her absence). The partner may be the father or maybe the female partner who is the co-parent of the baby, or a partner who is not the father. There are many ways of being a family, and how each family is configured is crucial to understanding the dynamic which is likely to be played out in the therapy. If we have a couple it could also be two men and a baby in the room; how is their triangle configured? What if the breast- or bottle-feeding parent is exhausted, has low feelings or is frightened, and the baby's response is fractious, unable to receive comfort? What does the partner do? Who does he or she attend to? So much needs to be observed, thought about, but not assumed. And how are the triangles pulled now?

What does feeding and being fed mean within each of the triangles – historically, traditionally and culturally? Can these differences be tolerated, managed, respected and harmonious?

Clinical example 2: Greta and Sven

Another couple and another story. A heterosexual couple, Sven and Greta, come to see me to discuss the pressure they are under; they come from two different cultures and yet share a similar history of trauma in previous generations. This history continues to cause conflict and tension in the wider family system. They remain in long-term couple therapy for several years, and we work together on how to manage the boundaries in this complex dilemma.

Over a period of time, they negotiate with the two families to achieve a satisfying enough extended family structure. Differences are debated and boundaries discussed, compromises made. Their parents increasingly accept their adult autonomy as they, the couple, name and claim it with more self-confidence. Their journey prior to and through the therapy was an extraordinary path from insecure fearful avoidance toward secure and deep attachment (Bartholomew & Horowitz, 1991;

Bowlby, 1979). They feel it is time to have a child and conceive more quickly than they expected – their fear of infertility had been explored in the therapy.

In the latter part of the pregnancy, Sven becomes rather anxious about his role as a father. He lays great emphasis on his commitment to and concept of "co-parenting" and how he wants all to be equal. Greta is alongside this in every way, at the beginning. Sven attends every ante-natal appointment with Greta and helps her with her diet and nutrition, as both are determined to protect the baby from anything they believe harmful passing through to the foetus. In the same spirit, Greta stops wearing makeup and only uses natural products in every area of her life. She avoids certain foods and cuts out all additives.

Throughout the pregnancy, they arrive with food for her to eat in the session, all healthy and prepared for her by Sven. She eats, but he never brings food for himself. In fact, he is following a "cleansing detox diet," and gradually I realise he is effectively starving himself. So, as Greta grows larger with the pregnancy, he appears to become slighter, to lose substance. I observe this, but as neither of them mentions it, I hold it in mind while the pregnancy continues.

Toward the end of the pregnancy Sven brings up something he says he has been thinking about for a long time. He wants to feed the baby himself. For a moment, Greta and I assume he means though expressed milk and a bottle. She makes this clear as she says, "Well of course you will; as the baby grows, you can bottle feed what I express and I can have a few hours off." But he says no, that is not what he had in mind, and tells us something he has heard about on the Internet. It is a gad-get linking a feeding bottle to a tube which attaches to the father's chest and into a teat that the baby can suck on. This, apparently, facilitates the nearest experience a father can have to breastfeeding. Just as he feeds Greta, he wants the experience of feeding their baby. He remains quiet and looks to see first his partner's and then my response.

Greta is gentle and says in a quiet voice, "I don't know what you mean? Why would we do that? It's so complicated and unnecessary." He looks shocked at her bewilderment; "I want to feel as close to our baby as you are going to be." She immediately responds with naming what she feels, and what I had seen; "Sven, I'm confused, I don't understand . . . I feel you're trying to make me redundant." Sven's reply is, "But that's exactly how *I* feel; there's nothing I can do, I can't carry and grow the baby, I can't deliver the baby, and I can't feed the baby. In fact, I feel totally impotent." Greta looks at him and shoots back, "Well, that's evidentially not true" – pointing at her tummy. He grins and we all laugh. The laugh loosens the tension, but it is still there, as is the depth of his feelings.

Listening, interpreting and exploring the feelings and thoughts of both is com-plex. They have such high expectations of themselves and each other, alongside tightly held anxiety which often spills out. This causes a kind of dissociative state in one or the other, resulting in agitation for them both. We've spoken about the terrorism of idealisation before in the therapy. It is implicit in so much of their idealistic hopes for their child and for their own ability to care for and bring the child up. Watching and listening to them through the gestation of the baby and their growth toward parenthood, I wonder if there is a worrying lack of the Winnicottian concept of "good enough" parenting (1976). And we all know why this is lacking, through the work we have done in sessions exploring and understanding their own childhood attachment experiences and relationships. Feeding was an important theme. How significant food was, mealtimes, who cooked, what was eaten, who was greedy or picky? When and how family rituals were observed, and what intimacy or hostility was associated with mealtimes? Each told and heard their stories; both could relate this to historical generational trauma. They were different traumas but left similar wounds.

And then we begin to make sense of how and why Sven's feeling of inadequacy has escalated again during the pregnancy. This is gentle and gradual work, as it entails exploring how each views their sexual identity and political adherence to equality. What emerges is a story of shame and further trauma on both sides, an unconscious yearning to repair, to cleanse, and change the family narrative through creating a perfect child, a child whose role, in part, is to repair historic trauma. This urge to heal is strongest in Sven. But there is also a fantasy of a combined parent, or two parents who can both do and be everything. Be everything in case one dies?

Learning about Winnicott's concept of "good enough" is painful but also a poignant relief as it challenges the fantasy of the perfect child and parent dyad.

The baby arrives, a good birth. They assume, and I support, their continuing to attend with the newborn baby. Over the following months I observe how they develop as a parental couple. They gain confidence as breastfeeding is established. Sven continues to feed Greta, but he also feeds himself. I'm relieved to see they can show me their exhaustion, irritability and frustration. This is normal and healthy, and they know it. They gain confidence and so does their child. I watch Sven feeding by proxy when he takes the expressed milk-filled bottle and feeds their child. Greta understands his needs as well as her own, and often naps when he feeds.

In line with a long-existing plan, they move away to another country, where neither has association with past trauma. They have created the possibility of a new beginning, a new chapter. Good enough is good enough.

Having a regular appointment time is a cornerstone of therapy ritual and ideology, incidentally, as it is also, traditionally and culturally, for mealtimes. If your consulting room happens to be near a café, maybe you notice a tendency for the therapeutic hours overlapping with lunchtime to contain references to or the actual presence of food. How do we react to this? While there is a school of thinking which says that only water belongs in the room (and some would say no even to water), many practitioners develop their own rules. And clients bring *their* own rules and needs to therapy as well. And these needs are not only psychological; they may be physiological. For instance, in the case of a client with diabetes, low sugar can cause a crisis or coma; a therapist only needs one experience of witnessing this in the consulting room (as I have) to learn to keep a packet of sweet biscuits handy. Rules can challenge humane care and need to be overridden on occasion.

Whatever happens in the consulting room is food for thought. And food for thought is food for talk.

Clinical example 3: Tara

A woman, Tara, has been in therapy for several months. On this occasion she comes to a session at an unusual time; the change in her appointment time has been forced on us due to an essential work commitment. She arrives carrying breakfast bought from a local shop. "You don't mind, do you?" She *states*, rather than asks. I notice my reaction to this; I feel slightly irritated and hold on to this to think about. She opens the package and the room fills with the aroma of eggs and bacon. She begins to eat. It is 7.30 in the morning. I find the smell off-putting. I am vegetarian, but that is not why I am irritated; what I eat is my choice and my business, and in my clinical opinion it is her choice how she uses this space and my job to interpret as I believe is helpful. So what is annoying me?

One of the beliefs I have about therapy is that it is and should be a space for almost anything to happen and that, as quoted before, "nothing good or bad is, but thinking makes it so." My internal supervisor leads me to take this to my external supervisor, who is also curious as to why I feel irritation. I have colleagues who would challenge this behaviour in a client, or interpret the action of bringing the food in to the session and refer to it as a breach in the frame. But that is not how I tend to react, so I question my irritated, critical reaction as she consumes her breakfast and tells me her concerns of the day ahead at work. Tara has to give a presentation to a client, and her immediate line manager will be observing. She is in the middle of an appraisal of her work and hoping for advancement, but fearing criticism. How she manages this situation is crucial to her, I know, as we have been discussing it in therapy for a while. As she talks about the presentation and eats, I see her becoming increasingly anxious, and her eating is becoming frenzied and rushed.

As she finishes her food she reaches across to the bin and drops the package in. She takes a couple of tissues and wipes her hands and drops these into the bin too. Then she sits back and suddenly says, "How are you? Are you OK?" I am taken aback for a moment, but also intrigued; she says this with genuine interest, and a searching gaze. No longer irritated and now curious, I wonder what is going on between us.

I say, "I'm fine thanks. How are *you* I think is more to the point?"

She comes back immediately with, "Well actually I'm scared shitless." We both laugh. I then say I think she's come into the session in battle dress, ready for the fray. This defence is really understandable with what is ahead today. In fact, she is doubly armed, with food for energy as well as anticipation and focus. I say, "The warrior has a hearty breakfast before the challenge." Tara laughs again.

I believe the annoyance I had felt was in picking up this defensive posture; it initially felt more of a sensory assault on me than a protective self-nurturing of herself against a feared attack. And as soon as she engaged with me directly, the irritation melted away. I was able to see the underlying fear, which the defence was protecting. The useful prompt for me was her comment regarding "feeling scared shitless." Shit is the waste product ejected from the body after a nurturing meal. The food she brought was both the defence and the nurturing to replace the evacuated shit. We worked on how she could understand her anxiety as perfectly normal and explored what coping mechanisms she had applied in the past in similar situations. We already knew a lot about her internal critic, her strategies for managing this and subduing it.

She went off to her challenge with a wobbly smile and appropriate defences, ready to face the world.

I opened the window to air the room, and emptied the bin – my responsibility. Not to erase her, but to allow another to enter the room without the impingement and evidence of a previous person intruding on their space.

Clinical example 4: Rosa and Patricia: the dance of attachment and intimacy, enacted through food

When I first met Rosa, she was clear that she was seeking couple therapy but felt she initially wanted some space to "set the scene" and have a chance to get her thoughts in order. Her partner, Patricia, knew she was coming and supported her intention, saying she would attend "as and when necessary." This is not such an unusual start to a couple therapy, but neither is it simple nor straightforward.

I take a history of the relationship, from Rosa's perspective, and ask what has brought her to therapy now? She describes a relationship of seven years which has been "rocky but creative," an interesting description. They have one child, carried and born by Patricia, from donor sperm. The decision to have the child had been long held and never a problem between them. What has been difficult is how they feel they cope as a couple with *difference*. Rosa's tale is of her wanting to negotiate and compromise, discuss and explain. She feels Patricia is "too certain, too sure, and won't negotiate or make concessions." No matter how hard she tries to rationalise, Patricia ends up storming off, and Rosa then turns to her family and friends to talk. She is concerned that this undermines their relationship. We end on this note, and I don't feel I really have a clue what this is about, but I feel that's understandable in a first session. This is an example of the need for Keats's "negative capability."

Our time is up, and I suggest she has a conversation with Patricia about this session. She immediately says, "It's been so helpful!" which surprises me; I can't see where or how. I ask how Rosa would feel if Patricia would like a one-to-one meeting as well, before coming to a couple session? "I would be delighted," she replies. The session ends. Within three days Patricia contacts and accepts the individual session.

She arrives and settles down, and we cover the fact that there is agreement regarding trust and open information between the three of us, if we begin couple work. I am curious to hear how Patricia presents the relationship. By the end of the session I am more confused than ever. I've heard a similar, rational, thoughtful description of the history and dynamic of the relationship. Whereas Rosa presented Patricia as "too certain, too sure, and won't negotiate or compromise," Patricia presents Rosa as "never lets anything go and goes on and on about the same thing until I want to run away."

We agree that Patricia and Rosa will talk together, decide what to do and let me know. The session ends with a mirroring of the previous session as Patricia thanks me for "such a helpful meeting." Once again I feel perplexed. I am reminded of Hamlet's sarcastic words; "O wonderful son, that can so astonish a mother."

When we finally meet as a triangle I can begin to formulate an attachment fit between this couple. As soon as I experience the interaction between them I recognise the pattern of avoidant/dismissing attachment in one and preoccupied in the other.

This is demonstrated immediately as they enter their first – and revealing – discussion which concerns food. This is a long story about last night's supper, and Rosa begins. She tells us, in detail, how she planned, prepared, cooked and delivered the food to the table. Patricia clearly knows how the story is going to pan out and tries to hurry her along; the more she does this, the more flustered Rosa becomes, retracing her steps and repeating the story. Patricia is increasingly prodding, critical and dismissive. She moves around awkwardly in her chair, gets up, walks around the room, sits down and taps her foot. I am picking up intense frustration, panic even. But I can also see Rosa's fear and a dogged determination to have her say, finish her story and be heard. I am not impervious to their height-ened mood and emotions but do feel I can empathise with both. I know from experience that this is helpful in such a couple fit in adult attachments.

This behaviour in the session is a pattern which establishes itself as a familiar mode of communication over the next weeks and months. The avoidant part of Patricia will try to rush on, not "go over all that again." She will be experienced as dismissive, contemptuous and cruel. In return, Rosa's endless, detailed mono-logues can take up a lot of therapy time and cause her great anxiety, as she feels unheard. Both feel I indulge and collude with the other.

My role in this dance of mis-intimacy is to observe and gradually feed back the dynamic I observe. We discuss the attachment patterns each demonstrate. They can see the other's pattern more readily than their own. But as we go through a kind of discourse analysis and I reflect back to them what I see and hear, they listen carefully and reflect on their internal process as the dance goes wrong. As soon as I engage with one, the other is able to simply be an observer of their part-ner. I ask them what they see. Rosa can recognise the frustration behind what she usually perceived as her partner cutting her off, not listening, being contemptuous and rude. This is a revelation and opens up room for further exploration. Patricia initially rejects the avoidant attachment category, but as I explore it with her and Rosa becomes the observer, again the triangulation creates a new thinking space.

As sessions progress, their locked-in battles become easier to identify as an attachment dance which can be harmonious and not rigidly hostile. The change from "battle" to "dance" is another example of the power of language to effect change and is directly named in the session.

Change begins and is reinforced with humour, as Patricia announces; "I'm avoidant, it's not my fault, blame my parents!" Rosa quips back, "at least your parents ignored you, mine drove me mad!" We all laugh. As a teacher on one of my training courses said, "Attachment theory is so easy to understand. Just spend an afternoon in the playground in a local park and watch the family interaction for a few hours; so much can be understood about ourselves as we observe others."

One day something different happens. Unusually, Rosa arrives first. She comes in with a takeaway bag containing food. She launches in on the latest row, last night, about a holiday they are contemplating, going into detail about their conflicting desires and plans. Their rows often remind me of Albee's play *Who's Afraid of Virginia Woolf?* What begins mildly as a difference of perspective rapidly escalates into an emotional tirade where power is used differently by each. They have separate but powerful weapons. Both hurt the other, and I fear also themselves, at the same time. Then Patricia crashes in and can't believe that Rosa has already arrived. "You're always late," she says. Rosa tells her that we are talking about the holiday, and immediately the row starts. They take up their well-practiced positions, and the dance begins.

However, at the same time, with no overt references, Rosa reaches into her bag and takes out lunch. She hands a sandwich, a banana and bottle of water to Patricia, who receives it while still talking. Rosa then opens her identical lunch and carefully munches away while her partner tells us what she wants for a holiday. The first opportunity Rosa gets to speak is when Patricia unscrews the water bottle to drink. She grabs the moment and repeats exactly what she has said prior to Patricia's arrival. Patricia sends me long-suffering glances, which Rosa sees and challenges. I – gently, I hope – remind Rosa that we all have this in mind. She nods, but I can see the compulsive need to be heard is overwhelming for her. Patricia also understands this, even if it drives her crazy. We have made a lot of sense of Rosa's childhood trauma with regard to not being listened to or heard. There is empathy in this relationship.

I grab the moment as Rosa finishes her story. I ask them what have they noticed going on in the room while the session has been running? They offer a synopsis of who arrives when and what we've discussed. I then describe what *I* have seen. I say, "I've seen two people caring for each other. Rosa arrives on time – unusual, Patricia is late, also unusual. Rosa has brought lunch for them both, Patricia has thanked her and eaten it enthusiastically. She then reached over to clear up Rosa's bag and crumbs and tidied them away. Rosa thanked her. And throughout all this they have rowed about a hypothetical holiday." When I stop speaking, there is a significant pause, and then a laugh.

Some couples are destined to row with each other all their lives; others grow weary and more tolerant. Rows can be vicious, cruel, bullying, but they can also be creative, playful, sexy and educational. If there is a power imbalance in the relationship, arguing is potentially very dangerous in many ways. Observing the structure and content of a dispute is essential in building a narrative between two people, enabling them to develop a shared perception and understanding of how they work, love, parent and live together. Whatever their differences – or perhaps *because* of their differences – this couple seemed to work.

To conclude

How does a therapy end, or a clinical paper finish? Is there a natural conclusion or an enforced ending – for instance, where there are only a limited number of sessions permitted in a therapy, or word count in a chapter? What is important is that a truthful and, as far as possible, contained ending is provided.

And how does a career end, "with a bang or a whimper?" (Eliot, 1917). The request for this chapter came in at a time of calm. Within a few weeks, life changed for all of us with the spread of Covid-19.

It was an extremely difficult time for everyone, whether affected directly or not. Many adjectives on people's lips and in the media attempted and failed to express the levels of society's intellectual and emotional reaction. As I write, we are still in the midst of it. At this time, the world of therapy represented in my chapter doesn't exist. It has largely moved online. And rather than bringing breakfast into the therapy room, the client may be sitting in his or her kitchen, tucking into a snack or keeping an eye on the children's lunch and home schooling. I hope by the time you, the reader, read this, face-to-face therapy, the work I knew and that sustained me, has resumed once again.

At the moment, both comforting and frightening elements have emerged in this "unprecedented" time. However, as I have recently been back in touch with Daniel Defoe's book *A Journal of the Plague Year*, is it unprecedented? His final footnote says:

A dreadful plague in London was
In the year sixty-five
Which swept an hundred thousand souls
Away; yet I alive!
(1722/2001)

And there have been good things too; individual acts of kindness, generosity of time and thoughtfulness, being alongside others in their concerns, fears and hopes. Sharing grief and not turning away. Comfort in living a simpler life, and the sense of connection, complementing each other's skills and resources in the spirit of community.

As to answering the question posed – how does a career end? I'll tell you when I've worked it through.

References

Albee, E. (1970). *Who's Afraid of Virginia Woolf*. London: Penguin.
Bartholomew, K., & Horowitz, L.M. (1991). Attachment styles among young adults: A test of a category model. *Journal of Personality and Social Psychology*, *61*(2), 226.
Bowlby, J. (1979). *The Making and Breaking of Affectional Bonds*. London: Tavistock.
Casement, P. (1985). *On Learning from the Patient*. London: Tavistock.
Defoe, D. (1722/2001). *A Journal of the Plague Year*. New York: Dover Publications.
Eliot, T.S. (1917). The hollow men. In (2004) *Complete Poems and Plays of T. S. Eliot*. London: Faber and Faber.
Frost, R. (1955). *Robert Frost Selected by Himself*. London: Penguin.

Keats, J. (1973). Letter December 1817 to his brothers. In H. Bloom & L. Trilling (Eds.), *The Oxford Anthology of English Literature*. Oxford: Oxford University Press.

Shakespeare, W. (1982). *Hamlet*. Edited by Harold Jenkins. The Arden Shakespeare (1.2: 249). London: Bloomsbury.

Steinbeck, J. (1939/2000). *The Grapes of Wrath*. London: Penguin.

Winnicott, D.W. (1976). The Maturational Processes and the Facilitating Environment. London: Hogarth.

Chapter 9

Guess who's coming to dinner

Culture, community, identity ... and food

Linda Cundy

Introduction

We are profoundly relational creatures, adapting ourselves to fit into the social and relational environment we are born into. Attachment theory tells us a great deal about our species and what motivates us – the need for protective relationships that make the world feel safer – and attachment research has identified many of the mechanisms and strategies we use to get our needs met in optimal and suboptimal circumstances. The themes, patterns and general categories identified have many uses, including guiding the practice of psychotherapy. However, we are all individuals; each person develops in a unique context with many complex influences; we each have our own original story and distinctive "aesthetic." Our food-related narratives give access to many ingredients that contribute to our identity: communities we belong to, family culture and dynamics, identifications, reactions, choices, values, aspirations . . . and our intergenerational inheritance.

Ancestors

I recall watching a television programme many years ago called "How to Live to 101" (2008). What stayed with me was footage filmed in Okinawa, one of the poorest regions of Japan that has the highest percentage of centenarians in the world. One lady, well over 100 years of age, comes in from her garden where she has been harvesting vegetables to make a thin soup for her son – who is in his eighties. The remarkable phenomenon of such healthy, active old age is believed to be due to the foods eaten by these elders for most of their lives. Traditionally, local people ate sweet potatoes rather than the rice grown in most of Japan, along with green vegetables and soy, supplemented with a little fish – these are island people. This low-calorie fare is rich in nutrients, and only small portions were eaten; it may be very like the diet of our distant ancestors who first learned to cook the starchy tubers they dug from the ground, long before grains and animals were farmed for food. Chronic but stable undernourishment was the norm for the Okinawans, not quite at malnutrition level, but the diet was severely impoverished compared to the rest of Japan – and yet the result was a long, active and healthy life. Heart disease and many cancers that limit life expectancy of Americans, Europeans and other Japanese are rare among the older generations there. Researchers conclude that "Okinawans . . . appear to be one of the few populations in the world that may have experienced mild long-term [caloric restriction] without significant malnutrition, and this may be linked to their exceptionally healthy survival" (Willcox et al., 2007, p. 446).

Our experience of ourselves, our emotions, how we engage with other people and the world depends upon our bodies. We have a relationship with our bodies, enjoying them, caring for them, worrying about them, abusing or neglecting them. What we feed ourselves has a major impact on our health, stamina, fatigue and well-being. But research suggests that it is not only what we eat and how much, that matters; what our parents and grandparents ate also has a significant bearing on our health.

Överkalix is a region in the far north of Sweden, an area historically affected by food shortages during the long, harsh Lapland winters. Kaati and colleagues examined records of near-famine periods in the nineteenth century and corre-lated this with health data concerning a cohort born in 1905. They discovered that the experiences of hunger or food plenty that affected parents or grandpar-ents had a significant influence on the health of the generation studied (Kaati et al., 2002). Surprisingly, periods of hunger during a critical stage of a child's life have a beneficial, protective impact on the health of subsequent children and grandchildren. We can appreciate that the nutritional condition of a woman preceding and during pregnancy is likely to impact on the child's health but, astonishingly, the researchers discovered that "if there was a surfeit of food in the environment when the paternal grandfather was a 9–12 year old boy a shortening of the [grandchild's] survival could be demonstrated" (Bygren & Kaati, 2018). In other words, there is a "nutrition-linked mechanism" *through the male line* associated with a significant increase of mortality due to cardio-vascular disease and Type 1 diabetes in later generations; grandchildren were four times more likely to die of these diseases, regardless of their own diet, if the grandfather was well-nourished as a boy. The same effect does not appear through the maternal lineage. Through such epigenetic changes, it is not simply "you are what you eat" but, to some extent, "you are what your grandparents ate."

Annual patterns of food scarcity and plenty would have been familiar to all our distant ancestors: hunter-gatherers are still affected by seasonal shortages of game, fruits and other foodstuffs, and early farmers must have contended with a time of hunger each year before their crops were ready to harvest. Harris (1990) concludes that these cycles of feast and shortage were responsible for our bodies' systems for storing energy as fat to see us through the hungry seasons. Now we in the developed world are rarely confronted with such cycles of shortage and glut, and the stored fat deposits are not "drawn down" as energy. Instead, we have a crisis of obesity and diabetes.

Mad with hunger

It is possible that epigenetic changes due to nutrition affect not only the physical but also the mental health of later generations. In the 1980s, working at a mental health day centre in North London, I noticed the high percentage of clients from an Irish background referred. I assumed this reflected the local demographic, but ten years later, teaching on a foundation course in counselling and psychotherapy, I researched statistics on admissions to psychiatric hospitals according to patients' ethnicity for a lecture on mental illness. I was shocked, as were my students, at the disproportionate levels of diagnoses and admissions of patients from an Irish background, hospitalised for every kind of mental suffering from depression, anxiety disorders and addictions through to schizophrenia and the psychoses. So it was with great interest that I recently read about the work of Professor Oonah Walsh, who notes that, as well as in Ireland itself, "admissions to asylums in Canada, Australia and Britain show that the Irish are disproportionately over-represented as inpatients in comparison with other migrant groups" (Walsh, 2016, p. 175). Immigration itself can be stressful, but this alone does not account for the psychiatric statistics. Walsh believes the shadow of the Great Famine of 1845–1852, *An Gorta Mór*, is cast over the Irish people as an enduring legacy. This terrible event killed around one million people and led to mass emigration, reducing the population by a quarter.

The impact of the potato crop's destruction by disease was exacerbated considerably by the policies of the British government that ruled Ireland at that time. While fertile farming land was used to produce grain for absentee landowners in England, poorer soil had produced good crops of potatoes that were the basis of the local diet. However, only one species of potato was cultivated, the Lumper, and once it was infected by blight the entire crop was wiped out. Meanwhile, the landlords continued to ship the grain harvest out, leaving the population to starve.

We can well understand the psychological toll of this horror, the sheer scale of suffering and loss. The original Irish diaspora left behind relatives ravaged by starvation. The consequences of massive unresolved grief, along with rage against those who allowed such a catastrophe to happen, would inevitably influence an individual's parenting: trauma handed down to the next generation through disorganised attachment between a parent who survived the famine and a child.

There is strong evidence linking famine conditions (Hoek et al., 1998; St Clair et al., 2005) with an increase in schizophrenia in the next generation: in both Holland and Anhui Province in China, rates of mental illness doubled in the cohorts conceived just before or during desperate food shortage. However, Professor Walsh believes that epigenetic changes due to near starvation in Ireland may also have affected the mental health of later generations:

> The Great Famine changed Irish society forever, altering social, political, economic and religious life . . . furthermore [it] changed our basic biological

makeup, laying down a specific mental and physical health profile in order to prepare whole communities for further famine and stress.

(Ibid. p. 180)

She concludes that; "the psychological and physiological trauma of the Great Famine . . . [left] a mark upon survivors and their descendants that continued well into the 20th century" (Ibid. p. 173). Patrick Tracey's family migrated to Boston in the United States fleeing the Great Hunger. In the 1970s, two of his sisters were diagnosed with schizophrenia, an illness that had also cursed an uncle, his maternal grandmother and her great-grandmother, Mary Egan. In 1847, Mary left Roscommon, the area of Ireland worst hit by the famine (or "Irish holocaust") and set sail with her husband for the United States, taking with her the affliction that would continue to haunt the family five generations later (Tracey, 2008). It seems that food abundance, undernourishment or starvation affect not just the physical and mental well-being of one generation but those of future ones too.

Perhaps the fear of hunger continued to haunt the Irish, and the instinct to protect and feed loved ones contributed to another phenomenon: the diaspora who emigrated to America to escape the Famine sent food parcels to relatives back home on a grand scale. And almost one hundred years later, families in Ireland sent supplies to relatives in Britain during the World War Two years of food rationing – the "five-pound food parcels." In the weeks before Christmas of 1948, more than fifty thousand such packages containing turkeys, fresh produce and other treats were posted. "The food parcel . . . came not only with food for tomorrow, but also as nostalgic gastronomy . . . fused with hope, renewal and a sense of solidarity" (Mulcahy, 2000, p. 173).

We inherit far more than epigenetic changes from our forebears; cultural practices, a sense of identity and belonging are handed down too. And much of this is expressed through the relationship with food.

Traditions, culture, identity and food

I am writing this in early October 2020. It is the beginning of Sukkot, the Feast of Tabernacles in the Jewish calendar. My neighbours have erected temporary outdoor shelters with roofs that lift so they can eat their festive meals under the stars, commemorating their ancestors who, expelled from Egypt, survived in the parched Sinai desert. I hear them chanting their prayers as the autumn rain gently falls.

The many holy days and festivals of religious and spiritual belief systems keep traditions alive. Rituals and memories are passed down from parent to child; observing these same practices connects us back to our ancestors in a phylogenetic chain. Food plays a significant role in all religions. Preparing, offering, sharing and eating specific foods at specific times keeps many people in touch with their lineage, identity and sense of belonging.

Last year, Christine arrived to talk to me about her upbringing in Taiwan and the place of food in her culture. She brought me gifts of delicious Chinese biscuits and panettone (Christmas was approaching). We drank tea and spoke about spiritual practices in her homeland, influenced by both Buddhism and Taoism, and she explained that most Taiwanese homes have a family shrine, the focal point for rituals that keep individuals anchored within their religious, cultural and family identity. Food, for the Taiwanese, is not only the way to connect with each other in the living world but is also the means to remain continuously connected with – attached to – the deceased. There are many traditions to honour one's ancestors and the gods, and most of these involve offerings of food. She described the specific practices and dishes associated with important events in the lunar calendar. Chinese New Year is marked by offering either six or twelve small dishes of food – the number must be even – including a "three-animal dish" of cooked pork, chicken and fish; also vegetables, fruits (though some fruits are prohibited for worshipping ancestors and gods), sticky rice cake and steamed sponge cakes. It is similar for the Lantern Festival, but offerings include three bunches of long fine noodles wrapped in red paper, and also for the Dragon Boat Festival, when the noodles are replaced by rice dumplings in bamboo leaves. Other significant dates are the Tomb Sweeping Day (the same six or twelve dishes but including boiled eggs) and Ghost Festival. This latter event, taking place in the seventh month of the Chinese year, marks the day the doors of hell open to allow ghosts home to visit their families. It is usual, on the fifteenth day of this month, to prepare a feast to ensure that ancestors and those ghosts without a home to go back to will have a banquet to please them.

Chopsticks are always provided so the ancestors can eat, and Christine explained: "Each time when we worship the gods and ancestors, after about an hour, we will use a pair of new-moon shaped objects made of red wood to ask the ancestors whether they have eaten. If they have, when we throw these on the floor, they will show one head and the other tail. If this is not the result, we have to wait for a while and ask them again until they are full and happy!"

At the end of the Second World War, industry was restarting in the United Kingdom, but labour was in short supply. One solution was to bring in "displaced" European workers, including Ukrainians whose country had been annexed by the USSR. There had not been a Ukrainian community in the United Kingdom previously, but within a few years of the war ending, around 34,000 exiles were living and working in textile towns such as Bradford. Unlike the Irish diaspora, they were cut off from their families back home behind the Iron Curtain; most had little education and spoke little English, and food rationing made it difficult to access familiar ingredients to cook. However, "those who settled in Britain in the late 1940s viewed food as symbolic expression of their identities," and they "ate what they ate in the way they did with a distinctive Ukrainian nationalistic purpose" (Forero & Smith, 2010, p. 92). Traditional dishes such as borscht, filled dumplings, cabbage rolls and pickles helped to confirm their group identity and their separateness from their native British neighbours. Very few ate British food; perhaps that would have felt like a betrayal. Like many migrants and refugees, they believed that one day they would return to their homeland, when it had thrown off the oppressive mantle of communism and was once more independent of the USSR. Food symbolised their lost nation.

The primary settlers portrayed pleasant childhoods interrupted by the war. In such narratives Ukrainians are invariably portrayed as victims reacting against irrational or evil external forces who deprived them of human security, including food. Food has a greater meaning in these stories than recalled individual hunger. After all, these are recollections of childhoods that were spent in communities in which farming and food processing were important determinants of peasant identity.

(Ibid. p. 82–83)

Equally important to these migrants was the Ukrainian Orthodox Church. Separated from relatives back home, godparents of children born and christened in the Church were adopted as surrogate family members to create new relational networks. And food was significant in religious observation too, especially at Easter, when each family filled a basket with traditional delicacies, covered it with a specially embroidered cloth and took it to be blessed by the priest.

But the original migrants did not return, and their children had a different experience. They viewed themselves as "British Ukrainians" and were committed to making their lives in the United Kingdom. They were more open to eating "foreign" foods in restaurants and cooked a range of dishes at home. However, for many of them, the rituals connected with the Church continued to be important. By the current third generation, the link with Ukraine is weak but these young people still recognise themselves as "Ukes" – of Ukrainian heritage. The foods they eat every day are no different from those of their school friends. Their knowledge of customs and traditional foods is important not so much to distinguish themselves from their "non-Uke" friends but rather as a means of socialising with them, an interesting and "exotic" feature of their heritage.

Some questions

- What influence did history, religion, culture and social class have on what, how, and when your family ate?
- What kind of foods did your parents and grandparents eat? And how were meals eaten when you were a child?
- In what ways are your eating habits and diet similar to and different from your parents and grandparents? Why?

Choice and agency

Identity is a blend of many ingredients, including our intergenerational story, our early attachments, and the independent choices we make that express our agency. We may choose to continue identifying with our family of origin, distinguish ourselves from it in some respects or reject it (although all rejected relationships continue to exist in and influence our internal worlds). We humans adapt to changing environments, and the world we inhabit now is different from the one our parents experienced. However, choices may express certain values and identifications, with the aim of belonging to a new "tribe." And sometimes choices are a purposeful reaction against traditions and systems experienced as oppressive and traumatic memories associated with them.

Amir was raised as a practicing Muslim by an overbearing, disciplinarian father and a passive, depressed mother. The meat eaten was halal, and he was instructed to use only his right hand to put food into his mouth. Because he was naturally left-handed, this caused problems, and he was frequently beaten. Ramadan was observed religiously. Now, Amir has become a committed and vocal socialist. He does not identify with his religious upbringing; although he is sympathetic to the compassionate message of the Quran, he does not attend mosque, has married out and is not raising his children in any religious tradition. However, he chooses to fast at Ramadan but for political reasons, to show solidarity with those throughout the world who are hungry and poor. Amir's rejection of the religious component of his childhood is meaningful, as are the carefully considered choices through which he defines himself. It is not Islam he has turned against but the Islam of his father. I am reminded of Freud's description of the super-ego as "not simply a residue of the earliest object choices . . . it also represents an energetic reaction-formation against these choices" (Freud, 1923, p. 34). Decisions we make about what we eat can be similar expressions of personal identity.

We each have our cultural and family inheritance, what we have in common with our "tribe," but our choices assert our individuality. Individuation is developmentally driven; in the Adult Attachment Interview, those who are classified "secure" are characterised by their capacity to act autonomously, and autonomy requires agency. One of the earliest opportunities for expressing agency is provided by the small child's mealtimes.

Loretta struggled to feed her toddler, Chantelle. Meal-times escalated into battles as mum tried to prise her daughter's clenched teeth apart to get a spoonful of food into her mouth while the little girl, strapped into her high chair, wriggled and turned her head away. Loretta complained "she has a mind of her own." Talking to other young mothers, she decided to try a different approach. Instead of preparing a big bowl of pasta for lunch she left small bowls of different options – chicken nuggets, cheese, carrot sticks, banana – within reach. And to her amazement, Chantelle helped herself happily to what she wanted. Then Loretta, feeling less stressed, devised a game. She would say, "I'm just leaving this pasta here for a minute while I go to the kitchen. And don't you dare eat any!" And of course, when she returned, some of the pasta had gone and there would be a cheeky grin – and lots of tomato sauce – on Chantelle's face.

Adolescence is another developmental opportunity to renegotiate one's place in the family of origin. It is Christmas Day, 1991, and I am working for ChildLine (at that time, a telephone counselling service for children and young people). It is quieter than other days, but I am asked to take a call from a distressed 17-year-old.

She tells me she is vegetarian, she has not eaten meat for a year. She feels revulsion at the sight of corpses under tea-towels in the kitchen, blood soaking through the cloth, and the smell of roasting flesh. All the family are there to celebrate Christmas together, and they have just sat down to a traditional lunch. Her mother served her a plate of vegetables but "everything is contaminated by gravy made with juices from the turkey." She refuses to eat it, and her father has shouted at her. Her mother is crying. The young woman feels manipulated and bullied, but she will not give in. She says: "I made my decision. I could stop eating meat or I could just stop eating."

I can empathise with her easily, having myself given up eating meat at the age of 13. Christmases had been difficult for me too. My reasons were different, but I also experienced the impact on my family. My mother worked full time and, I'm sure, had enough on her plate with her job and preparing food for us all without having to think about different options for me (and this was an era when vegetarianism was uncommon in the United Kingdom – no handy ready-meals from the supermarket to heat up in the oven). I was fortunate in having a friend whose Quaker mother was also vegetarian, and she taught me a few simple recipes. In preparing my own food, I was making a statement about growing independence (though, of course, my parents still paid for the ingredients). And in time my mother came to prefer what I ate, and I was pleased to cook for her too.

A different example comes from chef Valentine Warner. As a boy he lived in the country and loved fishing and shooting rabbits and hares. His father had served in the navy during the war and saw enough of killing but was reluctant to interfere in his son's hobbies; "There was an unbroken understanding between us which was, quite simply, if you kill it you eat it" (Warner, 2019, p. 27).

The choice of what to eat and what to refuse can be a matter of psychic life and death. Belfast teacher Brian Keenan was held hostage in Beirut for four and a half years by Shi'ite militia, from 1986 to 1990. His kidnappers came to take him to the bathroom once each day and delivered food. At night he was left alone without light. Some days nobody came. From time to time he was moved to a new location; chained and blindfolded, and with Kalashnikov rifles pointed at his head, he would be bundled into the boot of a vehicle and driven to another bleak basement. The first months were spent in isolation. He was powerless. Having some control over his life, however small, was vital to his psychic survival. He refused to shave his beard, and then, one day,

> The Shuffling Acolyte and I take part in our daily ritual, that long short walk to the toilet. That same walk back and I am home again. I don't look any more at the food, knowing its monotony will not change, not even its place on my filthy floor. The door closes, the padlock rattling, and it's over again for another day. With calm, disinterested deliberation I pull from my head the filthy towel that blinds me. . . . But wait. My eyes are almost burned by what I see. There's a bowl in front of me that wasn't there before. A brown button bowl and in it some apricots, some small oranges, some nuts, cherries,

a banana. The fruits, the colours, mesmerize me in a quiet rapture. . . . I lift an orange into the filthy flat palm of my hand and feel and smell and lick it. The colour orange, the colour, the colour, my God the colour orange. . . . I cannot, I will not eat this fruit.

(Keenan, 1993, p. 68)

The individual in context: the ingredients of identity

As a psychotherapist I am curious about the context of each person's life: their cultural origins, the political and geographical environment they grew up in, their relationship with the belief systems of their families of origin, and their matrix of relationships. An attachment-focused approach addresses the unique personal experience and the wider cultural, historical and social backdrop. Developing a self-narrative that spans the generations is a therapeutic activity, a search for a meaningful sense of self. The relationship with food often gives access to a rich seam of memories and associations that infuse a person's identity.

Hannah was 4 years old when her mother took her to Jerusalem "on holiday." They stayed until she was 9. Her grandparents became her main carers until she and her mum returned to London to rejoin her father. Her first coherent memories are of those five years and the love, warmth, security – and food – of her childhood. Despite her parents' troubled marriage and the intergenerational tragedy and trauma that haunted her family, Hannah felt special. In the United Kingdom, her parents were observant Jews but not orthodox, and they spoke English at home rather than the Hebrew spoken in Jerusalem. "Meals were my cultural education." She learned about the food traditions of each important event in the Jewish calendar: apples dipped in honey at Rosh Hashanah to welcome in a "sweet New Year" ("a rare opportunity for children to get their fingers sticky!"); the bitter herbs, horseradish and hard-boiled eggs dipped in saltwater of the Passover Seder that remind Jews of the sorrows of life and the Exodus of the Israelites from Egypt. As the youngest person at the Seder table, Hannah was asked to read a passage explaining why this night was different from all others. She felt very important and included in family life. She describes another religious festival for me:

> Sukkot was great fun when I was a kid. Our verandah was "roofed" with palm branches from the garden from which we hung pomegranates and other seasonal fruits. We ate all our meals in the Sukkah, checking at night that we could see the stars through the roof; I have no memory of it ever raining! On the eighth and final day, we celebrated Simchat Torah – the most joyous day in the Jewish calendar – by parading through the streets with palm leaves and clutching a delightfully fragrant ethrog [yellow citron].

Day-to-day eating was memorable too; mealtimes brought the extended family together, with aunts, uncles and cousins joining them at the dining table. The kitchen, however, was very much grandmother's domain, cooking in an oven fuelled by methylated spirits. Nobody else, not even Hannah's mother, was allowed to enter while food was being prepared and cooked, and this was significant, as recipes were passed down rather than written. But young Hannah was the exception and recalls sitting in the kitchen watching her grandmother bake on Thursday afternoons in preparation for the weekend. There were no scales in the kitchen; her grandmother judged all ingredients by instinct: "You can just *feel* it." And she watched as grandmother made the best Gefilte fish, chicken soup and dumplings. With nostalgia, Hannah recalls everybody taking their Shabbat meals to the neighbourhood bakery; the ovens were turned off but still hot enough to warm through the Friday evening dinner. And Hannah was introduced to foods that were unknown to her in England – aubergines, avocados and wonderful Jaffa oranges straight from her family's orchard.

Back in London "food was more of an issue." Her mother had been educated to be a professional and was not a good cook. Hannah's relationship with her Jewish identity was not straightforward either: "I was too English in Israel and too Israeli in the UK." As she grew up she was sensitive to the boycotting of Israeli produce, including Jaffa oranges like those her family grew. Now, as an adult, she no longer keeps kosher and has eaten seafood and even bacon, foods prohibited under Jewish dietary laws. But she also has a deeper understanding of her parents, the way their own histories and tragedies shaped them. And those years with her grandparents remain as precious and sustaining memories, a secure foundation for her sense of identity.

George was born in London in the late 1950s to a Greek Cypriot mother and a Sri Lankan father. His parents spoke their native languages with relatives and friends from their own communities, languages that George and his sisters did not understand. As a child of mixed heritage, he identified with neither parent. He grew up in a predominantly white part of town and felt like an outsider everywhere. At school he experienced racism – mostly from his teachers. What he wanted was to be like his school friends, for whom skin colour and ethnicity were not an issue. He was especially embarrassed by the foods his parents cooked and ate, the strange ingredients (olives, vine leaves, chillies, tamarind) and smells that wafted from the kitchen when his friends came to visit. Rather than spicy curries or dolmades, George liked fish fingers and peas, ideally in front of the television while watching *The Man from Uncle* – this was the Swinging Sixties.

As an adult, and in a different era, George has travelled widely. He is more sure of himself and his identity. He now loves dishes from many cuisines, including those his parents once prepared. When asked about his ethnicity he replies, "I'm a Londoner." (He no longer eats fish fingers.)

I talk to Nina about her first marriage. As a young British woman in the early 1960s she met and fell in love with a Jamaican lawyer, Edsel. They married in the Caribbean, and their children were born and raised there. It was a real culture shock; Nina knew nothing of Jamaica before she met Edsel. In her early twenties and in a totally different culture, she was "a shrinking violet, a frightened mouse." She was intimidated by all the confident, beautifully dressed women who were part of her husband's social scene. And . . . she could not cook! Her mother had never allowed her in the kitchen, and the only dish she could make was lemon meringue pie. "But they don't use lemons in Jamaica, only limes!" And food is a very important feature of West Indian life.

Nina describes the huge breakfasts of "ackee and salfish," explaining that salfish – salted cod – was once used to feed slaves, as there was no refrigeration, and is now the national dish. She talks of the big parties with barbecues, roast suckling pig and curry goat, and the spicy patties she loved to eat for lunch. She had to learn quickly how to prepare these dishes so she could fit into her new family and community, to cater for the thirty-strong family gatherings. One anecdote concerns a Christmas lunch. Her parents-in-law, who lived "way out in the bush," were coming over, and she decided to impress them with a roast turkey dinner. She had to buy an enormous turkey from a hotel supplier as they were not easily available in Jamaica at that time. As she proudly delivered the bird to the table, her father-in-law stared: "What kinda chicken that?!"

So many ingredients were unknown to her; the breadfruit that grew in abundance, the numerous varieties of mango, plantains and green bananas, and the avocados she could pick from a tree in her garden (but didn't like). And then there were the scotch bonnet chillies! She had not encountered any of these before marrying her Jamaican husband. Neither had she shopped in an open-air market where women sat with baskets of oranges, tomatoes, sweet potatoes or "Irish potatoes" and buyers haggled over the price. This was so different to the traditional English fare and supermarket shopping she was used to.

She says: *I went from being a girl in Thames Ditton to having servants in Jamaica. There were the "haves" and the "have nots" – and I was one of the "haves." Back then I just accepted it but I realise now how colonial it was – the cocktail parties, the entertaining and having help in the kitchen.* The family lived very comfortably, but Nina was acutely aware of the poverty suffered by many. Some of Edsel's clients had no money to pay for his legal services so paid in kind with yams or oranges.

When Edsel died, Nina returned to the United Kingdom with her teenaged children. At that time, it was difficult to find Caribbean ingredients in London. But now, whenever they all get together, they cook Jamaican food to share, a way to stay in touch with "home." And they return to visit family as often as they can. As Nina says: *It's like having two selves. Moving to Jamaica in the 1960s was a crazy thing to do, but I don't regret a minute of it.*

Into the melting pot

Surplus food was one of the first commodities to be traded by our distant relatives, but perhaps the most precious of resources that could be traded or exchanged was fire. Fire kept our ancestors warm, safe and fed. Before they discovered how to make fire they were keeping fire; finding it as a naturally occurring phenomenon, they learned how to control, transport, feed and protect it. And to contain it. An eternal flame took dedication, resources and skill to nurture. If one clan's fire was extinguished, another "mother log" would need to be quickly acquired from neighbours, either by theft, exchange or gift (Twomey, 2013). Where fire was given, Twomey suggests, systems of cooperation and obligation were established; there were mutual benefits involved. Being on good terms with one's neighbours, even when they have different practices and beliefs, made the world a safer place, and there could be opportunities to benefit in other ways; the exchange of information, new technologies and ideas, and new foods from further afield.

Whether bartered or traded, ingredients have been exported around the world for millennia: salt, spices, grain crops, potatoes and tomatoes; "If you go back far enough in time, you'll find that almost everything in your everyday pantry actually came from somewhere else" (Redzepi, 2018, p. 88). We have come to depend upon some of these as staples, central to our daily diets, while others haven't stood the test of time (the cultivation of dormice for consumption, a practice taken to its empire by the Romans, is one example). "Exotic" foods from distant lands bring status. Dishes from one cuisine can be adopted as favourites in another country, or adapted. Perhaps it is more difficult to fear and despise a people once we know and love their cooking.

It is not only ingredients and recipes that migrate but people too. Just like the ingredients in the pantry, every one of us had ancestors who hailed from a different part of the globe, and as they migrated they would have brought their own food knowledge, "foodways" and preferences with them. Most cities in the Western world are enriched by citizens from a myriad of cultures and faiths, with each district characterised by a unique blend of these ingredients. Every community contributes its own foods. I have the good fortune to live in a highly multicultural, multi-faith area of London; located just a few minutes from my home are Polish, Turkish and Gujarati grocery stores; a Salvation Army charity shop with café and a neo-humanist wholefood shop with community kitchen; a modern Pakistani restaurant (opened by a Karachi-born artist and social activist who describes his diner as "a new artwork") and a traditional Indian take-away. We also have a Seventh-Day Adventist church, a mosque and a synagogue. Perhaps the most visible population is the ultra-orthodox Jewish. Unlike the other communities represented locally, my Haredi neighbours are self-contained, with their own schools and facilities and shops catering to their particular needs regarding clothing and kosher foods. Many people who visit me are surprised, in particular, to see these traditional mostly Ashkenazi Jews living peaceably side by side with Muslim neighbours, despite historical discord between followers of these faiths over issues such as the ongoing Palestine–Israel tensions. The concord between these two populations owes much to the efforts of local Rabbi Herschel Gluck, co-founder of the Muslim-Jewish forum (along with Ismail Amaan) (*Al Jazeera*, 2015), who has devoted his life to mediating and breaking down barriers between groups locally, nationally and internationally. Individuals influence and shape the communities they are part of, and food can bring communities together, even when relations are strained or have been fractured.

In May 2019 I met Rabbi Gluck in the street. He was hurrying to the local mosque where he had been invited to join worshippers breaking their Ramadan fast. He had similar invitations to iftars elsewhere (iftars are community meals served after sunset during the month of fasting), including the Grand Mosque in Regent's Park. Rabbi Gluck is held in particular regard by those who attend the Finsbury Park mosque. In June 2017, a group of people outside its community centre were target of a far-right hate crime; one man was killed and nine others injured when a vehicle was driven into them. Rabbi Gluck was quickly on the scene, standing shoulder to shoulder with the mourners. Each year subsequently he is on the guest list for their celebratory meal. He tells me, "The Talmud teaches us that food brings hearts closer."

Bearing gifts

Another concern of the rabbi is the plight of refugees. Cultures, communities and individuals may pride themselves on their values, including their hospitality, but the arrival of large numbers of migrants and asylum seekers can challenge this self-perception; it is difficult to maintain compassion if we fear our security is threatened. In this defensive frame of mind, we no longer see refugees as individuals with their own stories and suffering; they become competitors for resources, "freeloaders," "other." Undertaking dangerous journeys to escape mortal danger, on arrival refugees are often treated almost as criminals, sent to bleak detention centres surrounded by barbed wire with long delays in processing applications to remain, and always with the threat of deportation hanging over them. But there are also numerous projects aimed at helping, housing and feeding them, including lunch clubs, often organised by churches, where the local community shares food with its "guests." What is often overlooked is that migrants and refugees are a great potential resource to receiving countries, bringing skills that can benefit us all.

One satisfying example of this is Migrateful, a London-based project that organises cookery classes taught by migrants, refugees and asylum seekers. They share their traditional recipes and cooking techniques to interested members of the public, and in return they receive basic catering and food hygiene training and opportunities to improve their language skills. The experience enables them to meet others from many different countries who are also often escaping war or persecution; they become part of the Migrateful community and, even if their English is initially minimal, a love of food and cooking unites them; "food *is* the language." Through not only teaching their culinary skills but also sharing knowledge of their homelands, they are helped to integrate into the wider community, and this can lead to paid employment when (and if) they are granted leave to stay and work in the United Kingdom.

Like so many aspects of life, these cookery lessons moved online when Covid-19 struck. Rather than people coming together to learn, cook, socialise and eat with their teacher, participants joined "remotely" from their own kitchens. One bonus of this was geographical. My first lesson took place one Monday evening; our teacher was Yusuf, who had arrived four years previously as an asylum-seeker from Syria. Also taking part were people from around the United Kingdom, the

Netherlands and Colorado (while most of us prepared an evening meal it was lunch-time there).

Yusuf explained that traditionally in Syria women prepare food in the home but men cook in cafés and restaurants. Also, during the obligatory four-year national service most men learn some cookery skills. As he demonstrated how to prepare ingredients and cook the dishes, he talked to us about his own experiences as a refugee; the frustrations and long delays in waiting for asylum to be granted, the hardship of being unable to seek paid work, and the kindness of host families who took him into their homes and took an interest in him. He also told us about Syria, its rich culture, long history and natural riches. But the city he grew up in, Aleppo, was reduced to rubble by the brutal civil war between government forces and rebel factions in recent years, in what the International Committee of the Red Cross described as one of the most devastating conflicts in modern times.

The dishes we prepared, mutabq (a delicious aubergine dish) and fattoush, the classic Levantine salad that includes coriander and mint, pomegranate seeds and croutons, were those he remembers as an everyday meal that could be rustled up if visitors dropped by; guests would always be offered food, and these were easy options made with ingredients everybody had in their store cupboards and fridges before the civil war. During the years he survived in the United Kingdom on a minimal income, Yusuf could not afford to buy many of these ingredients to make food from his homeland. I imagined how evocative these dishes must be of his childhood and family life, and a culture of hospitality in a world that no longer exists.

It is almost unthinkable that a society which traditionally welcomed guests warmly and where dishes were shared between neighbours could be destroyed by atrocities like barrel bombs, chemical warfare, civilians used as human shields and suicide bombings. Seventy-six percent of more than thirty thousand deaths in the siege and battle of Aleppo were civilian. But, for those who survive such horrors and take refuge elsewhere, bringing their cultures and cuisines to new communities is a gift, an act of hope.

Food to go

> What is patriotism but the love of the food one ate as a child?
>
> (Lin Yutang)

Particular ingredients, dishes, ways of preparing, cooking and serving foods are a powerful expression of one's identity, feeding nostalgia and longing. While unfamiliar foods can feel threatening, especially to those who now lack a secure base, the dishes we associate with our childhood provide a visceral link with attachment figures that nourish us and help us feel safe in alien environments. Cuisine is also highly portable, an edible transitional object. Pradhan reminds us that farming, catering and the hospitality industry rely heavily on unskilled migrant labour. Yet

> food is not only a means [for migrants] of making a living, but also a way of preserving their cultural identity. They contribute to their local economy and community by cooking and selling food that is meaningful to them. Cuisine is built this way, with immigrants arriving in new places and introducing and exchanging ingredients, flavors, and techniques.
>
> (Pradhan et al., 2018, p. 103)

"Food that is meaningful" rekindles a felt sense of what they have left behind. The aromas, flavours, textures and colours that conjure up sensory memories are particularly poignant for those who needed to flee, who may never be able to return to the country of their birth – and whose homelands may be transformed into something alien and unrecognisable should they ever make that journey.

Let me introduce you to my friend Shabibi. She was born in Afghanistan in 1947 and grew up there before the war with Soviet Russia, before communists came to power, and before the Taliban regime. Her family – her father, mother and older brother, were poor. Her mother was a good cook but "because of our poor budget she couldn't always cook the best food and we didn't always have a lot to eat. In Afghanistan, poor people ate lots of vegetables, aubergine, celery, spinach, onions. . . . We ate potatoes instead of rice because rice was expensive." Afghanistan is a very fertile country and vegetables are plentiful, but wealthier people ate more rice, meat and chicken. She comments; "It's the other way round in Britain! Rich people have healthy food, lots of fresh vegetables, and poor people eat fried chicken and burgers."

Shabibi's mother died when she was just 7, and she became responsible for feeding her father and brother. "Afghan men don't cook! It was the normal thing for me to do – I was the woman." With no one to teach her, she shopped at the local market and "invented" meals. If her father enjoyed what she cooked she would make it again. He was a kind, gentle man who, unusually for the time, was not strict about his daughter being unchaperoned outdoors. Just as well, as they moved to a small village when she was a teenager and she had to walk an hour each way to school. Her life was one of cooking, housework and study, but "I didn't suffer, except that I had lost my mum. I got emotional sometimes."

Shabibi studied hard and got into university at Kabul. Although she continued to live at home at first, still cooking for her family, her life completely changed direction. She enjoyed serious studying and mixed with both women and men. It was at university that she met Zafar, and later married him. Once married, she moved into his family home, a very different world for her. They were wealthy and had a cook and other staff, so, relieved of cooking duties, she was able to finish her degree and have her first child. However, she always felt that her husband's family thought he had married beneath him. Because he was very strong-minded and had studied in America, they had not arranged his marriage – he married Shabibi for love.

And then the communists came to power and Soviet troops invaded. Zafar was a journalist with strong political views, and he opposed the regime. He was arrested and imprisoned twice. On the second occasion he was beaten so badly that he suffered a brain injury. Shabibi had to manage with three small children and constant fear. The time had come to leave their homeland.

> We had to leave quickly, to get away. We couldn't take anything or say good-bye to anybody. My husband left first – he walked all the way to Pakistan through the mountains. Then I followed the same route with the children. It was very frightening. When we arrived in Pakistan there were so many refugees. Life was so sad – it was a bad situation.

The family of five lived in one room. It was very hot. The children could not go to school, and Zafar's mental health was deteriorating. Fortunately, they could afford to feed themselves. "In Pakistan the food is similar except they eat a lot of chilli. In Afghanistan we use just a little, and not so much spices. We were not used to such hot food."

Through his overseas contacts, Zafar was eventually helped to bring the family to Britain in 1984. "It was like a miracle! People were very nice, though I couldn't speak a word of English then. We had a flat and some food but no jobs, only money from the government. It was not pleasant." I asked about culture shock:

> Afghanistan was a very developed part of Asia in the 1960s and '70s, at least in the cities. Kabul was like Europe, so it was not such a shock to be in London. But the food was completely different – tasteless! We were used to rich, oily food with a little spice. Here it is healthy but had no flavour.

Shabibi continued to cook dishes from "back home," but as she couldn't yet speak English, she had difficulty finding the ingredients. This is where her creativity in the kitchen, developed when she was a young child, helped out. Now, partly due to her good language skills and partly a greater diversity in available foods, she can make more authentic meals that her children still love to eat. She occasionally eats out with British friends and has discovered that she likes fish and chips!

Sadly, Zafar died in 1993. Shabibi has kept busy doing voluntary work, including supporting refugees. She now fosters children and has a 16-year old Afghan boy living with her. I asked if she is teaching him to cook. "Not yet. He has only been here for six months and is getting used to the different culture, so I want to be careful with him. Still in some parts of Afghanistan it is shameful for men to cook, to be in the kitchen." This takes her back to reminiscing about her country.

> Everything grew there – spinach, coriander, apples, pears and the best watermelon. It was a wonderful country. Life must be so difficult for people who've lost everything. There was freedom, food – everyone was relatively happy. Now it is chaos. Rich people are very rich and the poor people are very poor. It's so sad.
>
> [Shabibi has written a book about her experiences (Shah, 2008).]

Guess who's coming to dinner

My parents were friendly people and enjoyed company, but I recall the anxiety when the doorbell rang as we were sitting down to eat. It was just not done for people to drop by unannounced; visitors came by appointment, especially when dining was involved. In the United Kingdom, we are generally accustomed to only sharing daily meals with immediate family, with exceptions made for eating out and special occasions. A more communal approach does not easily fit our lifestyles. Dinner table conversation can be limited unless sitting and eating together is the aim, rather than simply sating hunger. It is a common phenomenon, even in cafés and restaurants, to see diners more engaged with their mobile devices than with each other, or even the food on their plates. Many cooks will be familiar with the experience of planning a meal, shopping for ingredients, putting care, skill and time into preparing something delicious to find it has been devoured within minutes and everyone has scattered! But mealtimes can feed relationships as well as fill stomachs; the dinner table can be a place for connection and emotional refuelling as well as simply providing fuel. "We are not at table merely to eat, but in order to enjoy each other's company." (Visser, 2017, p. 285) Coming together with food nurtures the bonds between individuals and groups.

> Since the Byzantine era, feasting in the form of mezze was a means of facilitating socialisation around the table, with the continuous offering of delicacies to stimulate appetite and keep conversations going, sometimes up to a whole day. The social connection inherent in Greek Cypriot food is demonstrated by the tendency for food to not be individually plated. Instead, it is an abundance of food for sharing that adorns the table.
>
> (Oskis, unpublished)

It can be argued that too strong an affiliation with our immediate group, our "tribe," leads to splitting, with those outside the group excluded, sometimes vilified, scapegoated, feared and attacked. It is sadly undeniable that we humans are capable of such behaviour, yet we are more open to and interested in those from different backgrounds when we feel assured of support from within our own group (Mikulincer & Shaver, 2001). There are many traditions that welcome strangers, that value the "Other." We benefit from what is new and different, and there are undoubted evolutionary advantages to remaining adaptable; we can think of this as the "diversity principle." Alongside the need for attachment goes the drive to explore the world, and exposing ourselves to ways of life and world views other than our own feeds that appetite. And food can mediate, a vehicle for dynamic personal and cultural exchange that enriches all involved. But during the Covid era it has not been possible to gather together for a leisurely emotional refuelling and group bonding at the dinner table.

Food and community in the time of Covid

Eating together has special significance in Sikhism. Every gurdwara has a community kitchen, *langar*, that provides food for all visitors; everybody eats seated on the floor together as equals, whatever their creed, social position, colour or gender.

When the Coronavirus pandemic struck, I spoke with two women from the Guru Maneyo Granth Gurdwara in Slough. It was painful when the Gurdwara was closed as a place of worship but "Langar has never stopped in five hundred years. We decided, if people can't come to us, we'll go to them. It is part of Sikh DNA; if there is a need we will act." A huge voluntary task force was mobilised, and the four-acre site became an industrial-scale food store. "It has been incredible. Nothing runs out! We have pallets of rice and lentils filling the langar hall, all provided by voluntary contributions from individuals or funded by donations from the golak (collection box)." There was enough space for social distancing, and volunteers, wearing face coverings and protective clothing, worked in shifts through the day and night preparing 9,300 hot meals each day to be distributed to local people who were in need. The effort attracted many new volunteers of different backgrounds. "You can't underestimate the power of doing the right thing."

Deep explained the tradition of langar, providing free food for whoever is present regardless of background or faith. "We put our beliefs into action. Sikhism is not a religion but a way of life." The three basic tenets, introduced by the founding father, Guru Nanak Dev Ji, are *simran* (meditation to still and awaken the mind), *sangat* (coming together, community, meditating and eating together) and *seva* (selfless service). All food prepared in the langar is vegetarian, and simran is done while preparing, cooking and packing it for distribution to ensure that the meals provided are infused with spiritual nourishment.

Charanjot Kaur and her husband were among the many who offered to distribute food to those who had requested it. Most recipients were not Sikh. She described the gratitude expressed by many who were elderly, vulnerable and isolated and commented on the significance of them approaching those of a different religion and culture for food support, which spoke to the integration that Covid brought about. Real human relationships developed between people who would not have encountered each other without these extraordinary circumstances. She told me that they will continue to help any individuals who ask for support, and all recipients in the community know that, when it is possible to reopen, the Gurdwara will welcome them whenever they would like to visit, to share a sit-down meal with the rest of the congregation.

Gurdwaras have a centuries-long tradition of feeding large numbers of people and the infrastructure to prepare and cook these meals. However, the Coronavirus pandemic highlighted some unanticipated areas of food shortage. One unexpected source of need came from the very people who were putting themselves at risk to care for the sick: NHS medical staff. Because it was essential to restrict contamination in hospitals, staff initially had no access to canteens. Pop-up non-profit Furloughed Foodies was created within days of lockdown starting to provide nutritious hot meals for NHS workers. Via word of mouth and social media one man, Floris ten Nijenhuis, mobilised a team of volunteers who were either furloughed from their jobs or permanently laid off due to the pandemic. Almost overnight, eight hundred people had signed up to either make food or deliver it, far more than were needed. Volunteers began preparing meals, in batches of fifty, in their own kitchens. They cooked whatever they could make – curries, Chinese food, pasta, burritos. Donations were raised, though many volunteers chose to not only give their time but also pay for ingredients as an expression of gratitude to those who were battling this deadly virus on the front line. As a result, they were able to deliver almost 2,500 meals per week between fifteen London hospitals.

Will McFadden, the organisation's fundraiser, told me that volunteers were motivated by a strong desire to support the medical teams: "If we can do this for them, they can focus on getting people better." Will told me of the pleasure he felt distributing meals, – "it's home-cooked and comforting, like mothers' cooking. It is made with love" – and the touching appreciation from doctors and nurses who took delivery. Some volunteers wrote messages of support on the carton lids – "we're rooting for you" – and one little girl decorated lids with drawings. In time, hospital catering services reopened, but Furloughed Foodies' volunteers voted to continue longer, providing food for homeless shelters.

Attachment and helping

Those of us in the developed world are used to having control over our lives; we take a lot for granted. In those early days of the pandemic, mandatory lockdown changed that. There was a tangible sense of shock and fear. Perhaps helping others was, among other things, an expression of agency, doing *something* rather than waiting passively for the crisis to unfold. As social creatures, many of us wanted to pull together, to do our bit.

There is a large research literature concerning altruism and "selfishness." It appears that very young children are predisposed to help others; in one experiment, toddlers not only shared toys but gave away their own food to someone who had none. Graham Music has synthesised much of this research and presented it accessibly in a fine book, *The Good Life*. He writes:

> Altruistic tendencies and empathy normally emerge alongside being able to conceptualise oneself as part of a story with a past, present and a future. . . . Those with more grey matter at the junction between the parietal and temporal lobes are seemingly not only better able to see things from another person's perspective but are also more altruistic. . . . There can be a shift with maturity from a spontaneous, almost unthinking empathy which leads to altruistic gestures [in children], to what some see as deeper compassion for others.
>
> (Music, 2014, pp. 45–46)

The mature capacity to hold a coherent self-narrative that encompasses and makes links between the past, present and future is a feature of secure attachment, as is the mentalisation that enables us to see things from someone else's point of view. But an infant's innate altruism needs certain conditions in his relational environment in order to develop into this more mature compassion for other people. If children feel safe, loved, understood, respected and protected by their caregivers, their internal resources flourish. Feeling well-resourced internally, they are not depleted by acts of generosity toward others. Being "secure" is not equated with being financially comfortable: many compassionate, generous individuals and peoples are poor – their "wealth" is of a different nature. Whatever they have, a little or plenty, they are happy to share.

But our original prosocial natures can be perverted or obliterated under certain conditions. It stands to reason that when people feel insecure they are less inclined to genuine hospitality. If they have grown up in families where reserves are scarce – not only of money and food, but most importantly of time and loving attention – then they may jealously guard what is "theirs" and compete with others for what they see as their rightful share. Research has found that individuals with a more avoidant attachment pattern, who learned early on to be self-sufficient and fend for themselves rather than turn to others for help and support, are less likely to be prosocial. This is summed up neatly by Sue Gerhardt: "The moral impulse to care about other people's needs and feelings is very dependent on having had your own needs and feelings cared about" (Gerhardt, 2011, p. 98).

There is poverty and parents desperate to feed their children even in the first world countries, people in need of food aid, soup kitchens, food banks. The words of Deep Kaur come back to me: "You can't underestimate the power of doing the right thing." It feels good to help. Just as welcoming and feeding guests in our homes brings pleasure to us, the brain's reward circuits are activated through "doing the right thing." It raises an interesting question: when we help others, is it for their benefit or our own? But perhaps that doesn't really matter. Helping, sharing, donating, feeding are all aspects of the "caregiving system" and ultimately make for more welcoming, secure communities and society for all of us.

I am deeply grateful to everyone who was prepared to talk with me about the place of food in their lives, histories, relationships, values and sense of self.

References

Bygren, L.O., & Kaati, G. (2018). Slow growth period and epigenetics. In V. Patel & V. Preedy (Eds.), *Handbook of Nutrition, Diet, and Epigenetics*. Cham: Springer. https://doi.org/10.1007/978-3-319-31143-2_119-1.

Forero, O., & Smith, G. (2010). The reproduction of 'cultural taste' amongst the Ukrainian diaspora in Bradford, England. *The Sociological Review, 58*(2), 78–96. https://doi.org/10.1111/j.1467-954X.2011.01963.x.

Freud, S. (1923). The ego and the super-ego. In *The Standard Edition of the Complete Psychological Works of Sigmund Freud, Volume XIX (1923–1925): The Ego and the Id and Other Works* (pp. 28–40). London: Hogarth Press.

Gerhardt, S. (2011). *The Selfish Society: How We All Forgot to Love One Another and Made Money Instead.* London: Simon and Schuster.

Harris, M. (1990). *Our Kind: Who We Are, Where We Came from and Where We Are Going.* New York, NY: Harper Perennial.

Hoek, H.W., Brown, S.S., & Susser, E. (1998). The Dutch famine and schizophrenia spectrum disorders. *Journal of Social Psychiatry and Psychiatric Epidemiology, 33*(8), 373–379.

How to Live to 101 (2008). Horizon, BBC Two, Television 19th February, 21.00.

Kaati, G., Bygren, L.O., & Edvinsson, S. (2002). Cardiovascular and diabetes mortality determined by nutrition during parents' and grandparents' slow growth period. *European Journal of Human Genetics, 10*, 682–688. www.nature.com/ejhg/. Accessed on 03 September 2020.

Keenan, B. (1993). *An Evil Cradling.* London: Vintage.

Mikulincer, M., & Shaver, P. (2001). Attachment theory and intergroup bias: Evidence that priming the secure base schema attenuates negative reactions to out-groups. *Journal of Personality and Social Psychology, 81*(1), 97–115.

Mulcahy, J. (2000). Eating abroad, remembering home: Violent disruption, the Irish diaspora, and their food parcels, 1845–1960. *A paper presented to the Dublin Gastronomy Symposium 2020, Food and Disruption.* https://arrow.tudublin.ie/cgi/viewcontent.cgi?article=1184&context=dgs. Accessed on 18 November 2020.

Music, G. (2014). *The Good Life: Wellbeing and the New Science of Altruism, Selfishness and Immorality.* London: Routledge.

Oskis, A. (2019). *From the Cradle to the Table: Food, Attachment and the Power of Relationships.* Unpublished Essay.

Pradhan, B., Patel, H., & Caudillo, I. (2018). Food is a gateway. In C. Ying (Ed.), *You and I Eat the Same* (pp. 103–123). New York: Artisan.

Redzepi, R. (2018). If it does well here, it belongs here. In C. Ying (Ed.), *You and I Eat the Same* (pp. 87–95). New York: Artisan.

Shah, S. (2008). *Where Do I Belong? From Kabul to London: A Refugee's Life.* London: Longstone Books.

St Clair, D., Xu, M., Wang, P., Yu, Y., Fang, Y., Zhang, F., Zheng, X., Gu, N., Feng, G., Sham, P., & He, L. (2005). Rates of adult schizophrenia following prenatal exposure to the Chinese famine of 1959–1961. *Journal of the American Medical Association, 294*(5), 557–562. https://doi.org/10.1001/jama.294.5.557.

Tracey, P. (2008). *Stalking Irish Madness: Searching for the Roots of My Family's Schizophrenia.* New York, NY: Bantam.

Twomey, T. (2013). The cognitive implications of controlled fire use by early humans. *Cambridge Archaeological Journal, 23*(1), 113–128.

UK Jews and Muslims team up against hate. (2015). *Al Jazeera.* www.aljazeera.com/features/2015/01/27/uk-jews-and-muslims-team-up-against-hate/.

Visser, M. (2017). *The Rituals of Dinner: The Origins, Evolution, Eccentricities and Meaning of Table Manners.* London: Penguin.

Walsh, O. (2016). "An invisible but inescapable trauma": Epigenetics and the Great Famine. In C. Kinealy, J. King, & C. Reilly (Eds.), *Women and the Great Hunger* (pp. 175–183). Hamden, CT: Quinnipiac University Press.

Warner, V. (2019). *The Consolation of Food*. London: Pavilion.

Willcox, B.J., Willcox, D.C., Todoriki, H., Fujiyoshi, A., Yano, K., He, Q., Curb, J.D., & Suzuki, M. (2007). Caloric restriction, the traditional Okinawan diet, and healthy aging: The diet of the world's longest-lived people and its potential impact on morbidity and life span. *Annals of the New York Academy of Sciences, 1114*, 434–455. https://doi.org/10.1196/annals.1396.037. https://s.put.re/edWLkDBZ.pdf. Accessed on 03 September 2020.

Index